Experimental Methods for Evaluating Herbage

Compiled by
J. BADEN CAMPBELL
Research Station, Canada Department of Agriculture
Swift Current, Saskatchewan

Publication 1315   1969
CANADA DEPARTMENT OF AGRICULTURE

CONTENTS

Chapter

Chapter

FOREWORD

This book has been prepared for researchers who must understand and appraise measurement techniques that may be applied in a great variety of situations. In Canada, about 100 scientists are working on forage research in 40 locations over the 4000 miles from Victoria, British Columbia, to St. John's, Newfoundland. Our growing season is one of the shortest and our winters are among the most severe encountered in agriculturally advanced countries. We therefore have unique problems in evaluating herbage quality and yield, and they have prompted the development and use of a wide range of specialized research methods.

A special feature of this book is the diversity of authorship. The chapters were contributed by specialists from almost every discipline of biological science. They have been brought together by J. Baden Campbell, an outstanding scientist of broad experience in both rangeland and cultivated forages. This book will therefore be a valuable reference text for research establishments and advanced classes wherever herbage measurement and evaluation are studied.

J. E. R. Greenshields
Research Station
Canada Department of Agriculture
Saskatoon, Saskatchewan

INTRODUCTION

If you can measure that of which you speak,
and express it by a number, you know something
of your subject. If you cannot measure it,
your knowledge is meagre and unsatisfactory.

Lord Kelvin

Techniques to evaluate the yield and quality of herbage are still in a formative period that began many centuries ago. Xenophon, Cato, Varro, Virgil, Pliny the Elder, and other philosophers wrote about farm husbandry, commenting on grazing practices, the benefits of manuring, the need for drainage, and the good which the "face of the master" gave to land, crops, and livestock. The practices they advocated were followed in small districts throughout Europe until after the Renaissance (Prentice, 1939), and agriculture progressed in those areas. Wherever farming stagnated, systems of land tenure, wars, social prejudices, educational inequalities, and poor communications were greater obstacles than lack of practical agricultural knowledge (Prentice, 1939; Beddows, 1965). Though the Greek and Roman philosophers cannot be called scientists, they sifted the progressive from the traditional and the enlightening from the magical, and they stimulated good agricultural practices.

Sinclair (1816) was the first to report yields of herbage. Sir Humphrey Davy conducted a few chemical analyses of Sinclair's samples. Sinclair attempted to prove "comparative degrees of nourishment in different plants" by feeding and weighing animals, but reported inconclusive results. Boussingault (1845) undertook a similar experiment and stated that "a horse foddered most regularly, and weighed at the same time on consecutive days, presented differences in daily weight of up to 30 pounds." Thus, over a century ago, scientists realized the importance of measurement and the limitations that inadequate techniques and biological variations imposed on their findings. The experiences of these pioneers and their successors suggest four basic objectives of herbage research:

- To determine physiological, ecological, and biochemical characteristics of plants and animals
- To relate livestock production to crop characteristics
- To determine the role of herbage in soil stabilization and land rehabilitation
- To develop, for both crops and animals, laboratory and field techniques that estimate yield and quality of herbage more critically than the procedures used at present.

Studies to evaluate herbage are concerned with two biological systems: the plant and the animal (Spedding, 1965). Two environmental complexes are also involved: the soil and the climate. Studies of either the plant or the animal may be relatively simple, but when both systems are studied together it is often necessary to compromise between perfection and practicality. In addition, the influence of soil or climate may confound the most carefully organized program. The only factor that can be controlled completely is experimental design.

The problems associated with assessing the yield and quality of a new herbage commence before its seed is planted and continue until it is accepted or rejected for agricultural use. Some of the problems may be answered by literature research or simple experiments, whereas others require detailed and time-consuming studies. An example of a lengthy and involved study is the Canada Department of Agriculture's program to improve Russian wildrye, *Elymus junceus* Fisch., a species recommended for pasture in the Northern Great Plains of North America. Because of its apparently low yield, the grass was not recommended for farm use until recently. The factors that tilted the scale in its favor were high digestibility, a relatively high crude-protein content after curing, production of a good liveweight gain in cattle per hundredweight of herbage eaten, and the development of cultural practices to produce good seed yields.

Yield of herbage will not normally be increased greatly by improving only one variable of production. The best possible seedbed and the best seed mixture are required. The soil fertility level and the sward composition need to be maintained. Utilization practices should also be considered. For example, what is the most efficient way to use a new herbage? If pastured, it may be best to graze it in continuous, rotational, complementary, repeated-seasonal, or daily-break patterns. Alternatively, a crop may be utilized better if it is harvested and fed in a feed yard; then soiling or dry processing may be more profitable.

Herbage cut for hay produces 10 to 40 percent more total energy per acre than herbage that is grazed. This advantage introduces a problem in economics: What percentage increase in yield will pay the harvesting, processing, and investment costs for drylot feeding? There is information to support soiling when the feeding animal is a production unit, such as a fattening steer or a milking cow. There is less evidence when the feeding animal is not the finished product, as when a beef cow raises a calf or a ewe rears a fat lamb.

The appraisal of a herbage by livestock may give different results from assessments by agronomic and chemical methods. For this reason animal response should be investigated early in a testing program. The comparative acceptability of herbage as hay, pasture, or silage should be determined. Its resistance to trampling and how it recovers from different methods of grazing should be known. There is also the question of when animal data should assume more importance than information gained from agronomic studies. At this time two further variables must be considered: the size of the herd or flock needed for a representative sample, and the sensitivity of a genus or even of a breed of animals to the conditions of an experiment. An apparently valuable feed may cause stress in animals; stress, in turn, may be reflected in energy conversion.

Research has attempted to resolve the plant–animal complex by developing laboratory techniques to estimate the nutritive qualities of herbage. Since Sir Humphrey Davy's early analyses, the search for short-cuts has continued with increasing interest. This field of investigation is one of the most diligently studied today. Several standards have been proposed and developed; each has adherents; each exhibits a fairly constant relationship with the others (Heaney and Pigden, 1963).

Experimental work is based on small-scale techniques. The land area reserved for field testing, the quantities of seed sown, the amounts of herbage harvested for yield determinations and laboratory analyses, and the number of livestock used are minute when compared with those used in agricultural production. Generally, a microtechnique creates a favorable environment that needs to be balanced against the macro-environment of the industry. One problem is to equate the results in terms of time, and to realize that the intensive production techniques of today may be the extensive production practices of tomorrow.

How is a new crop or practice incorporated into a farming system? Usually, readily applied research information is quickly put to use, but sometimes further experimentation is needed. Alder and Redford (1958), as well as others, have established "farmlets" or "pilot farms" to test and demonstrate the application of advanced research results; these projects are flexible, permitting a new crop or a new management practice to be introduced when research information warrants such a move.

Undoubtedly the human race will continue to eat; but in what form will food be processed and stored 50 years from now? This question poses a challenge to imaginative thinking and sound scientific judgment. The techniques required for progressive development may be unknown at present. But trends will be made clearer if curiosity leads to thorough literature research and to imaginative programs of experimentation. Most research programs will be concerned with immediate and local problems, but some time is needed to probe probabilities. A way to fall behind a changing economy is to stay too close to field plots or laboratories; a way to prepare for the future is to carry out a survey project that takes sociological trends into consideration.

Undoubtedly, many of the experimental procedures and analytical techniques accepted at present will be superseded by more exact methods within a decade. This is inevitable and desirable. Many of the procedures presented in this book will be recognized readily because they have been used by research workers for decades; modifications have simplified and increased the reliability of others. A few techniques that have not been reported previously are presented. Some portions of the book may deviate from the experimental approach. If so, it should be realized that the inquiring mind and the subjective analyses of the philosophers are legacies that underwrite and complement the objective approach of twentieth century research.

References

Alder, F. E., and R. A. Redford. 1958. Further observations on grassland management for meat production. J. Brit. Grassl. Soc. 13:239–246.

Beddows, A. R. 1965. The provision of year-round succulent feed for livestock in Great Britain, 1957-1963. Herb. Abstr. 35:151–157.

Boussingault, T. D. 1845. Rural economy in its relation with chemistry, physics, and meteorology. 2nd ed. H. Dailliere, London.

Heaney, D. P., and W. J. Pigden. 1963. Interrelationships and conversion factors between expressions of the digestible energy value of forages. J. Anim. Sci. 22:956–960.

Prentice, E. Parmalee. 1939. Hunger and history. Harper and Brothers, London and New York. 269 p.

Sinclair, G. 1816. *Hortus gramineus woburnensis.* D. McMillan, London.

Spedding, C. R. W. 1965. The physiological basis of grazing management. J. Brit. Grassl. Soc. 20:7–14.

Chapter 1

PLANT PHYSIOLOGY AND MORPHOLOGY

DONALD B. WILSON
Research Station, Canada Department of Agriculture
Lethbridge, Alberta

LEONARD P. FOLKINS
Ottawa Research Station, Canada Department of Agriculture
Ottawa, Ontario

D. GRANT WOOLLEY*
Research Station, Canada Department of Agriculture
Lethbridge, Alberta

Fundamental information on the physiology and morphology of herbage plants is essential to continued refinement of herbage management techniques. Unfortunately, this type of information is limited because herbages have not been popular subjects for physiological or morphological studies. The fund of information is growing but is not yet sufficient to permit a theoretical explanation of many phases of herbage growth. Rapid development in this field will depend mostly on the enterprise of workers whose research is oriented specifically toward herbages rather than plant physiology in general. In particular, studies specific to herbages are needed in the fields of plant–soil and interplant relationships, light and carbon dioxide utilization, water and nutrient uptake, translocation, storage and remobilization of metabolites, and plant morphogenesis. In this chapter, some of the techniques now being used to study the physiology and morphology of herbages are reviewed and their further development and application are discussed.

DEVELOPMENTAL MORPHOLOGY

Bud and Shoot Development

In grasses the meristematic tissue of the shoots is in the stem apex and the intercalary meristem. New leaves arise from successively higher nodes on alternating sides of the apex, each leaf being partly enclosed by its predecessor. As the leaf primordium develops, the ligule is formed, separating the lamina from the sheath and dividing the intercalary meristem into two parts. Ligule formation may occur when the leaf is less than 1 cm in length. The leaf continues to elongate within the sheath of the next oldest leaf, but by the time the lamina emerges the exposed portion has ceased to expand. The sheath continues to expand

---

*Present address: Department of Agronomy, Iowa State University, Ames, Iowa.

1

until the ligule is exposed. Several leaves on each stem will usually be growing at one time, but only two or three of these will be visible. The number is a function of the species and the environmental conditions (Evans and Grover, 1940).

In many grasses, such as brome grass, *Bromus inermis* Leyss., elongation of the internodes begins at an early stage of growth. The stem apex soon rises above ground level and is accessible to grazing animals. When this growing point is removed by defoliation, new growth must come from buds at the base of the plant. If the growing point is removed at an early stage of development, growth of the secondary buds may be slow because of insufficient carbohydrate accumulation. The height of the growing point can be determined by cutting off representative samples at crown level and splitting them lengthwise with a sharp knife.

In certain other grasses, such as perennial ryegrass, *Lolium perenne* L., there is little or no internodal elongation of the flowering stem until the growing point enters the reproductive phase. During the vegetative phase, the growing point remains close to the surface of the ground, and the leaves may be grazed without removal of the meristematic tissue. After a temporary slowing down caused by reduction of leaf area, the plant continues to grow. If the ratio of vegetative to reproductive shoots is wide, relatively few growing points are removed at any time by defoliation.

Tiller formation in grasses has been studied by attaching a small plastic label on a colored nylon thread to each tiller or by labeling the tillers with colored plastic rings (Grassland Research Institute, 1961). The threads or rings are slipped over the tillers and placed as low as possible. Rings are preferred as they are not easily displaced during recording and do not become buried in the soil. Current knowledge of the vegetative development of grasses has been summarized by Jewiss (1966) and Anslow (1966).

In broad-leaved plants, the growing cells are found in the terminal bud. The terminal bud is thrust upward when growth starts and is soon within reach of grazing animals. If the terminal bud is removed before a leaf joint is formed, that stem grows no more. In many plants, if the terminal bud is removed above a leaf joint, the stem may continue to grow from a new bud formed at the leaf joint.

Bartels (1956) examined the regrowth of alfalfa, *Medicago sativa* L., by digging plants and recording the number of new shoots. The shoots were classed according to their points of origin: from the crown, from the base of cut stems (axillary growth), and from leaf axils farther up the stems (stem growth). Difficulty was experienced in distinguishing between crown and axillary growth when the crop approached the flowering stage, making it necessary to group both types under one heading. Some of the new shoots died as the crop grew, the greatest mortality being among those arising from farther up the stems cut at the previous mowing.

2

Development of a crop through its growth cycle can be followed by means of growth-curve studies. In this technique, cutting is begun in the spring, when plants are in the vegetative stage, and is continued at regular intervals until the crop matures. A previously uncut plot of herbage is harvested at each cutting date. Yield is plotted against time to portray the rate of dry-matter accumulation. Concurrent phenological records are used for interpreting the results and as reference points on a biological calendar. If only vegetative growth is to be studied, separate parts of each treatment can be harvested at frequent intervals within a regular schedule of repeated cuttings (Anslow and Green, 1966).

Root Development

Many techniques have been used to study root development. Often it is necessary to remove a sample from the field and wash the soil from the roots. A core sampler, which is a cylindrical metal tube sharpened at one end, can be forced into the ground to remove a known volume of soil. After the tube is pulled out, the core of soil it contains is pushed out with a piston. The diameters of core samples generally range from 2.5 to 10 cm, although a 15-cm sampler has been used (Burton and Jackson, 1962). A tractor-mounted core sampler has been described by Boehle and others (1963). A device for removing single-plant samples has been developed by Rivers and Faubion (1963). In their method a hexagonal ring is attached to a frame and placed around the plant to be removed. Triangular cutting blades are inserted into six slots in the ring and driven into the ground. The blades converge at a point about 35 cm below the soil surface. A lever attachment removes the sample.

Washing roots by hand, a tedious and slow procedure, has prompted the development of mechanical methods. A machine suitable for the initial washing, in which the greater part of the clay, silt, and fine sand are washed away, and the roots, other macro-organic matter, coarse sand, and stones are left on a sieve, has been described by Williams and Baker (1957). McKell, Wilson, and Jones (1961) obtained better separation of roots and soil by placing the soil and root mass in a 5-gallon can, and then washing under a stream of water. With this method the fine soil particles and detached roots are carried into suspension and, as the water rises in the can, they pass by way of an overflow spout onto a fine-mesh screen that lets the soil pass through but retains the roots. The heavier particles of soil and gravel settle on the bottom of the can. Good water pressure and some stirring is necessary to separate all the soil from the roots. The advantages of this method are its speed and the retention of all root tissue.

There may be considerable contamination by soil particles even after careful washing. A correction for this can be made by igniting the sample and expressing the weight of roots as ash-free organic matter. Although the method will not give completely accurate results, inter-

3

pretation is likely to be affected less by the omission of plant ash from the root weights than by the inclusion of soil contamination.

Growing roots have been examined by using glass-faced planter boxes (Crider, 1955; Crowder, Vanegas, and Silva, 1960; Muzik and Whitworth, 1962). The boxes are placed at an angle of 30 to 45 degrees, with the glass facing downwards. As the roots grow against the glass plate the rate of growth can be measured by marking the position of the roots on the glass. The roots can be kept in darkness by covering the glass with a removable shutter.

A root-blacking method has been used to study the growth of roots in pots (Crider, 1955). A plant is temporarily removed from its pot and the surface of the soil–root mass is painted with carbon black, a material that dissipates slowly in water and is not injurious to the plant. The plant is replaced in the pot and removed at later dates for additional measurements. The growing roots, which characteristically follow the inside of the pot, can be distinguished readily as all new growth is white.

Some of these and other methods to estimate root development are discussed in more detail in reports of the Subcommittee on Range Research Methods (1962) and Troughton (1957).

Top–Root Interrelations

Troughton (1956) points out that in a young grass plant the rates of growth of the root and shoot are seldom the same. The distribution of weight between the root and shoot varies with the total weight and age of the plant. The effect of various cultural treatments on the shoot: root ratio may be misinterpreted if plant weights are recorded only at the end of an experimental period. It is then difficult to know if the treatments have affected the relative rates of root and shoot growth directly, or only indirectly through an overall effect.

This difficulty may be overcome by periodically harvesting plants and plotting growth curves of the roots and shoots under each treatment. A different plant must be used at each time interval, and a large number of plants must be grown and measured to offset the variation between plants receiving the same treatment. An alternative proposed by Troughton (1956), which requires fewer plants, is to use the allometric formula $(y = bx^k)$ to compare the effects of various treatments on the relative growth rates of the roots and shoots. In this formula, $y =$ root weight, $x =$ shoot weight, $b =$ the value of y when x equals unity, and $k =$ the ratio (log weight of the root)/(log weight of the shoot) at a given point of time. If the values of log y and log x are plotted against each other on a double logarithmic grid, the resulting points will lie along a straight line. Fewer points are required to define a straight line than a curved one. Theoretically, two points should be sufficient if the variation between plants is due only to the experimental treatments. The value of k is equivalent to the regression of log y on log x, and this value is the main basis for comparing treatments.

Using this formula, Troughton (1960) found that flower formation was associated with an increase in shoot growth relative to root growth. Within varieties of perennial ryegrass there was a greater shoot:root ratio as intensity of heading increased.

Vose (1962) found widely different shoot:root ratios between genotypes of perennial ryegrass. He visualized the shoot:root ratio as representing the net product of the differential distribution of carbohydrates between shoot and root. This distribution is genetically controlled but is subject to modification by environmental factors.

Defoliation of a growing plant causes a temporary reduction in the rate of root growth. Crider (1955) demonstrated that a single clipping, which removed most of the foliage, caused root growth to stop for periods ranging from 6 to 18 days in all species studied except orchard grass, *Dactylis glomerata* L. The percentage of roots that stopped growth varied in proportion to the amount of foliage removed.

Growth Analysis

Watson (1958) points out that the total dry-matter production of a crop may vary through changes in either the size or the amount of activity of the photosynthetic system, together with the length of the growth period during which photosynthesis continues. The photosynthetic capacity of crops is expressed in terms of leaf area index (LAI), which is the ratio of leaf area to land area. Crop growth rate (CGR) is the increase in weight of the crop per unit area of land during a stated time interval.

For individual plants, other measurements are more useful. Leaf area ratio (LAR) is the leaf area (including sheath in grasses) per unit weight of plant material present (including roots). It is usually expressed as cm^2/g at a given point in time. Photosynthetic efficiency is measured as net assimilation rate (NAR), which is the rate of increase in dry weight per unit of leaf area, usually expressed as g/dm^2 per week. NAR can be considered a measure of the excess of rate of photosynthesis over the rate of dry-matter loss by respiration. The LAR and NAR determine the plant's relative growth rate (RGR): the increase in plant weight per unit weight already present during a stated time interval.

The mean NAR for a sampling interval is calculated from the initial and final values of dry weight and leaf area obtained from similarly treated plants. Mean NAR is generally calculated by the formula:

$$\text{NAR} = \frac{(W_2 - W_1)\,(\log_e A_2 - \log_e A_1)}{(t_2 - t_1)\,(L_2 - L_1)}$$

where W_1 and W_2 are initial and final dry weights,
A_1 and A_2 the initial and final leaf areas, and
t_1 and t_2 the initial and final points in time.

5

This expression gives an accurate estimate of mean NAR only when the relationship between L and W is linear over the interval t_1 to t_2. It appears that this condition is approximated for short intervals of 1 to 2 weeks, under constant environmental conditions.

Limitations in the concept of NAR and possible sources of error in estimating it are discussed by Watson (1947, 1952). In field crops, the whole root system cannot always be recovered, and often the NAR has to be estimated from the tops of the plants only. This results in an underestimation of NAR when the root system is increasing in dry weight, but the error may be almost negligible at some stages of growth.

Mean RGR is calculated by the formula:

$$RGR = \frac{\log_e W_2 - \log_e W_1}{(t_2 - t_1)}$$

The only assumption required is that W varies without discontinuity over the period t_1 to t_2.

In growth analysis it is normal to destroy the plants at the time of measurement so that the separate parts can be recovered and weighed. Troughton (1963) has suggested a method of measuring root and shoot size by volume displacement of water, thus leaving the plant intact. The derivation and proper use of growth analysis formulas have been treated by Radford (1967).

Non-structural Carbohydrates

The carbohydrates formed by a plant may be used directly as the substrate for growth and respiration, or they may be stored for future use. In herbages, the major non-structural carbohydrates, or total available carbohydrates, are soluble carbohydrates (sugars and fructosan), dextrin, and starch. The relative importance of each varies with the species. It is characteristic of the common perennial and biennial forage legumes to accumulate sucrose and starch. The common perennial forage grasses native to tropical and subtropical latitudes also accumulate sucrose and starch, whereas those native to temperate latitudes accumulate sucrose and fructosan (Smith, Paulsen, and Raguse, 1964).

Non-structural carbohydrates are found in the basal, aerial, and underground parts of plants. The leaf base and stem base of grasses usually contain larger amounts than the roots (Reynolds and Smith, 1962; Sprague and Sullivan, 1950). The roots of alfalfa and red clover have a considerably higher carbohydrate content than the crowns (Jung and Smith, 1961).

The effect of stored carbohydrates on regrowth and winterhardiness has been studied. Carbohydrates accumulated in the basal portions of grasses and legumes are utilized for respiration and regrowth immediately after defoliation. Davidson and Milthorpe (1966) found that the changes in reserve carbohydrates following lenient defoliation of orchard grass would account for respiration and regrowth requirements. They speculated that under severe defoliation proteins would also have to be remobilized.

In reviewing the association between carbohydrates and winter survival of plants, Weinmann (1961) concludes that the relationship is complex. Although large quantities of available carbohydrates are indirectly important, cold-resistance may be more closely related to the sugar and amino acid content of the storage organs. The subject of carbohydrates in grassland herbage has been reviewed by McIlroy (1967).

Various methods have been used to preserve plant material for carbohydrate analysis. Because soluble carbohydrates undergo rapid changes after cutting, immediate and complete inactivation of the enzymes in cut material is essential if samples are stored before analysis. Wylam (1953) notes that freeze-drying produces no change in the individual soluble carbohydrates of grass samples, but that changes may occur during subsequent storage. Rapid heat-drying is effective, but it involves the risk of some destruction of the component sugars. Jones (1962) found differences in soluble carbohydrate constituents at various drying temperatures, but considered that controlled drying in a forced-draught oven was justified when only gross differences in composition were to be measured. Smith (1962) oven-dried samples for analysis of total available carbohydrates at 100 C for 1 hour, and completed drying at 70 C. Other techniques are autoclaving for 5 minutes for rapid killing of the material, followed by drying at 30 to 40 C for 72 hours, then at 100 C for 20 minutes (Baker, 1960), or by immersion in boiling alcohol (Waite and Boyd, 1953). Negligible differences were found between the latter method and oven-drying when the samples were placed in the oven within 10 to 15 minutes after cutting.

For many purposes, Weinmann (1947) considers that the determination of total available carbohydrates is of greater significance than determination of individual or groups of carbohydrates. He developed a method to assess the available carbohydrate content by a single determination. In his method the plant material is subjected to enzyme digestion to break down starch, dextrin, and maltose to glucose. Other sugars and fructosan are extracted at the same time and, after clarification, are converted to reducing sugars by acid hydrolysis. This method, as modified by Lindahl, Davis, and Shepherd (1949), has been used by many workers. Smith (1962) has outlined a technique that is more rapid, though it gives carbohydrate percentages slightly higher than those obtained by Weinmann's method.

With plant material that contains no starch, or only negligible amounts of it, analysis for water-soluble carbohydrates has the same physiological significance as total available carbohydrate analysis (Weinmann, 1961). Total soluble carbohydrates can be extracted from plant material with water. If a separation of soluble sugars and fructosan is

7

required, the sugars can be extracted with alcohol, and the fructosan separated from the residue with hot water (Jones, 1962) or oxalic acid (Laidlaw and Reid, 1952).

The carbohydrates in both the soluble sugar and fructosan extracts can be estimated from the quantities of free hexoses by using an anthrone technique (Baker and Garwood, 1961). A green color is produced when carbohydrates are heated with anthrone in an acid solution. This technique is much more sensitive for hexoses than for pentoses. Fructosan content can be calculated from the amount of fructose, measured colorimetrically (Teel, 1956). Laidlaw and Reid (1952) used paper chromatography to separate and estimate the various sugars present in the extracts, and Waite and Boyd (1953) measured the reducing sugars by a copper-reduction method. Several other useful techniques for estimating the reducing power of the hydrolysate are noted by Weinmann (1961).

A direct estimation of food reserves can be made by taking plants from an actively growing situation and placing them in a dark room until growth ceases (Burton and Jackson, 1962). Because photosynthesis is prevented, the weight of the new growth is a measure of the quantity of carbohydrates and other energy-yielding materials that were stored in the plants.

ENVIRONMENTAL PHYSIOLOGY
Light

One goal in physiological investigations is to determine how plants can make more efficient use of light energy. The energy in light is usually expressed as calories striking a unit area per unit of time. The caloric content of herbage plants can also be measured, and comparisons can be made between the energy received and that stored. In such comparisons, the efficiency of conversion is found to be very low, even when the energy required for nutrient uptake, respiration, photosynthesis, and chemosynthesis is considered.

Loomis and Williams (1963) calculated that under average summer conditions in the United States, if only 5.3 percent of the total radiant energy falling on a crop surface was stored in carbon compounds, dry-matter production could be 77 g/m^2 per day. In 100 days of growth at this rate, crop yields (including minerals) approaching 80 metric tons per hectare would be produced. This is about ten times the yield normally obtained under good crop management. Black (1964) found a similar gap between potential and actual yields of subterranean clover in South Australia, and attributed the discrepancy largely to inefficient utilization of light. The prospect of making better use of light energy is encouraging enough to justify intensive investigation of the problems involved. The efficiency with which energy is stored can be calculated by assuming a calorie content of 3,440 cal/g of dry herbage, and a radiant energy receipt appropriate to the area. Loomis and Williams (1963) estimated a daily receipt of 500 cal/cm² over much of the United States during the summer.

Though the energy concept best expresses the usefulness of light, the foot-candle is a more popular unit of measurement. Ten thousand foot-candles of natural daylight, which is about the maximum intensity at noon on a cloudless day, is approximately equivalent to 1.75 cal/cm² per minute at sea level. Photographic meters will measure illumination in foot-candles, but they have definite shortcomings. These meters have their maximum sensitivity to green light, but plant processes such as photosynthesis, chlorophyll synthesis, phototropism, and photomorphogenesis reach their peak activity under red or blue light and are at a minimum under green light. This does not make all measurements with photographic meters valueless, for in natural daylight there is a relationship between the light measured and the light that influences the plants. Interpretation is required, however, because the spectral composition of natural daylight varies with atmospheric conditions and the angle of the sun, and the composition of artificial light varies with the type of lamp used. Measurement with a photographic meter can be very misleading. Ideally, the meter should measure the intensity of the light only at the wavelengths concerned in the plant process under study. Photosynthesis appears to have peak responses to wavelengths of 435 and 675 mμ. At 560 mμ, where most photographic light meters are most sensitive, the rate of photosynthesis is about one-fifth of its maximum. Instruments that will measure wavelengths with a high degree of exactitude can be obtained, and though they are more costly than ordinary photographic meters, the expense can be justified (McCree, 1966; Robertson and Holmes, 1963). Stern (1962) has reviewed the problems of light measurement in pastures.

To study the effects of light, it is necessary to have control over its intensity. This is a simple procedure in the laboratory, where artificial sources are available, but a light meter of the correct sensitivity should be used to establish the conditions. There are fluorescent lights especially designed for plant growth, but a combination of cool white fluorescent and incandescent sources can also be used. Helson (1965) compared two fluorescent sources and found that both required supplementation with incandescent light to promote efficient growth of tomatoes. There are three main differences between laboratory and field lighting that should be considered in evaluating results. Laboratory light is usually of lower intensity than outdoor light; laboratory light is usually supplied from directly overhead, whereas light in the field comes from changing directions; and, as plants in the laboratory are close to the source of light, there is a greater relative reduction in illumination from the top of a plant to its base. The precise light requirement in the laboratory cannot be specified because of the complication of light quality and the varying requirements of plants. For reasonable growth of most herbages, 800 to 1000 foot-candles measured on a photographic meter would be a minimum, and increased growth might be obtained with up to 3000

9

foot-candles or more. At the higher light levels, disposal of heat from the lamps becomes a serious problem.

In the field, light can be regulated through the selection of companion species in mixtures, by sowing, mowing, or grazing at critical times, or by selection of the topography on which a crop is grown. Shading with cotton, nylon, or wire mesh is useful for small experimental plots.

Black (1957) has reviewed the influence of light on dry-weight increases in herbages. Other aspects that have been reported are the influence on chemical composition (Bathurst and Mitchell, 1958); seedling growth (Bula, Rhykerd, and Langston, 1959); carbon dioxide utilization, root and rhizome growth, and nutrient uptake (Burton, Jackson, and Knox, 1959); nodule development in legumes (Butler, Greenwood, and Soper, 1959); and various combinations and extensions of these.

In experiments involving light as a variable, it may be necessary to know the area of leaf surface exposed. The usefulness of techniques that measure leaf area varies with the size and shape of leaves. The simplest method is to establish a relationship between weight and area, and then calculate areas on the basis of weight. This method must be used with caution because the weight–area relationship is affected by environmental conditions. Another method for grass leaves uses the relationship: Area $= LB$ (0.905), where $L =$ length, and $B =$ breadth at a point midway along the length (Kemp, 1960). More elaborate means are necessary for irregularly shaped leaves. Jenkins (1959) has described a device that measures the reduction in air flow when a leaf is placed over a perforated plate through which air is forced, and Voisey and Kloek (1964) used the same principle in measuring light reduction when a leaf was placed in the pathway between a light source and a photoelectric cell. In a further adaptation of this method the leaves are photographed, and the negative placed between a light source and a photoelectric cell. A rough estimate of individual leaf areas can be made by comparing leaves with standard photographs showing known areas (Williams, 1954).

The concept of LAI, the area of leaf (one surface) per unit area of ground, is more useful than leaf area alone. As the LAI increases, the light supplied to the lowermost leaves of a plant diminishes because of shading. In the lower leaves, respiration might exceed photosynthesis, and instead of being an asset to the plant these leaves could become a liability. Stern and Donald (1961) calculated the LAI necessary for photosynthesis to balance respiration at various levels of light energy. They reasoned that when the intensity of usable radiation is increased a higher LAI can be maintained profitably.

Temperature

Air temperature within the normal range required for plant growth is easily secured in growth rooms. However, indoor studies on the effects of temperature can be misleading unless other conditions of the environment such as light, humidity, and carbon dioxide supply can be interpreted. Broad aspects of the problem are discussed by Went (1957) and Hudson (1957). Possible complications are illustrated in work reported by Hull (1958), who noted the difference in foliar wax between plants grown outside and inside the greenhouse and thus the inadequacy of greenhouse plants for the evaluation of some herbicides.

It is often desirable to control soil temperature independently of air temperature. Cooper and others (1960) used water baths held at various temperatures, into which plastic, soil-filled pots were immersed. Natural temperature conditions can be simulated with this arrangement.

Interspecies Relations

The most-studied interspecies relationship is that between grasses and legumes, but it is still not well understood. There is no doubt that the nitrogen nutrition of grass is enhanced through association with a legume, but the precise mechanism remains obscure. Martin (1960) lists four possible routes of transfer of nitrogen from a legume to a grass: directly from the legume nodules, from decayed nodules, from decomposed aerial parts, and through grazing animals. Bakhuis and Kleter (1965) confirm that transfer occurs both above and below ground, but have been unable to assess the relative importance of each mechanism.

The difficulty of maintaining legumes with grass under high nitrogen fertilizations is usually attributed to shading by the rank growth of the associated grasses. Stern and Donald (1962) believe that shade is harmful when legumes are in the seedling stage, but state that shading is not the only cause of poor growth. Richardson, Jordan, and Garrard (1957) found that alfalfa nodulation was actually inhibited at high NH_4 and NO_3 levels, although nodulation did occur when levels of soil nitrogen were moderate. Allos (1956) showed that small amounts of nitrogenous fertilizer increased nitrogen fixation in several legumes.

Nodulation alone is not sufficient evidence that the nitrogen nutrition of a legume is adequate, because antagonisms between *Rhizobium* strains may lead to an unsatisfactory symbiotic relationship (Hely, Bergersen, and Brockwell, 1957; Nutman, 1953). Allen and Baldwin (1954) have presented a review of the techniques in use up to 1953 to study the *Rhizobium*–legume complex. A more recent technique, using a strain of subterranean clover, *Trifolium subterraneum* L., that has a red coloration until effectively nodulated (the Red Leaf Strain), has been described by Brockwell (1956). When this method was used, significant differences in the effectiveness of *Rhizobium* strains could be detected 18 days after inoculation.

Nitrogen fixation by nonleguminous plants has received some attention also. Bond (1957) has described work with *Casuarina*, and Gardner and Bond (1957) with *Shepherdia*.

11

The effects of toxic root exudates on interspecies relations has been summarized (Woods, 1960; Garb, 1961). Garb (1961) lists several herbage species that react to root exudates. He suggests that species that tend to grow in pure stands might do so because of the antagonistic effect of their exudates on other species, and he believes that such plants might be useful objects of study.

Many investigations have been made on the effect of physical extracts from one plant on the growth of another. Nielsen, Cuddy, and Woods (1960) tested the mutual effects of water extracts from ground plant material of several herbage species on germination and seedling growth. Alfalfa extract had the widest range of inhibition. Alfalfa was the most tolerant to extracts of other species, and timothy the least. These unidentified substances would not necessarily be exuded by intact plants. Bhuvaneswari and Sulochana (1955) have described a simple laboratory technique for obtaining root exudates without disturbing a growing plant. In their method the plant was grown in a soil-filled porous tube immersed in a flask of water. The root exudates passed from the tube into the water and could be recovered at any time. Stotzky, Culbreth, and Mish (1962) developed a more elaborate apparatus that permitted collection of both exudates and carbon dioxide released by the roots. Persidsky and Wilde (1954) were able to evaluate the effect of volatile gases emanating from the soil by placing the soil to be tested in the lower chamber of a desiccator and the excised roots of the plant to be tested in the upper chamber.

In investigations involving plant growth regulators, an attempt should be made to identify the active substances. For any soluble substance, paper chromatography is probably the simplest method by which to attempt identification and it requires a minimum of equipment. The techniques are well described by Lederer and Lederer (1957); Smith (1958); and Vlitos and Meudt (1953).

WATER AND PLANT NUTRIENT RELATIONS

Approximately 99 percent of the water that enters roots moves upward in response to diffusion pressure gradients and is lost to the atmosphere. This water acts as a solvent and a conductor of nutrients, and aids in regulating plant temperature. If the supply of moisture is reduced, growth processes are restricted. Plant growth terminates long before death is caused by moisture stress.

Soil Moisture Control

Several methods have been used to measure the effect of soil moisture supply on the rate of absorption and the transfer of nutrients by a plant. Each method has certain advantages and disadvantages.

The method most often used allows the soil moisture to decrease by evapotranspiration to a predetermined level, after which sufficient water is applied to bring the soil mass to field capacity. The principal justification for this method is the similarity between the cyclic soil moisture system it presents to the plant and the dynamic situation that occurs under field conditions. An objection to the procedure is that in a cyclic moisture pattern the availability of some nutrients, especially potassium and phosphorus, is decreased. If plant nutrient responses are related to some average soil moisture content, erroneous conclusions with regard to these differentially available nutrients may be reached. There is also a problem with moisture stratification, which is very common with high evapotranspiration from the shallow soil that is used in most greenhouse studies. Through a modification of this method, the moisture stratification and also the cyclic effect can be reduced. A ceramic cone or plate is placed in the soil to maintain the soil at a moisture level determined by a manometric thermocap relay system (Taylor, 1955).

In a method described by Mederski and Wilson (1960), water and nutrients are supplied to the plant from separate layers of soil in a glazed crock. The lower layer of soil is used as a reservoir for plant nutrients, and the upper layer of wet sand for water. The two layers are separated by a film of wax that is permeable to plant roots but not to water. A plant such as corn is able to draw water from the sand and nutrients from the soil. Moisture in the soil layer is regulated before sealing, and remains at an adequate level during a short-term experimental period.

Osmotic agents such as sucrose, glucose, D-mannitol, and polyethylene glycol have been used to regulate moisture availability in nutrient solutions (Lagerwerff, Okata, and Eagle, 1961; Wiggans and Gardner, 1959; Woolley, 1963). Some success in restricting water and nutrient uptake from soils has been attained by incorporating octadecanol in the soil (Olsen and others, 1962).

Several methods are used to measure soil moisture in the field. Baver (1956) discusses procedures that use electrical resistance and moisture tension techniques. The use of radioactive materials to measure soil moisture and other soil properties has also been described (Kirkham and Kunze, 1962).

Soil Moisture and Nutrient Availability

Studies with grasses and legumes show that at a given level of fertility a reduction in the soil moisture supply causes an increase in plant nitrogen, a decrease in potassium, and a variable effect on the calcium, phosphorus, and magnesium contents (Jones, 1948; Thomas, Mack, and Cotton, 1942). The nitrogen content of legumes exposed to high moisture tensions may decrease because of the adverse effect on symbiotic fixation.

Some of the effects of soil moisture on plant nutrient contents have been explained by the fixation processes that occur in many soils. Volk

(1934) reports that there is very little soil fixation of potassium when the soil is kept moist, but that alternate wetting and drying causes fixation of potassium in a nonreplaceable form. Acid soils fix very little potassium when moist, but fixation increases sharply when the soil is dried. Calcareous soils fix potassium when moist and the rate increases upon drying.

Soil moisture stress is also conducive to the fixation of phosphorus and explains the low phosphorus content of plants under these conditions (Trumble, 1947). The clay content of soil determines the extent of phosphorus fixation upon drying (Neller and Comar, 1947). The wide variation in clay content of soils helps to explain the variable response observed in phosphorus uptake.

Magnesium tends to become concentrated in plants as soil moisture decreases (Jones, 1962; Thomas and others, 1942). Calcium and magnesium deficiencies occur under similar conditions, and often the symptoms of magnesium deficiency are not evident until calcium is applied.

Generally, the percentage content of calcium in plants is increased as soil moisture is decreased, but it is also influenced by the status of other soil constituents such as potassium and magnesium. The entry of calcium and potassium into a plant follows a reciprocal relationship.

During prolonged periods of drought, the moisture content of the fertile surface soil may be reduced below its wilting percentage. There is some evidence that roots transfer water from a moist region to a drier one, thus permitting roots to grow into soils that are below the wilting point (Hunter and Kelley, 1946; Volk, 1947), but contrary results have also been reported (Shantz, 1927; Loomis and Evans, 1936; Hendrickson and Veihmeyer, 1931).

Plant roots in soils below the wilting point are able to absorb some nitrogen, phosphorus, and potassium (Volk, 1947; Hunter and Kelley, 1946), but this source appears to be inadequate even in the most fertile soils (Wadleigh and Richards, 1951). Even when the subsoil was kept moist, Hobbs and Bertramson (1949) found that boron was not available in sufficient amounts in dry surface soil.

Adequate root zone aeration is essential for the development of healthy plants. This has been emphasized many times in soil studies (Baver and Farnsworth, 1940; Ellis and Morris, 1945; Smith and Cook, 1946), and also in solution cultures (Gilbert and Shive, 1942; Shive, 1941). The rate of nutrient entry into a plant is conditioned by the rate of respiration of the absorbing tissue, which in turn is conditioned by the oxygen supply.

Lawton (1945) found that plants grown in soils at or near moisture saturation had a low percentage composition of nitrogen, phosphorus, and potassium, but no consistent effects were noted for calcium or magnesium. Letey and others (1961) verified these results, reporting an increase in growth and water uptake but a decrease in the sodium content of plants when soil oxygen was increased. Reviews by Russell

(1952) and by Page and Bodman (1951) deal with the effects of oxygen on nutrient absorption.

Excess soil moisture affects nutrition, not only through reduced oxygen supply but also by increased partial pressure of carbon dioxide. Carbon dioxide bubbled through nutrient solutions can reduce both water and nutrient uptake (Chang and Loomis, 1945). Toxic concentrations of carbon dioxide in soils may be more common than limiting concentrations of oxygen. Interactions between soil moisture and oxygen level have been investigated by Gingrich and Russell (1956). They found root growth to be at a maximum in soil with a moisture tension of $\frac{1}{3}$ atmosphere and an oxygen content of 21 percent. Growth was restricted when either the moisture stress was increased or the oxygen level decreased.

Anaerobic conditions resulting from excessive soil moisture may cause a relatively high accumulation of reduced iron, sulfur, and manganese, all of which may be toxic to plant roots (van't Woudt and Hagen, 1957). Wet soils tend to have low soil temperatures that depress the microbial activity on which nutrient availability depends. Letey, Stolzy, and Blank (1962) point out the importance of the duration and timing of low soil oxygen levels because a low supply is most detrimental during the early stages of plant growth.

The literature shows conclusively that nutrient availability and absorption are influenced by soil moisture. In general, the uptake of nutrients increases with increasing soil moisture up to field capacity. There are notable exceptions, and extreme moisture conditions cause perceivable changes in the uptake patterns of many nutrients.

Nutrition and Root Cation-exchange

It has been recognized for some time that plant roots exhibit cation-exchange properties (Jenny and Overstreet, 1939). Marked species differences in cation-exchange capacity (CEC) have been demonstrated (Drake, Vengris, and Colby, 1951; McLean, Adams, and Franklin, 1956). Heintze (1961) has reviewed several methods that have been used to determine root CEC. By applying the Donnan equilibrium theory to the root–soil complex, differences in root CEC have been used to explain the differential uptake of phosphorus (Drake and Steckel, 1955), calcium and potassium (Drake and others, 1951; Gray, Drake, and Colby, 1953; Smith and Wallace, 1956), and strontium (Mouat, 1960).

There is no general agreement on the significance of root CEC in nutrient absorption (Epstein, 1956; Laties, 1959). It is possible that CEC exerts a quantitative influence by increasing the proportions of ions of different valency in the apparent free-space of the root, and also by raising the concentration of cations in the apparent free-space above the level in the soil solution (Asher and Ozanne, 1961).

In comparison with grasses, legumes seem to have a relatively high CEC, dicotyledons having two to three times the CEC of monocotyledons. The CEC of a plant may be increased by nitrogen applications, as has been observed on plants with a naturally low CEC (Asher and Ozanne, 1961; McLean and others, 1956).

The ratio of potassium to calcium adsorbed onto plant roots should decrease as the root CEC increases. Thus, when plants differing in CEC are grown in association on soils deficient in potassium, the plants with a low CEC should have a competitive advantage (Gray and others, 1953). Positive correlations between root CEC and uptake of phosphorus and calcium have been reported (Asher and Ozanne, 1961; Drake and others, 1955; Rossiter and Ozanne, 1955). Further application of root CEC theories to herbage plant associations may clarify some of the nutrient responses that have been difficult to explain.

References

Allen, O. N., and I. L. Baldwin. 1954. *Rhizobia*–legume relationships. Soil Sci. 78:415–427.

Allos, Hazim F. 1956. Influence of inorganic nitrogen on the inhibition of symbiotic nitrogen fixation. Dep. Agron., Iowa State Coll., Doctoral Thesis.

Anslow, R. C. 1966. The rate of appearance of leaves on tillers of the Gramineae. Herb. Abstr. 36:149–155.

Anslow, R. C., and J. O. Green. 1966. The seasonal growth of pasture grasses. J. Agr. Sci. 68:109–122.

Asher, C. J., and P. G. Ozanne. 1961. The cation-exchange capacity of plant roots, and its relationship to the uptake of insoluble nutrients. Austral. J. Agr. Res. 12:755–766.

Baker, H. K. 1960. The production of early spring grass. 1. The effect of autumn management and different levels of nitrogenous manuring on the production of early spring grass from a general purpose ley. J. Brit. Grassl. Soc. 15:275–280.

Baker, H. K., and E. A. Garwood. 1961. Studies on the root development of herbage plants. V. Seasonal changes in fructosan and soluble-sugar contents of cocksfoot herbage, stubble and roots under two cutting treatments. J. Brit. Grassl. Soc. 16:263–267.

Bakhuis, J. A., and H. J. Kleter. 1965. Some effects of associated growth on grass and clover under field conditions. Neth. J. Agr. Sci. 13:280–310.

Bartels, L. F. 1956. Cutting lucerne hay—new shoots a doubtful guide. J. Dep. Agr. Victoria 54:595–597.

Bathurst, N. O., and K. J. Mitchell. 1958. The effects of light and temperature on the chemical composition of pasture plants. New Zeal. J. Agr. Res. 1:540–552.

Baver, L. D. 1956. Soil physics. 3rd ed., p. 290–298. John Wiley and Sons, Inc., New York.

Baver, L. D., and R. B. Farnsworth. 1940. Soil structure effects in the growth of sugar beets. Proc. Soil Sci. Soc. Amer. 5:45–48.

Bhuvaneswari, K., and C. B. Sulochana. 1955. Assay of root exudates. Current Sci. 24:376–377.

Black, J. N. 1957. The influence of varying light intensity on the growth of herbage plants. Herb. Abstr. 27:89–98.

Black, J. N. 1964. An analysis of the potential production of swards of subterranean clover (*Trifolium subterraneum* L.) at Adelaide, South Australia. J. Appl. Ecol. 1:3–18.

Boehle, J., Jr., W. H. Mitchell, C. B. Kresge, and L. T. Kardos. 1963. Apparatus for taking soil–root cores. Agron. J. 55:208–209.

Bond, G. 1957. The development and significance of the root nodules of *Casuarina*. Ann. Bot. 21:373–380.

Brockwell, J. 1956. The use of the Red Leaf strain of subterranean clover for rapid evaluation of strain effectiveness in *Rhizobium triplii*. J. Austral. Inst. Agr. Sci. 22:260–265.

Bula, R. J., C. L. Rhykerd, and R. G. Langston. 1959. Growth response of alfalfa seedlings under various light regimes. Agron. J. 51:84–86.

Burton, G. W., and J. E. Jackson. 1962. A method for measuring sod reserves. Agron. J. 54:53–55.

Burton, G. W., J. E. Jackson, and F. E. Knox. 1959. The influence of light reduction upon the production, persistence and chemical composition of Coastal bermudagrass, *Cynodon dactylon*. Agron. J. 51:537–542.

Butler, G. W., R. M. Greenwood, and Kathleen Soper. 1959. Effects of shading and defoliation on the turnover of root and nodule tissue of plants of *Trifolium repens, Trifolium pratense* and *Lotus uliginosus*. New Zeal. J. Agr. Res. 2:415–426.

Chang, H. T., and W. E. Loomis. 1945. Effect of carbon dioxide on absorption of water and nutrients by roots. Plant Physiol. 20:221–232.

Cooper, D. J., K. F. Nielsen, J. W. White, and W. Kalbfleisch. 1960. Note on an apparatus for controlling soil temperatures. Can. J. Soil Sci. 40:105–107.

Crider, F. J. 1955. Root-growth stoppage resulting from defoliation of grass. U.S. Dep. Agr. Tech. Bull. 1102.

Crowder, L. V., J. Vanegas, and J. Silva. 1960. The influence of cutting interval on alfalfa production in the high Andes. Agron. J. 52:128–130.

Davidson, J. L., and F. L. Milthorpe. 1966. Leaf growth of *Dactylis glomerata* following defoliation. Ann. Bot. 30:173–184.

Drake, M., and J. E. Steckel. 1955. Solubilization of soil and rock phosphate as related to root cation exchange capacity. Proc. Soil Sci. Soc. Amer. 19:449–450.

Drake, M., J. Vengris, and W. G. Colby. 1951. Cation-exchange capacity of roots. Soil Sci. 72:139–147.

Ellis, N. K., and R. Morris. 1945. Preliminary observations on the relation of yield of crops grown on organic soil with controlled water table and the area of aeration in the soil and subsidence of the soil. Proc. Soil Sci. Soc. Amer. 10:282–283.

Epstein, E. 1956. Mineral nutrition of plants: mechanisms of uptake and transport. Ann. Rev. Plant Physiol. 7:1–24.

Evans, M. W., and F. O. Grover. 1940. Developmental morphology of the growing point of the shoot and the inflorescence in grasses. J. Agr. Res. 61:481–520.

Garb, Solomon. 1961. Differential growth-inhibitors produced by plants. Bot. Rev. 27:422–443.

Gardner, I. C., and G. Bond. 1957. Observations on the root nodules of *Shepherdia*. Can. J. Bot. 35:305–314.

Gilbert, S. G., and J. W. Shive. 1942. The significance of oxygen in nutrient substrates for plants. I. The oxygen requirement. Soil Sci. 53:143–152.

Gingrich, J. R., and M. B. Russell. 1956. Effect of soil moisture tension and oxygen concentration on the growth of corn roots. Agron. J. 48:517–520.

Grassland Research Institute. 1961. Research techniques in use at the Grassland Research Institute, Hurley. Bull. 45. Commonwealth Agr. Bur., Farnham Royal, Bucks.

Gray, B., M. Drake, and W. G. Colby. 1953. Potassium competition in grass–legume associations as a function of root cation exchange capacity. Proc. Soil Sci. Soc. Amer. 17:235–239.

Heintze, S. G. 1961. Studies on cation-exchange capacities of roots. Plant and Soil 13:365–383.

Helson, V. A. 1965. Comparison of gro-lux and cool white fluorescent lamps with and without incandescent as light sources used in plant growth rooms for growth and development of tomato plants. Can. J. Plant Sci. 45:461–466.

Hely, F. W., F. J. Bergersen, and J. Brockwell. 1957. Microbial antagonism in the rhizosphere as a factor in the failure of inoculation of subterranean clover. Austral. J. Agr. Res. 8:24–44.

Hendrickson, A. H., and F. J. Veihmeyer. 1931. Influence of dry soil on root extension. Plant Physiol. 6:567–570.

Hobbs, J. A., and B. R. Bertramson. 1949. Boron uptake by plants as influenced by soil moisture. Proc. Soil Sci. Soc. Amer. 14:257–261.

Hudson, J. P. 1957. Control of plant environment for experimental work and notes on environmental control equipment for use in Britain. Dep. Hort., Univ. Nottingham. Misc. Pub. 8.

Hull, H. M. 1958. The effect of day and night temperature growth, foliar wax content and cuticle development of velvet mesquite. Weeds 6:133–142.

Hunter, A. S., and O. J. Kelley. 1946. The extension of plant roots into dry soil. Plant Physiol. 21:445–451.

Jenkins, H. V. 1959. An airflow planimeter for measuring the area of detached leaves. Plant Physiol. 34:532–536.

Jenny, H., and R. Overstreet. 1939. Cation interchange between plant roots and soil colloids. Soil Sci. 47:257–272.

Jewiss, O. R. 1966. Morphological and physiological aspects of growth of grasses during the vegetative phase, p. 39–54. In F. L. Milthorpe and J. D. Ivins (ed.) The growth of cereals and grasses. Butterworths Sci. Publications, London.

Jones, Byron E. 1948. The effect of varying amounts of irrigation on the composition of two varieties of snap beans. Proc. Amer. Soc. Hort. Sci. 51:457–462.

Jones, D. I. H. 1962. Note on the pre-treatment of herbage samples for determination of soluble carbohydrate constituents. J. Sci. Food Agr. 13:83–86.

Jung, G. A., and Dale Smith. 1961. Trends of cold resistance and chemical changes over winter in the roots and crown of alfalfa and medium red clover. 1. Changes in certain nitrogen and carbohydrate fractions. Agron. J. 53:359–364.

Kemp, C. D. 1960. Methods of measuring the leaf area of grasses from linear measurements. Ann. Bot. 24:491–499.

Kirkham, D., and R. J. Kunze. 1962. Isotope methods and uses in soil physics research. Advances in Agron. 14:321–358.

Lagerwerff, J. V., Gen Okata, and Harold E. Eagle. 1961. Control of osmotic pressure of culture solutions with polyethylene glycol. Science 133:1486–1487.

Laidlaw, R. A., and S. G. Reid. 1952. Analytical studies on the carbohydrates of grasses and clovers. 1. Development of methods for the estimation of free sugar and fructosan content. J. Sci. Food Agr. 3:19–25.

Laties, G. G. 1959. Active transport of salt into plant tissue. Ann. Rev. Plant Physiol. 10:87–112.

Lawton, K. 1945. The influence of soil aeration on the growth and absorption of nutrients by corn plants. Proc. Soil Sci. Soc. Amer. 10:263–268.

Lederer, Edgar, and Michael Lederer. 1957. Chromatography. 2nd ed., 711 p. Van Nostrand, Princeton, New Jersey.

Letey, J., O. R. Lunt, L. H. Stolzy, and T. E. Szuszkiewicz. 1961. Plant growth, water use and nutritional response to rhizosphere differentials of oxygen concentration. Proc. Soil Sci. Soc. Amer. 25:183–186.

Letey, J., L. H. Stolzy, and G. B. Blank. 1962. Effect of duration and timing of low soil oxygen content on shoot and root growth. Agron. J. 54:34–37.

18

Lindahl, I., R. E. Davis, and W. O. Shepherd. 1949. The application of the total available carbohydrate method to the study of carbohydrate reserves of switch cane, *Arundinaria tecta*. Plant Physiol. 24:285–294.

Loomis, R. S., and W. A. Williams. 1963. Maximum crop productivity: an estimate. Crop Sci. 3:67–72.

Loomis, W. E., and L. M. Evans. 1936. Hydrotropic responses of roots in soil. Bot. Gaz. 97:728–743.

Martin, T. W. 1960. The role of white clover in grassland. Herb. Abstr. 30:159–164.

McCree, K. J. 1966. A solarimeter for measuring photosynthetically active radiation. Agr. Meteorol. 3:353–366.

McIlroy, R. J. 1967. Carbohydrates of grassland herbage. Herb. Abstr. 37:79–87.

McKell, C. M., A. M. Wilson, and M. B. Jones. 1961. A flotation method for easy separation of roots from soil samples. Agron. J. 53:56–57.

McLean, E. O., D. Adams, and R. E. Franklin, Jr. 1956. Cation exchange capacities of plant roots as related to their nitrogen contents. Proc. Soil Sci. Soc. Amer. 20:345–347.

Mederski, H. J., and J. H. Wilson. 1960. Relation of soil moisture to ion absorption by corn plants. Proc. Soil Sci. Soc. Amer. 24:149–152.

Mouat, M. C. H. 1960. Interspecific differences in strontium uptake by pasture plants as a function of root cation-exchange capacity. Nature (London) 188:513–514.

Muzik, T. J., and J. W. Whitworth. 1962. A technique for the periodic observation of root systems *in situ*. Agron. J. 54:56.

Neller, J. R., and C. L. Comar. 1947. Factors affecting fixation of phosphorus in soils as determined with radioactive phosphorus. Soil Sci. 64:379–387.

Nielsen, K. F., T. F. Cuddy, and W. B. Woods. 1960. The influence of the extract of some crop and soil residues on germination and growth. Can. J. Plant Sci. 40:188–197.

Nutman, P. S. 1953. Studies on the physiology of nodule formation. 4. The mutual inhibitory effects on nodule production of plants grown in association. Ann. Bot. 17:95–126.

Olsen, S. R., F. S. Watanabe, W. D. Kemper, and F. E. Clark. 1962. Effect of hexadecanol and octadecanol on efficiency of water use and growth of corn. Agron. J. 54:544–545.

Page, J. B., and G. B. Bodman. 1951. The effect of soil physical properties on nutrient availability, p. 133–166. *In* E. Truog (ed.) Mineral nutrition of plants. Univ. Wisconsin Press.

Persidsky, D. J., and S. A. Wilde. 1954. The effect of volatile substances released by soil humus and composts on the growth of excised roots. Plant Physiol. 29:484–486.

Radford, P. J. 1967. Growth analysis formulae—their use and abuse. Crop Sci. 7:171–175.

Rechenthin, C. A. 1956. Elementary morphology of grass growth and how it affects utilization. J. Range Manage. 9:167–170.

Reynolds, J. H., and D. Smith. 1962. Trends of carbohydrate reserves in alfalfa, smooth bromegrass, and timothy grown under various cutting schedules. Crop Sci. 2:333–336.

Richardson, D. A., D. C. Jordan, and E. H. Garrard. 1957. The influence of combined nitrogen on nodulation and nitrogen fixation by *Rhizobium meliloti* Dangeard. Can. J. Plant Sci. 37:205–214.

Rivers, G. W., and J. L. Faubion. 1963. A uniform technique for comparing root systems of sesame, *Sesamum indicum* L. Crop Sci. 3:182–183.

Robertson, G. W., and R. M. Holmes. 1963. A spectral light meter: its construction, calibration, and use. Ecology 44:419–423.

19

Rossiter, R. C., and P. G. Ozanne. 1955. The short-term effects of rock phosphate and superphosphate on a subterranean clover pasture. Austral. J. Agr. Res. 6:553–564.

Russell, M. B. 1952. Soil aeration and plant growth, p. 253–301. *In* Agronomy management. Vol. 2. Academic Press Inc., New York.

Shantz, H. L. 1927. Drought resistance and soil moisture. Ecology 8:145–157.

Shive, J. W. 1941. The balance of ions and oxygen tension in nutrient substrates for plants. Soil Sci. 51:445–457.

Smith, Dale. 1962. Carbohydrate root reserves in alfalfa, red clover, and birdsfoot trefoil under several management schedules. Crop Sci. 2:75–78.

Smith, D., G. M. Paulsen, and C. A. Raguse. 1964. Extraction of total available carbohydrates from grass and legume tissue. Plant Physiol. 39:960–962.

Smith, F. W., and R. L. Cook. 1946. The effect of soil aeration, moisture and compaction on nitrification and oxidation and the growth of sugar beets following corn and legumes in pot cultures. Proc. Soil Sci. Soc. Amer. 11:402–406.

Smith, Ivor. 1958. Chromatographic techniques. Inter-science Publishers Inc., New York. 309 p.

Smith, R. L., and A. Wallace. 1956. Cation-exchange capacity of roots and its relationship to calcium and potassium content of plants. Soil Sci. 81:97–109.

Sprague, V. G., and J. T. Sullivan. 1950. Reserve carbohydrates in orchard grass clipped periodically. Plant Physiol. 25:92–102.

Stern, W. R. 1962. Light measurements in pastures. Herb. Abstr. 32:91–96.

Stern, W. R., and C. M. Donald. 1961. Relationship of radiation, leaf area index and crop growth rate. Nature (London) 189:597–598.

Stern, W. R., and C. M. Donald. 1962. The influence of leaf area and radiation on the growth of clover in swards. Austral. J. Agr. Res. 13:615–623.

Stotzky, G., W. Culbreth, and L. B. Mish. 1962. Apparatus for growing plants with aseptic roots for collection of root exudates and CO_2. Plant Physiol. 37:332–341.

Subcommittee on Range Research Methods. 1962. Basic problems and techniques in range research. Nat. Acad. Sci., Nat. Res. Council, Pub. 890. Washington, D.C.

Taylor, S. A. 1955. An instrument for controlling pressure, vacuum, and temperature. Soil Sci. 79:327–328.

Teel, M. R. 1956. The physiological age of bromegrass, *Bromus inermis* Leyss., as it affects growth rate following defoliation. Ph.D. Thesis, Purdue Univ.

Thomas, W., W. B. Mack, and R. H. Cotton. 1942. Foliar diagnosis in relation to irrigation. Proc. Amer. Soc. Hort. Sci. 40:531–535.

Troughton, Arthur. 1956. Studies on the growth of young grass plants with special reference to the relationship between the shoot and root systems. J. Brit. Grassl. Soc. 11:56–65.

Troughton, Arthur. 1957. The underground organs of herbage grasses. Bull. 44. Commonwealth Agr. Bur., Farnham Royal, Bucks.

Troughton, Arthur. 1960. Further studies on the relationship between shoot and root systems of grasses. J. Brit. Grassl. Soc. 15:41–47.

Troughton, Arthur. 1963. A comparison of five varieties of *Lolium perenne* with special reference to the relationship between the root and shoot systems. Euphytica 12:49–56.

Trumble, H. C. 1947. Research report Western Australian Branch. J. Austral. Inst. Agr. Sci. 13:198.

van't Woudt, B. D., and R. M. Hagan. 1957. Crop responses at excessively high soil moisture levels. Agronomy Management. Vol. 2. Amer. Soc. Agron., Madison, Wisc. p. 514–578.

Vlitos, A. J., and Werner Meudt. 1953. The role of auxin in plant flowering. 1. A quantitative method based on paper chromatography for the determination of indole compounds and of 3-indolacetic acid in plant tissues. Contrib. Boyce Thompson Inst. 17:197–202.

Voisey, Peter W., and Martin Kloek. 1964. A portable leaf area measuring instrument. Can. J. Plant Sci. 44:389–391.

Volk, G. M. 1947. Significance of moisture translocation from soil zones of low moisture tension to zones of high moisture tension by plant roots. J. Amer. Soc. Agron. 39:93–106.

Volk, N. J. 1934. The fixation of potash in difficultly available form in soils. Soil Sci. 37:267–287.

Vose, P. B. 1962. Nutritional response and shoot/root ratio as factors in the composition and yield of genotypes of perennial ryegrass, *Lolium perenne* L. Ann. Bot. 26:425–437.

Wadleigh, C. H., and L. A. Richards. 1951. Soil moisture and mineral nutrition of plants, p. 411–450. *In* E. Truog (ed.) Mineral nutrition of plants. Univ. Wisconsin Press.

Waite, R., and J. Boyd. 1953. The water-soluble carbohydrates of grasses. 1. Changes occurring during the normal life cycle. J. Sci. Food Agr. 4:197–204.

Watson, D. J. 1947. Comparative physiological studies on the growth of field crops. I. Variations in net assimilation rate and leaf area between species and varieties, and within and between years. Ann. Bot. 11:41–76.

Watson, D. J. 1952. The physiological basis of variation in yield. Advances in Agron. 4:101–145.

Watson, D. J. 1958. The dependence of net assimilation rate on leaf area index. Ann. Bot. 22:37–54.

Weinmann, H. 1947. Determination of total available carbohydrate in plants. Plant Physiol. 22:279–290.

Weinmann, H. 1961. Total available carbohydrates in grasses and legumes. Herb. Abstr. 31:255–261.

Went, Fritz W. 1957. The experimental control of plant growth. The Ronald Press Co., New York. 343 p.

Wiggans, S. C., and F. P. Gardner. 1959. Effectiveness of various solutions for simulating drouth conditions as measured by germination and seedling growth. Agron. J. 51:315–318.

Williams, R. F. 1954. Estimation of leaf area for agronomic and plant physiological studies. Austral. J. Agr. Res. 5:235-246.

Williams, T. E., and H. K. Baker. 1957. Studies on the root development of herbage plants. 1. Techniques of herbage root investigations. J. Brit. Grassl. Soc. 12:49–55.

Woods, Frank W. 1960. Biological antagonisms due to phytotoxic root exudates. Bot. Rev. 26:546–569.

Woolley, D. G. 1963. Effects of nutrition, osmotic pressure, and temperature of the nutrient solution on plant growth and chemical composition. I. Spring wheat at the 4- to 6-leaf stage. Can. J. Plant Sci. 43:44–50.

Wylam, C. B. 1953. Analytical studies on the carbohydrates of grasses and clovers. III. Carbohydrate breakdown during wilting and ensilage. J. Sci. Food Agr. 4:527–531.

Chapter 2

PLANT SOCIOLOGY AND ECOLOGY

ROBERT W. LODGE and JAN LOOMAN
Research Station, Canada Department of Agriculture
Swift Current, Saskatchewan

H. J. KNUTTI*
Experimental Farm, Canada Department of Agriculture
Kapuskasing, Ontario

Field analyses to evaluate species in pasture swards can be grouped under two related disciplines: plant sociology, or phytosociology, and plant ecology. The primary aim of phytosociology is to study plant communities, their floristic compositions, and their classification into manageable units. The primary aim of plant ecology is to study a plant or a species in relation to its environment. The information recorded can be used to map grazing units and to plan pasture development and management programs.

Vegetation must be sampled to find ways and means of improving pastures and their management. These goals can be reached after research has demonstrated the most desirable type of vegetation, that is, the one that gives the greatest return for the longest period of time, and when methods are found to establish and maintain this vegetation type. Thus it is necessary to study the behavior of plant species in relation to three factor complexes: climate, soil, and grazing.

PLANT SOCIOLOGY

Classifying vegetation by phytosociological methods before making ecological studies has several advantages. The work can be done qualitatively and the presence or absence of species noted in relatively little time. Large areas can be studied and important differences in swards may become obvious. Units established may form the basis for ecological studies.

Classification procedures, especially those of the Zürich-Montpellier school (Braun-Blanquet, 1951), have been criticized as being subjective and nonrandom. However, these methods assume that plant species are not distributed randomly in nature, but are usually grouped in recognizable combinations that indicate definite environmental conditions. Complicated objective methods (de Vries and Baretta, 1952; Goodall, 1953; Looman and Campbell, 1960) confirm the existence of these combinations of species or associations.

*Present address: CIBA Company Ltd., Dorval, P.Q.

Although sociological surveys can be strictly qualitative, this does not mean that ecological observations cannot be made simultaneously. On the contrary, a survey may be improved considerably if relationships are observed between the association and soil type, climate, or other factors. If surveys are made over large areas where there are wide differences in climate or soil, these observations will be very valuable. Climatic change is often indicated by the distributions of different species of plants, and transitions from one climatic region to another can be outlined by the surveys. Because recommendations for pasture management and pasture improvement may differ according to climatic regions, each region recognized should be treated separately (Clarke, Campbell, and Campbell, 1942; Brown, 1954).

A plant association is essentially a group of stands floristically and ecologically similar but distinct from other associations. In a given association, some species may find optimal conditions, whereas others barely survive. Hence, ecological studies made in associations allow comparisons between stands of an association, as well as between different associations. Yields of stands within an association will give a fairly accurate estimate of the carrying capacity of large areas on the basis of recognized associations.

Most plant associations are too broad for use in recommending management and improvement practice on farms and ranches and for other detailed sociological work. Within a plant association several "agricultural types" must be distinguished for detailed mapping (Campbell and others, 1962). As types are best distinguished on the basis of dominance of one or more species, ecological studies are required for this purpose. Classification of plant communities, however useful, should therefore be considered not as an aim in itself but as another tool to evaluate swards.

PLANT ECOLOGY

Plant ecology, or the study of a plant's household, is the study of the plant in relation to its environment. This environment may be divided into three factor complexes: climatic, edaphic, and biotic.

Climatic factors determine whether a given species can grow and survive in a given area (Good, 1953). Extremes in climatic factors are more decisive than averages, because plant species that do well during years with average environmental conditions may be killed in a year of extreme drought or cold, or by excessive icing or ponding. Indigenous species are usually well adapted to the extremes of climate in their areas, and introductions should be made from similar climatic regions.

An edaphic complex includes soil composition and texture, fertility, drainage, and topography. Edaphic complexes are secondary in determining plant distribution because, within an area of homogeneous climate, soil factors determine where species will grow. All plants cannot

23

grow everywhere because many species have very special requirements. For example, some species grow only on saline soils and others on acid soils. Knowledge of the edaphic requirements of species is, therefore, valuable in choosing seed mixtures and in planning irrigation, land use, and soil management programs.

The biotic complex, or the effect of living organisms on a plant, includes neighboring plants, grazing pressure, pests, microorganisms, and man. In pastures, the primary pressures are grazing and man. Grazing by any animal affects all parts of the plant; grazing by different types of livestock affects the vegetation differently through preferential use and compaction of the soil. Man, as a biotic factor, exerts his influence by mowing, burning, fertilizing, removing unwanted species, introducing exotic plants, irrigation, and hunting.

The objectives of ecological studies are threefold:

• To secure information about the composition of a sward to compare it with swards in other areas
• To obtain data on the distribution of species within specified regions
• To learn about the behavior of individual plant species in relation to one or more environmental influences.

The above objectives are basically the same as those of plant sociology, the distinction being that ecology uses *sampling* rather than *listing* methods to obtain the data required. Because sampling allows the use of statistics on the data obtained, ecological studies are more precise. Sampling, even with the most rapid methods, takes more time than a sociological survey. Ecological studies should, therefore, be used where great precision is required, as in the third objective noted above. At the same time, the data can be used to check the results of sociological studies. Though it may be possible to attain all three objectives with one sampling method, the highest level of precision often requires different methods for different purposes (Greig-Smith, 1964).

Kruyne and de Vries (1957) determined the relative abundance of species in relation to utilization, moisture conditions, soil texture, acidity, and P- and K-status of more than 1000 permanent pastures. Rating their estimates in each factor as correct, satisfactory, or wrong, they found that the accuracy of the estimates on the basis of sociology (species presence lists) was significantly better than expected for moisture conditions, soil texture, and acidity ($P<0.01$), but on the basis of quantitative data that recorded both presence and abundance of species, the accuracy was increased for all factors studied ($P<0.001$). Better correlation estimates should be expected when quantitative data are analyzed because plant species indicate certain environmental conditions, not only by their presence, but particularly by their abundance.

Wherever possible, quantitative studies should include reliable information about the utilization of a pasture. Past and present classes of livestock, grazing intensities, or applications of fertilizer or manure can have important influences. A change from sheep to cattle many years

24

ago may be reflected in the present vegetation and lead to erroneous conclusions if unknown to the investigator.

For studies of plant–climate relationships, the meteorological data of the weather stations in the area are usually accurate enough to correlate distribution limits of species to climatic factors (*see* Chapter 3).

SAMPLING

The best quantitative sampling method is the one that gives the greatest precision of the parameters. Thus, if the behavior of species in relation to climate, soil, and grazing is to be traced, precise data about many species in any one trial are required. And as most of the species involved are probably in the low density classes, methods that are not precise for the parameters of these species are unsuitable. But when only the relationship between the abundance of a few important species and grazing intensity is to be traced separately, the method used may be less precise if extraneous influences are excluded. In other words, to determine increasers and decreasers with a sampling method of relatively low precision, soil and climate should be kept constant.

The inclusion of many species in a vegetation sample is desirable. Whereas the dominants may not react noticeably to a change in a given factor-complex, less common species may react sharply. This is particularly true in relation to climatic and edaphic factors. Methods that sample only the more common species in an average-size sample are less desirable for correlative work, because less than half the species growing in the sward will be recorded in many samples.

Soil samples can be obtained when the vegetation is studied. By using the random points established for the vegetation samples, a randomized bulk-sample of the soil can be obtained. Though the depths to which soil samples are taken depends on the objective of the work, the best correlation between vegetation and soil is often found with soil samples taken to a 2-inch depth.

Random and Systematic Sampling

Vegetation sampling can be random or systematic. Both procedures give means of the properties measured, but only random sampling gives an estimate of the precision of the means. Hence, wherever this estimate is desirable, a random sample should be taken. A certain amount of subjectivity in sampling is rarely avoidable, but this does not detract from the validity of random sampling. The requirement that an area selected for sampling appear homogeneous is, therefore, not in conflict with randomness. Use of previously established associations as sampling units is allowable, as it falls in the same category as sampling separate parts of a "nonhomogeneous" field. However, within the stands selected for sampling, the samples must be selected at random.

25

Random sampling may be either entirely or restrictedly random. For the former, the requirement is that all parts of the stand must have equal chances of being sampled. For restricted random sampling, the stand may be divided into segments, but all parts within each segment must have equal chances of being sampled. Restricted random sampling is truly random and, as it is more precise than entirely random sampling, the amount of extra work involved is worthwhile. Use of a standard sampling plot, set out on squared paper and marked in the field with lines on which the sampling points are indicated, can save much time in this respect.

Sampling Methods

Many sampling methods are in use, most of which are intended to give an estimate of frequency, density, and cover, separately or in combination. The choice of method depends on the character of the vegetation and on the purposes of sampling (Hanson, 1950; Brown, 1954; Greig-Smith, 1964).

Frequency can be defined as the chance of finding a given species in a particular site in any one trial, as determined by the observed frequency in one trial. Because frequency determinations are based on the work of Raunkiaer (1934), the term frequency actually refers to the occurrence of a given species in samples of a defined size (for example, quadrats). The usual expression of frequency is a percentage, or the number of samples in which the species occurs divided by the total number of samples taken and multiplied by 100.

Density can be defined as the estimate of the number of entities per unit area. Either whole plants or specified parts of plants may be counted. If all species are counted, the density of the whole population as well as that of each species can be obtained; the latter can be expressed as the percentage density of the total cover or the total quadrat area.

Cover can be defined as the proportion of the ground occupied by the perpendicular projection onto it of aerial parts of individuals of the species under consideration (Greig-Smith, 1964). A variant of this measure is basal cover, in which only that portion of the ground surface occupied by a plant is measured (Clarke and others, 1942). Both can be expressed as percentage cover if the cover of individual species as well as that of the whole population is measured.

Methods of Vegetation Sampling

Of the several sampling methods used, the quadrat, point-quadrat, transect, and plotless are the most useful.

With the *quadrat method* (Raunkiaer, 1934) a unit sample of fixed shape and size is used in any one trial. Quadrats may be square, rectangular, circular, triangular, or elliptic and, depending on the objectives

26

of a study, they may be less than one to several square meters in size. In each quadrat an observer can record the presence or absence of species, count the number of individuals, measure the cover of each species and, if desired, obtain the yield and weight of each species by clipping. Thus, many properties of the vegetation can be secured at one time. But if samples are to be comparable throughout several vegetation types, the same size and shape of quadrat must be used in each stand. Because quadrat size influences frequency, and as frequency is in part dependent upon density, a large quadrat may show a higher frequency than a small quadrat. Long, narrow, rectangular quadrats reduce the variability of samples but increase the possibility of greater edge effects because of wider area-to-circumference ratios than square quadrats of equal area. Very small quadrats (¼ m² or less) have wide area-to-circumference ratios also, and an observer has to decide if a plant is inside or outside the boundary of a small quadrat more often than he does with larger quadrats (1 m² or more). If a measure of within-plot-variability is desired, square quadrats must be used; if a reduction of variability is the objective, then rectangular, circular, or elliptic quadrats are recommended. The quadrat method is reliable and versatile, but the work is expensive and time-consuming when only one character is being measured at a time.

The *point quadrat method* (Levy, 1933; Levy and Madden, 1933) was designed to measure cover. As the unit sample is a point, it is either covered or not covered. Hits can be recorded and expressed as percentage cover. The method has been applied to foliage cover (Levy and Madden, 1933), and basal cover (Clarke and others, 1942). Point quadrat sampling is usually done with a frame containing a number of pins. The frames can be placed randomly, but the position of the pins in the frame is interdependent. Consequently, hits lack statistical independence, the variance in the sample is increased, and the precision of the mean is decreased. With frames, a much larger number of points is required to obtain the precision possible with a smaller number of single points, but less time may be needed to place 200 frames of ten pins than to place 500 single pins.

Point quadrat sampling is essentially a frequency determination with quadrats of infinitesimally small size. Because of the very small size of the quadrats it is likely that only species of high density will be present in an average-size sample, and only a small number of the species comprising a stand will be represented. Expression of frequency as percentage of frames at which the species occurs does not alter the result, because this is an expression of frequency of the species in blocks of quadrats. As species of very different density may appear with equal frequency in the sample, the density-to-frequency relationship is lost.

In the *line intercept method* a line transect consisting of a thin wire is stretched tightly between two pins; it may be used to determine cover (Canfield, 1941; 1942). In randomization of the transects, one pin per line must be located, and the lines run parallel to each other. The length of intercept is recorded for each species along the line and expressed as a percentage of the total cover. Measurements of basal cover, height, and weight can also be made on each plant occurring in a sample. The line transect can be converted to a rectangular quadrat for frequency and density determinations by recording species within a given distance from the line.

Plotless methods can be illustrated by the distance methods of Cottam and Curtis (1949; 1955; 1956). The *point-centered quarter method* gives the greatest precision. With this method, random points are located and the distances from these points to the nearest plant in each of four quadrants are measured. The average distance is the square root of the mean area occupied by the plant and, from this distance, density can be calculated. Though the area calculated from the mean distance is taken to be a square, in reality plants occupy more or less circular areas. Because touching circular areas leave some space unoccupied, the effective mean area takes the shape of a hexagon. Hence, if the mean distance is 5 cm, the plant occupies a circular area of 25 cm^2 but an effective mean area of 27.6 cm^2. As no two plants can occupy the same space, the distribution of plants at densities high enough to cause their occupied areas to touch is no longer random. Distance methods give accurate results only in random distributions, and results with these methods in dense or patterned vegetation are not reliable. The methods cannot be used with turf-forming and stoloniferous plants. In vegetation of low density, however, the methods are relatively accurate, and can be used to advantage because of their simplicity and rapidity.

There are several other methods. Among these are *charting* (with or without mechanical aids), *step-point, point observation plot* (square-foot density), *weight estimate, reconnaissance, sod analysis,* and *range condition.* All are discussed by Brown (1954). No single method has every advantage and no disadvantages. The purposes of sampling, the data desired, and the accuracy required are the factors determining the choice of method.

STATISTICAL ANALYSIS

In practice, the quadrat method is the most reliable. It can give the precision required for all parameters and the data from the same sized quadrats can be analyzed statistically. However, it is not necessary to apply involved statistical analyses to arrive at conclusions; the ordination technique for individual species (de Vries, Kruyne, and Mooi, 1957), or that of Bray and Curtis (1957) for entire stands will give satisfactory assessments.

In the ordination of individual species, the average frequency (aF) of a species in all stands sampled, and its relative frequency (rF) in classes of a given environmental factor are determined. The rF is expressed as a percentage of *aF*; thus, a species with an *aF* of 10 percent on all soils but an *aF* of 40 percent on "wet soils", has an *rF* of 400 percent in this soil class, but if the *aF* of the species on dry soils is 2 percent, the *rF* would be only 20 percent. The *rF* values can be converted into "indicator numbers" for the factor, and these numbers, between + 100 and − 100, can be used as coordinates in graphs or three-dimensional models.

The ordination of entire stands can be done on the basis of sociological or quantitative data. In either case pairs of stands are compared, and the result expressed as a similarity coefficient. The formula used for comparison is usually:

$$100 \left(\frac{2c}{a+b} \right) = K \text{ (or } S\text{)}$$

where *a* and *b* are the number of species in stands A and B
and *c* is the number and quantity of species common to the two stands.

The *K* values can be used to ordinate the stands in graphs or three-dimensional models where the axes represent environmental factors or factor complexes; the stands become arranged in groups according to these factors. In contrast to the method of de Vries and others (1957), where the factors represented by the axes are known from the outset, the exact meaning of the axes in the method of Bray and Curtis (1957) must be inferred from the position of the stands and known characteristics of the habitats. With either method, the quantitative characters used are a matter of choice (frequency, density, weight proportions, cover), or a combination of two or more of these characters may be used. However, in grassland, where fluctuations in the performance of individual species occur from year to year or from season to season, rooted frequency and density are probably the most stable characters. As large numbers of stands must be studied before reliable conclusions can be drawn, these two characters are probably preferable. Because of the relationship between density and frequency in random distributions, and because distribution often approaches randomness in apparently homogeneous stands, frequency alone is adequate for many purposes.

Though the quadrat method of analyzing cover is slow, the data obtained with an adequate sample have good precision. By planning studies so that data can be expressed easily in computer language, much time can be saved in statistical analysis. For this purpose, species presence lists can be mimeographed with species indicated by code numbers and followed by columns for the characters measured. Data on soil, climate, grazing intensity, and other pertinent factors can be entered under code numbers, and fed to computer tape or punch cards directly from field forms.

29

References

Braun-Blanquet, J. 1951. Pflanzensoziologie: Grundzüge der Vegetationskunde. 2nd ed. Spring Verlag, Wien. xi and 631 p.

Bray, J. R., and J. T. Curtis. 1957. An ordination of the upland forest communities of southern Wisconsin. Ecol. Monographs 27:325–349.

Brown D. 1954. Methods of surveying and measuring vegetation. Commonwealth Agr. Bur., Farnham Royal, Bucks. Bull. 42. xv and 233 p.

Campbell, J. B., R. W. Lodge, A. Johnston, and S. Smoliak. 1962. Range management of grasslands and adjacent parklands in the Prairie Provinces. Can. Dep. Agr. Pub. 1133.

Canfield, R. H. 1941. Application of the line intercept method in sampling range vegetation. J. Forestry 39:388–394.

Canfield, R. H. 1942. Sampling ranges by the line interception method. Plant cover-composition-density-degree of forage use. Res. Rep. 4, U.S. Dep. Agr., Forest Serv., Southwest Forest Range Exp. Sta. 28 p. (Mimeo)

Clarke, S. E., J. A. Campbell, and J. B. Campbell. 1942. An ecological and grazing capacity study of the native grass pastures in southern Alberta, Saskatchewan and Manitoba. Can. Dep. Agr. Pub. 738.

Cottam, G., and J. T. Curtis. 1949. A rapid method of making surveys of woodlands by means of pairs of randomly selected trees. Ecology 30:101–104.

Cottam, G., and J. T. Curtis. 1955. Correction for various exclusion angles in the random pairs method. Ecology 36:767.

Cottam, G., and J. T. Curtis. 1956. The use of distance methods in phytosociological sampling. Ecology 37:451–460.

Good, R. 1953. The geography of flowering plants. Longmans, Green & Co., London. xiv and 452 p.

Goodall, D. W. 1953. Objective methods for the classification of vegetation. I. The use of positive interspecific correlation. Austral. J. Bot. 1:39–63. II. Fidelity and indicator value. Austral. J. Bot. 1:434–456.

Greig-Smith, P. 1964. Quantitative plant ecology. 2nd ed. Butterworth & Co. Ltd., London. xii and 256 p.

Hanson, H. C. 1950. Ecology of the grassland. II. Bot. Rev. 16:283–360.

Kruyne, A. A., and D. M. de Vries. 1957. Een methode tot benadering van de voornaamste milieu-eigenschappen van grasland aan de hand van de botanische samenstelling. Mededeling 54, I.B.S., Wageningen, Netherlands.

Levy, E. B. 1933. Technique employed in grassland research in New Zealand. 1. Strain testing and strain building. Imp. Bur. Plant Genetics. Bull. 11. p. 6–16.

Levy, E. B., and E. A. Madden. 1933. The point method of pasture analysis. New Zeal. J. Agr. 46:267–279.

Looman, J., and J. B. Campbell. 1960. Adaptation of Sörensen's K (1948) for estimating unit affinities in prairie vegetation. Ecology 41:409–416.

Raunkiaer, C. 1934. The life forms of plants and statistical plant geography. Clarendon Press, Oxford. 648 p.

Vries, D. M. de, and J. P. Baretta. 1952. De constellatie van graslandplanten. Verslag C. I. L. O. over 1951:26–29. Wageningen, Netherlands.

Vries, D. M. de, A. A. Kruyne, and H. Mooi. 1957. Veelvuldigheid van graslandplanten en hun aanwijzing van milieu-eigenschappen. Mededeling 27, I.B.S. Wageningen, Netherlands.

Chapter 3
CLIMATE–PLANT RELATIONSHIPS

WILLIAM L. PELTON
Research Station, Canada Department of Agriculture
Swift Current, Saskatchewan

ROBERT M. HOLMES
Inland Waters Branch
Department of Energy, Mines and Resources
Calgary, Alberta

Climatology deals with the collective state of the earth's atmosphere. The individual states are called weather; their summation is called climate. Agrometeorology, or agricultural meteorology, is that branch of climatology that measures and interprets the climatic forces affecting soil, plant, and animal relationships. As variations in climatic forces are the rule as much as the exception, reliable records can be obtained only by making observations at many sites and for as long as it takes to measure and describe their environments accurately. The records obtained may apply to vast forests, to steppes or deserts, to paddocks of a few acres, to the shadow under a single leaf, or to animals on pasture or in feedlots.

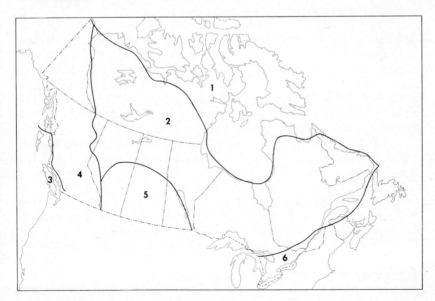

Climatic regions of Canada. 1, Arctic; 2, Northern; 3, Pacific; 4, Cordillera; 5, Prairie; 6, Southeastern.

31

Summaries of climatic measurements usually report a static condition of a dynamic environment. For this reason, to relate climatic forces to plant or animal response, numerous and reliable records are needed. In general, a macroclimate can be described adequately by records obtained at a "standard site," as defined by the World Meteorological Organization. But the description of a microclimate involves more refined instrumentation and more critical measurements.

CLIMATIC FACTORS

Temperature

Temperature is a qualitative term that denotes the quantity of heat energy available for plant growth; it is a fairly good indicator of the energy available at the time of measurement. For many years, temperature was the only climatic criterion used to explain the complex physiological processes of plant development. But it is realized now that many of the direct effects of temperature are obscured by their dependence on other climatic forces. Four examples illustrate the dependence: a moist soil may contain more heat than the same soil when dry, even if the temperature of the dry soil is several degrees higher than that of the moist soil; averages do not reflect the duration or intensity of extreme temperatures; plants may withstand extremely high or low temperatures for a short time, whereas the same temperatures during a longer period would be fatal; the rate of change of temperature may be more harmful to plant cells than the magnitude of the change.

There are optimum and lethal temperatures. Plants grow rapidly at optimum temperatures. Lethal temperatures, both high and low, damage plant tissue; they are not constant for a species during a season, because a temperature low enough to damage or kill a seedling might have no effect on the same plant in the boot stage. Likewise, a low temperature could be lethal to reproductive tissue but not to vegetative tissue. Respiration and photosynthesis in individual plants within and between species may have different optimum temperatures.

Air temperatures several feet above herbage are seldom the same as the temperatures of the plants or of the air within a cover. The differences are greatest when the air is still and radiation is intense. During daylight, when plants and soil absorb solar radiation, surface temperatures often exceed air temperatures by 20 F (11 C). At night, when plants re-radiate energy, the reverse is generally true; this may result in freezing on calm, clear nights during the spring and early fall.

Some plants will not flower unless there is a marked temperature reduction, either during successive summer nights or as the mean daily temperature drops in the fall. Hovin (1958) notes that night temperatures above 68 F (20 C) arrest the development of anthers in *Poa annua* L. Laude, Stanford, and Enloe (1958) report that low night temperatures accelerate floral initiation in *Trifolium repens* L. var.

Ladino. Knight and Hollowell (1958) indicate that high night temperatures inhibit flower production in *T. incarnatum* L.

Temperature may affect plants indirectly through its influence on plant diseases and harmful organisms. A particular temperature regime may cause pathogens to multiply rapidly, or create a condition that reduces the resistance of plants (for example, a lot of dew on leaves). Conversely, temperature can be an important regulator in the control of insect infestations or pathogenic organisms (Smith and Gibson, 1960).

Precipitation

Precipitation includes all forms of moisture reaching the earth's surface. Rain, snow, and hail are the most important sources, although dew and frost may add to the supply in localized areas.

Herbage yields are influenced largely by total precipitation, but they are also influenced by the intensity of storms and their distribution throughout the growing season as well as by other climatic factors. The variation of these factors from place to place makes it difficult to establish empirical relationships or formulas to correlate precipitation with herbage yields that are valid for a large area, though many have been proposed. In the southwestern United States, for example, a rain of less than half an inch is ineffective in promoting growth of native perennial grasses unless preceded or followed soon by other rainfall. Farther north, in southern Saskatchewan, a smaller amount is beneficial because evaporation is less (Smoliak, 1956). Shortgrass range in the Southern Great Plains requires 21 inches of total precipitation to make average growth, but 1000 miles north in the Northern Great Plains average growth requires only 14 inches of total precipitation. Ineffective showers are much more common than useful rains: at Swift Current, Saskatchewan, the probability of a day with rain during the growing season is 32 percent, but the probability of a day with more than a quarter inch of rain—a minimum for effectiveness—is less than 8 percent. Plants respond differently to summer and winter precipitation, and to a modal or a bimodal distribution of seasonal precipitation. The month of heaviest rainfall is also important. The characteristics of precipitation are local, and there is little probability of similar patterns existing between adjacent districts. More extensive instrumentation is required for accurate measurement of precipitation than for any other climatic factor.

Solar Radiation

Solar radiation is the source of power for all physical processes on the earth. Radiant energy has a twofold influence on plant growth: it links plant chemical processes and solar energy through chlorophyll, and its energy in the infrared region heats plant tissue.

Plant growth processes are affected differently by the energy in different spectral bands. Some processes are believed to be somewhat sensitive to all wavelengths, making analysis of wavelength composition difficult to interpret in some ecological work. Photosynthesis, for example, is mainly influenced by the violet-blue and orange-red wavelengths, but is affected somewhat by all wavelengths in the visible spectrum. The influence of light quality differs greatly between plant species, and specific effects are the subject of present-day research. Investigators are now relating the amount of energy in exact, narrow spectral bands to specific plant processes.

Infrared radiation comprises nearly half the solar energy spectrum, but it is not powerful enough to stimulate chemical reactions. Wassink and Stolwijk (1956) report, however, that infrared radiation exerts a stimulating effect on stem growth and germination that is unrelated to its heating effects. Ultraviolet radiation is of little apparent significance to plant growth.

Radiation intensity varies seasonally and diurnally. There is no apparent relationship between the visible radiation intensity and the energy content of any spectral band.

The length of the photoperiod, or, more correctly, the dark period, is of considerable importance. Plants can be classified broadly into long-day, short-day, or indeterminate-daylength groups. Short-day plants become vegetative at the expense of their reproductive organs when grown under long daylengths.

Net radiation is the difference between total incoming solar radiation and the radiation that is reflected and re-radiated from the earth's surface. This represents the energy that is available for plant processes. In humid regions, alfalfa uses 80 to 90 percent of the net radiation for evapotranspiration (Peck, Vittum, and Miller, 1958).

Other Climatic Factors

A climatic force does not act alone. Relative humidity, evaporation, and wind influence the effectiveness of available precipitation. A high atmospheric moisture content leads to lower evapotranspiration rates and vice versa. Wind velocity and air temperature affect evaporation rates. Drought years are usually characterized by high temperatures, low relative humidity, rapid evaporation and, occasionally, high wind velocities; all affect herbage production adversely.

HOW TO RECORD OBSERVATIONS

It is difficult to describe a microclimate, or the climate of a very small area which differs from that of the area surrounding it, because wind, temperature, humidity, and radiation vary within a crop canopy in space and time. Its complete description requires continuous and precise measurements of many atmospheric forces, and a computer is needed to analyze these complex data. With incomplete measurements, the environment has to be described in simple terms, such as arid or humid. Because plants and animals respond to all meteorological forces in degree, an investigator must decide which factors exert the greatest influence and organize instrumentation and observations accordingly.

Plants cannot complete their normal life cycle if their environment does not meet certain conditions. There are both optimum and lethal conditions for all stages of development and growth. Relatively simple instruments can measure optimum conditions because these conditions vary widely during most stages of plant growth. But lethal conditions are usually defined sharply, and their measurement requires careful observation and more complex instrumentation. Sometimes, lethal limits vary somewhat because of interactions between the duration and degree of climatic forces.

World Meteorological Organization procedures (WMO, 1961) should be followed in recording agrometeorological data. These require that "standard" meteorological equipment be set up on a "standard" site, which is representative of the area. The site must not border roads or highways, and should be free from obstructions and in the center of a grassed area about 400 feet in diameter. A level site is necessary unless topographical variations are common in the study area. If observations cannot be obtained according to WMO standards, the observer must ensure that his records are as reliable as possible. When reporting results, he should describe the site in detail. Meteorological measurements used by the aviation industry are seldom specific enough for agricultural research.

The agrometeorological observation site at Swift Current, Saskatchewan. The instruments are, from left to right: United States Weather Bureau Class A evaporation pan with a totalizing anemometer set at 18 inches; Canada Department of Agriculture Experimental Farm 4-foot buried tank with screen; black Bellani plate evaporimeter with mercury valve; black porous disc evaporimeter; recording anemometer with direction vane; power outlet (in foreground); standard 3½-inch rain gauge; Nipher shielded precipitation gauge; Suomi ventilated net radiometer (in foreground); tipping bucket recording rain gauge; Stevenson screen; junction box for wiring terminals with asbestos conduit leading to recorders in field building; Eppley pyrheliometer; Campbell-Stokes sunshine recorder.

35

Standard equipment, as defined by WMO, indicates or records air and soil temperatures, precipitation, atmospheric and soil moisture, evaporation, radiation, and the direction and daily run of the wind. An observer should record seasonal and phenological factors that are related to plant activities. These observations are fairly well correlated with the growth of crops during parts of their life cycles. However, specialized observations should supplement the standard observations so that the immediate plant environment can be defined. Relationships may then be established between the standard records and those of the microenvironments of plants or plots. Instruments for both standard and specialized observations should conform to WMO specifications. In Canada, information about the acquisition of standard meteorological instruments can be obtained from the Meteorological Branch, Canada Department of Transport, Toronto, Ontario.

Air and Soil Temperatures

Maximum and minimum thermometers are standard instruments to measure air temperature; they are installed in a louvered shelter, called a Stevenson screen, 5 feet above the ground, and are read twice daily. Thermographs placed in the Stevenson screen may be used if continuous measurements are needed, if twice-daily readings are not possible, and when an accuracy of $\pm$ 3 F (1.5 C) is adequate. Thermocouples and thermistors (thermally sensitive resistors) measure temperature for many applications; their electrical output can be measured intermittently or continuously. When temperatures are measured in other than standard exposures, for example under a crop canopy, instruments need to be shielded from direct solar radiation.

Soil temperatures are usually measured with a standard mercury or resistence soil thermometer. However, these instruments have inherent faults: they usually have to be read by an observer personally; they measure only at discrete depths; and their readings may be influenced unduly by stones, organic matter, or soil moisture. Equipment with multiple sensing units that measure the average soil temperature at a given depth, or through a depth range, has been described by Tanner (1958) and Burrows (1959).

Precipitation and Evaporation

A 3½-inch rain gauge is standard equipment to measure rainfall in Canada. For measuring weekly or monthly rainfall at remote locations, a ¼-inch layer of light oil is added to prevent evaporation. The duration, intensity, and amount of rainfall can be recorded daily by electrical or spring-driven rain gauges. Daily snowfall can be measured best on a large flat area with a ruler graduated in tenths of an inch, and the total depth measured on permanently installed graduated stakes. Although the density and water content of snow varies from storm to storm, generally 10 inches of snow equals 1 inch of water. Instruments to measure the duration and intensity of dew are still largely in the development stage. No measuring instrument can be recommended without qualification.

Many types of open pans and atmometers are used to measure evaporation and each exhibits individual characteristics. Most commonly used is the United States Weather Bureau Class A pan, which is 1 foot deep and 4 feet in diameter; its base is 4 inches above the soil surface. The black Bellani plate and the porous-disc atmometer are easy to install and operate; both measure evaporation close to the estimates of potential evapotranspiration calculated from empirical equations. Lysimeters have been designed to measure evapotranspiration and, although they are bulky and expensive to build and operate, they provide very reliable data.

Atmospheric and Soil Moisture

Dew-point temperatures (DP) and relative humidity (RH) can be calculated from dry- and wet-bulb temperatures obtained with aspirated or sling psychrometers. Dew-point temperatures can also be measured with recording equipment such as that described by Tanner and Suomi (1956).

Soil moisture is often the most important variable affecting plant growth. Most measurement techniques are inadequate. Gravimetric methods require that each sample of soil be dried in an oven and its moisture content calculated by differences in weight. As many samples are needed for a statistically reliable average, this method is laborious and slow. Soil moisture may also be determined by measuring the electrical resistance of gypsum or fiber glass blocks buried in the soil; the method is subject to hysteresis error, and is generally unreliable in stony land and in clay soils that shrink and swell. The most promising method for volume sampling is the neutron-moisture probe; it is rapid and reliable and is particularly useful for measuring changes in soil moisture over a 3- or 4-day period. A neutron probe assembly that is within the budgets of most research institutions is available.

Radiation

Total radiation can be estimated from the hours of bright sunshine, measured by a Campbell-Stokes sunshine recorder. More expensive instruments measure either total (sun plus sky) or net (total downward minus total upward) radiation, and usually require recording devices to obtain integrated values (Suomi, Franssila, and Islitzer, 1954). Less expensive radiometers have been described (Suomi and Kuhn, 1958), but they are not all-weather instruments.

Wind

Totalizing anemometers are placed 6 feet above ground level to measure the daily run of the wind. Additional anemometers can be placed within the vegetation cover or at other levels to determine wind travel at other elevations. Certain anemometers record direction as well as total travel, and recording equipment can be added to them to estimate wind speed throughout a day or for a longer period. Other models with an impulse counter are useful for measuring wind travel at remote locations where total run over a period of days is the only record required.

Seasonal and Phenological Records

A number of climatic factors are recorded only once during a season or a year. They are often overlooked because they do not fit into the regular schedule of recording. They include the last spring frost and the first frost in the fall, the first and last snowfall of the winter, the cumulative depth of snow, the depth of frost penetration, the number of thaw days throughout the winter, and the length of a drought period during the summer.

Phenological records should be maintained so that climatic factors can be associated with a biological calendar. All stages of plant development should be noted, including dates of sowing, emergence, stooling, flowering, and ripening, as well as measurements of leaf sizes and plant heights, the incidence of lodging, and counts of tillers, florets, and seeds.

PROCESSING AGROMETEOROLOGICAL DATA

The reduction of meteorological data is a tremendous task. It requires a very clear understanding of the relationships to be studied, and how to obtain the necessary data with the fewest possible observations.

Reliable observations require proper sampling techniques. Meteorological measurements are usually obtained from time-averaged observations at fixed points in space. Suitable time-averaging can be realized by applying Shannon's sampling theorem, which states that a variable with highest frequency f, may be satisfactorily specified by a sampling frequency of 2_f. This means that the daily air temperature cycle, which has a frequency of one, must be measured twice a day to obtain an acceptable approximation. The air temperature around an individual plant or leaf may have to be measured more often, because the frequency of a microvariation is usually much larger than one. The sampling frequency requirement depends also upon the time constant of the sensor, because a damped sensor will average highly variable fluctuations.

A sampling period equal to twice that of the instrument time constant is satisfactory for temperature. Thus, if a time average of a rapidly fluctuating variable is required for periods of several minutes to an hour, a heavily damped sensor is helpful. When the variable that is measured (for example, soil temperature) changes slowly, the sampling time may be adjusted to the variable fluctuations rather than to the instrument time constant. It must be remembered that average values, especially over long periods of time, may be misleading if associated with specific events. For this reason, agriculturists should not rely heavily on mean monthly or even mean weekly values of temperature, precipitation, evaporation, or other parameters.

In most countries, climatic observations are standardized and co-ordinated by a government agency. In Canada, this is done by the Meteorological Branch of the Department of Transport. Observation sites, instruments, and exposures are standardized as much as possible so that observers may follow a routine pattern when observing, recording, and reporting. Thus, continuity and regularity of observations are necessary to characterize a climate over a long period of time. Special information may be needed for a specific research project, and observations may differ considerably from routine procedures. There must be a clear understanding of the type of information required, and of the analytical procedures needed to reduce and interpret data.

The analysis and evaluation of meteorological data makes considerable use of statistics. Arithmetic means are often used to characterize the relationship of single climatic variables to plant response and, although helpful, they must be used cautiously to avoid misinterpretation. Weighted means and frequency distributions are also used, particularly to show climatic trends. More complicated analyses involve probability estimates, and simple and multiple correlation analyses. Time-series analyses necessitate the use of periodicity computations and harmonic analyses. Empirical relationships have been developed through the use of these statistical methods and, though many are extremely valuable, some can be used only under specific conditions. More thorough discussion of these matters may be found in the publications of G. Azzi (1956), F. A. Brooks (1959), Brooks and Carruthers (1953), Conrad and Pollak (1950), Geiger (1957), Landsberg (1958), and Sutton (1953).

References

Azzi, Girolamo, 1956. Agricultural ecology. Longmans, Green and Company, Toronto. 424 p.

Brooks, F. A. 1959. An introduction to physical microclimatology. University of California Press, Davis, Calif. 264 p.

Brooks, C. E. P., and N. Carruthers. 1953. Handbook of statistical methods in meteorology. Her Majesty's Stationery Office, London, England. 412 p.

Burrows, W. C. 1959. Multiple thermocouples for automatically averaging soil temperatures at several sites. Agron. J. 51:370–371.

Conrad, V., and L. W. Pollak. 1950. Methods in climatology. Harvard University Press, Cambridge, Mass. 459 p.

Geiger, Rudolf. 1957. The climate near the ground. Harvard University Press, Cambridge, Mass. 494 p.

Hovin, A. W. 1958. Reductions of self-pollination by high night temperature in naturally self-fertilized *Poa annua* L. Agron. J. 50:369–371.

Knight, W. E., and E. A. Hollowell. 1958. The influence of temperature and photoperiod on growth and flowering of crimson clover, *Trifolium incarnatum* L. Agron. J. 50:295–298.

Landsberg, Helmut. 1958. Physical climatology. Gray Printing Co., Inc., DuBois, Penn. 446 p.

Laude, H. M., E. H. Stanford, and J. A. Enloe. 1958. Photoperiod, temperature and competitive ability as factors affecting the seed production of selected clones of Ladino clover. Agron. J. 50:223–225.

Peck, N. Y., M. T. Vittum, and R. D. Miller. 1958. Evapotranspiration rates for alfalfa and vegetable crops in New York State. Agron. J. 50:109–112.

Smith, J. H., and P. B. Gibson. 1960. Influence of temperature on growth and nodulation of white clover infected with bean yellow mosaic virus. Agron. J. 52:5–7.

Smoliak, S. 1956. Influence of climatic conditions on forage production in shortgrass rangeland. J. Range Manage. 9:89–91.

Suomi, V. E., M. Franssila, and N. F. Islitzer. 1954. An improved net-radiation instrument. J. Meteorol. 11:276–282.

Suomi, V. E., and P. M. Kuhn. 1958. An economical net-radiometer. Tellus 10:160–163.

Sutton, O. G. 1953. Micrometeorology. McGraw-Hill Book Co., Inc., Toronto. 333 p.

Tanner, C. B. 1958. Soil thermometer giving the average temperature of several locations in a single reading. Agron. J. 50:384–387.

Tanner, C. B., and V. E. Suomi. 1956. Lithium chloride Dewcel properties and use for dewpoint and vapor pressure gradient measurements. Trans. Amer. Geophys. Union 37:413–420.

Wassink, E. C., and J. A. J. Stolwijk. 1956. Effects of light quality on plant growth. Ann. Rev. Plant Physiol. 7:373–400.

World Meteorological Organization. 1961. Guide to meteorological instrument and observing practices. WMO, No. 8, T.P. 3, Secretariat, Geneva, Switzerland.

Chapter 4

SOIL–PLANT RELATIONSHIPS

LAWRENCE E. LUTWICK
Research Station, Canada Department of Agriculture
Lethbridge, Alberta

Differences in plant growth within and between areas can be explained partly by differences in soil. This relation of soil to plant is often overlooked, but present concepts of soil genesis, and present methods of soil sampling and analysis are helping to explain the soil–plant complex more accurately.

Soil genesis may be considered as resulting from the interaction of a number of different factors, which not only contribute to the development of the soil but also react on each other. These factors include parent material (the geological deposit), topography (the kind of land surface), drainage (which is closely related to topography), climate, flora, fauna, time, and man himself. Climatic and biotic factors are the most active; parent material and topography are more passive. All these factors result in the differentiation of the soil into different soil types and classes, which may be recognized by their characteristics and the degree of their horizon development.

Horizon differentiation is ascribed to four processes: additions, removals, transfers, and transformations. These work together, or against one another, in different parent materials and under different climatic conditions. The relative importance of each, or a shift in the importance of one, is reflected in the soil profile. The character of a profile may change when a climatic factor changes from average to extreme, or when inadequate management affects the balance necessary for normal soil genesis. Simonson (1959) has discussed the presently accepted theory of soil genesis and points out that:

- The soils of the world form a continuum
- Similar changes occur in all soils
- There are seldom sharp boundaries between adjacent soils
- There are local differences within soils
- Some properties are shared by all soils.

PEDOGENIC AND EDAPHIC FACTORS

Where the soil pattern is complex, marked differences in productivity may occur over short distances and often reflect variations in soil characteristics (Rennie and Clayton, 1960). The influence of soil texture has been shown by Hubbard (1950), who reported a positive association between the dominance of western wheat grass, *Agropyron smithii* Rydb., and the percentage of clay content in southern Alberta soils; conversely he noted that the density of blue grama grass, *Bouteloua gracilis* (H.B.K.) Lag., was negatively associated with the percentage of clay fraction. Fox, Weaver, and Lipps (1953) have reported that certain chemical properties of Nebraska soils account for differences in plant response: low exchangeable calcium or low nitrogen content restricted the development of grass roots; low available phosphorus in the subsoil produced shallow-rooted stands of Kentucky bluegrass, *Poa pratensis* L. They demonstrated also that the branching of grass roots was restricted in claypan soils. Spilsbury and Tisdale (1944) correlated the genetic development of soils and plant associations in southern British Columbia with variations in available moisture, temperature, and length of frost-free period. Moisture was the most important climatic influence on genetic soil development and the corresponding plant cover at the lower elevations; at higher elevations, temperature and the duration of the frost-free period were the important factors determining zonal development.

MacLean and Summerby (1945) established plots within a single soil type on four Quebec farms and analyzed soil samples from these plots for pH, total nitrogen, easily oxidizable carbon, exchangeable potassium, and easily soluble inorganic phosphorus. Their objective was to determine variations in availability of the elements. They report that variations between samples were greater than duplicate analyses of a single sample, and that variations between farms were greater than those within a farm. These variations were associated with fertility gradients and different management practices. As a result of this study it may be possible to show by replicated herbage trials that variations occur, but the results may not show the cause of the variations; this often requires further work, usually analysis of samples obtained in an adequate sampling program.

EFFECTS OF SOIL MOISTURE

Rates of plant growth are dependent on transpiration rates (Perrier, McKell, and Davidson, 1961). There is a progressive decline in the transpiration rate (consumptive use of water) from field capacity to wilting (Bloodworth, Page, and Cowley, 1956; West and Perkman, 1953; Wilcox, 1960), though this viewpoint is questioned by Veihmeyer and Hendrickson (1955). Gravitational losses from the root zone occur over a wide range of decreasing soil moisture (Wilcox, 1959). Hence, a soil may contain a relatively large supply of water, but crops growing on it can neither obtain nor use it all. Methods to estimate moisture contents of soils have been discussed by Baver (1956); they are considered also in Chapter 3.

Under irrigation, highest yields of herbage are obtained with large applications of water, and water-use efficiency is improved by increasing the level of fertility (Krogman and Lutwick, 1961). On dry land, highest yields of grain are harvested when soils contain the greatest amount of water (Staple and Lehane, 1954), and the water use efficiency is usually, though not always, increased by application of a suitable fertilizer (Michalyna and Hedlin, 1961). Any relation between response to fertilizers and consumptive use of water depends on the available moisture and the stage of plant growth when the moisture supply is depleted (Zook and Weakly, 1950). Denmead and Shaw (1959) have shown that evapotranspiration from a corn crop increased from emergence to silking, but decreased thereafter. The increasing use was associated with an enlarging leaf area; the decreasing rate was caused by a declining physiological activity.

There is a dynamic relationship between plant growth and soil moisture, because crops use increasing amounts of energy to extract water from the soil as its moisture content declines. Static data, such as the amount of moisture in a soil at any stage of plant growth, are of limited value. But the soil moisture supply and an estimate of the energy needed to remove it are useful criteria to interpret plant growth and development.

Jamison (1956) points out that soil properties are not the only factors that control the consumptive use of water by plants. Plants themselves, as well as the weather, may have considerable influence. Perrier and others (1961) demonstrated the effect of plants with two subspecies of orchard grass, *Dactylis glomerata* L., that extracted moisture from the soil at different rates when grown under the same environmental conditions.

EFFECTS OF SOIL TEMPERATURE

Soil temperatures are measured with soil thermometers that are read by eye, or with thermocouples and thermistors when continuous recording is required. The advantages and limitations of each have been discussed by Bloodworth and Page (1957), Fluker (1958), Penrod, Elliott, and Brown (1960), Richards and Campbell (1948a, b), and Willis and others (1961). Within any field, soil temperatures may vary considerably from point to point, depending on slope, aspect, color, litter, vegetation, soil moisture, or organic matter. The annual variation is nearly simple harmonic, and it follows a pattern similar to the annual variation in air temperature (Penrod and others, 1960). Rainfall with cloudiness affects the temperature in the top 2 feet of soil for a period of up to 3 days after the rain ceases; diurnal changes are greatest in the surface soil and decrease to zero at the 3-foot depth (Fluker, 1958).

Nielsen and others (1960) have reported that soil temperature affects plant growth and the mineral composition of plants. Oats grown

43

in a temperature-controlled soil produced more grain and straw at 67 F and less at 80 F than at 41 F. Root weights usually decreased as the soil temperature increased. At a soil temperature of 67 F the uptake of nutrient elements, particularly phosphorus, was greater than at 41 F.

Influence of Litter

Krantz (1949) states that litter reduces soil temperatures. With an air temperature of 95 F, the temperature of bare soil was 118 F at the half-inch depth, but only 81 F when the soil was covered with 3 tons of straw per acre.

Because of its insulating effect, litter has a significant influence on plant growth. Its removal from the crowns of big bluestem, *Andropogon gerardii* Vitman, increased flower production sixfold and culm height by 60 percent; where the litter was left, spring growth did not start till nearly a month later (Curtis and Partch, 1950). Where litter accumulates, the dominant species maintain their stands (Sampson, 1921; Johnston, 1961), but the small and early-season species may disappear from the community (Weaver and Fitzpatrick, 1934).

Johnston (1961), working in the foothills of the Rocky Mountains, compared grazed and ungrazed fescue prairie (the *Festuca scabrella* association of Moss and Campbell, 1947). Where a region was lightly grazed there were more species, a greater basal plant area, more litter, and a greater root weight per unit area than on a heavily grazed site. When it was heavily grazed, the soil temperature was higher, there was little or no litter, and soil moisture and herbage yields were less than on the lightly grazed area. Different results were obtained in a drier environment of mixed prairie in North Dakota (Larson and Whitman, 1942), where, with zero to 0.5 inch of litter, herbage yields varied directly with litter depth. Consequently it is necessary to consider not only the amount but also the environment when the beneficial or detrimental effects of litter are being determined.

SAMPLING PROCEDURE

A poorly designed sampling program may not indicate the cause of variations, or the results may be so variable that no conclusions can be drawn. Jacob and Klute (1956) used components of variance obtained from analyses of several soil properties to illustrate an adequate sampling procedure. In uniform fields, multistage sampling was more efficient than single random sampling (Hammond, Pritchett, and Chew, 1958). Cost considerations show that a number of samplings at one location is preferable to samples at several locations, because the cost of moving between locations increases relative to the cost of processing samples (Sayegh, Alban, and Petersen, 1958).

A shovel is the most convenient tool to expose a profile, though power drills are necessary when deeper deposits are studied. After a profile is exposed, it is examined for its morphological characters, and samples are collected from all horizons for physical and chemical analyses. Special sampling tools and procedures are needed if the soil structure is to be retained.

Welsh and Fitts (1956) collected samples from different depths with different tools, and analyzed them for pH, organic matter, and available phosphorus and potassium. They found no significant differences between samples collected with a spade, trowel, or tube, but pH and organic matter were less in samples collected with an auger. No differences were found between samples placed in a bucket or in a box. For further information about the principles of soil sampling and the collection and preparation of samples, see Cline (1944, 1945), and Lutz (1947).

MEASUREMENTS OF LIMITING FACTORS

When there are variations in soil and climate, estimation of the level of fertility from crop yields is often hazardous. It is seldom that all the causes of variation in crop yield are known or, if known, measured. It would be useful to know the amount of the variation in the dependent variable (crop growth) that is explained by the independent variables (soil characteristics). The independent variables may be imposed by the conditions of an experiment and so be considered controlled variables, or they may be uncontrollable but measurable factors of the environment. The variation that is not explained by the measured or controlled independent variables must be assigned to unknown factors and to error. Wadleigh and Fireman (1954) state that "multiple regression analysis provides a convenient method for summing up all the evidence of a large number of observations into a single statement that expresses the extent to which differences in the dependent variables tend to be associated with differences in each of the other variables." In a soil erodibility study in California, the variations contributed by several factors were partitioned among those factors by the calculation of partial regression coefficients (André and Anderson, 1961).

Harris and others (1961) suggest that the ordinary multiple regression analysis can lead to errors in conclusions that might be drawn from a particular study. They propose a model to evaluate several parameters and the interactions of those parameters that may affect a common entity. In their procedure, a rule for selecting the most important predictors and removing their effects from the remaining variables is given, as well as a rule to stop the selections. A multiple regression equation using only the selected variables is then calculated.

References

André, J. E., and H. W. Anderson. 1961. Variation of soil erodibility with geology, geographic zone, elevation and vegetation type in Northern California Wildlands. J. Geophys. Res. 66:3351–3358.

Baver, L. D. 1956. Soil physics. 3rd ed. John Wiley & Sons, Inc., New York. 489 p.

Bloodworth, M. E., and J. B. Page. 1957. Use of thermistors for the measurement of soil moisture and temperature. Proc. Soil Sci. Soc. Amer. 21:11–15.

Bloodworth, M. E., J. B. Page, and W. R. Cowley. 1956. Some applications of the thermoelectric method for measuring water flow rates in plants. Agron. J. 48:222–228.

Cline, M. G. 1944. Principles of soil sampling. Soil Sci. 58:275–288.

Cline, M. G. 1945. Methods of collecting and preparing soil samples. Soil Sci. 59:3–5.

Curtis, J. T., and M. L. Partch. 1950. Some factors affecting flower production in *Andropogon gerardi*. Ecology 31:488–489.

Denmead, O. T., and R. H. Shaw. 1959. Evapotranspiration in relation to the development of the corn crop. Agron. J. 51:725–726.

Fluker, B. J. 1958. Soil temperatures. Soil Sci. 86:35–46.

Fox, R. L., J. E. Weaver, and R. C. Lipps. 1953. Influence of certain soil-profile characteristics upon the distribution of roots of grasses. Agron. J. 45:583–589.

Hammond, L. C., W. L. Pritchett, and V. Chew. 1958. Soil sampling in relation to soil heterogeneity. Proc. Soil Sci. Soc. Amer. 22:548–552.

Harris, B., A. L. Sharp, A. E. Gibbs, and W. J. Owen. 1961. An improved statistical model for evaluating parameters affecting water yields of river basins. J. Geophys. Res. 66:3319–3328.

Hubbard, W. A. 1950. The climate, soils and soil–plant relationships of an area in southwestern Saskatchewan. Sci. Agr. 30:327–342.

Jacob, W. C., and A. Klute. 1956. Sampling soils for physical and chemical properties. Proc. Soil Sci. Soc. Amer. 20:170–172.

Jamison, V. C. 1956. Pertinent factors governing the availability of soil moisture to plants. Soil Sci. 81:459–471.

Johnston, A. 1961. Comparison of lightly grazed and ungrazed range in the fescue grassland of southwestern Alberta. Can. J. Plant Sci. 41:615–622.

Krantz, B. A. 1949. Fertilize corn for higher yields. N. C. Agr. Exp. Sta. Bull. 366.

Krogman, K. K., and L. E. Lutwick. 1961. Consumptive use of water by forage crops in the Upper Kootenay River Valley. Can. J. Soil Sci. 41:1–4.

Larson, F., and W. Whitman. 1942. A comparison of used and unused grassland mesas in the Badlands of South Dakota. Ecology 23:438–445.

Lutz, H. J. 1947. Apparatus for collecting undisturbed soil samples. Soil Sci. 64:399–401.

MacLean, A. J., and R. Summerby. 1945. A study of the variability of certain chemical properties in soils. Sci. Agr. 25:221–230.

Michalyna, W., and R. A. Hedlin. 1961. A study of moisture storage and nitrate accumulation in soil as related to wheat yields on four cropping sequences. Can. J. Soil Sci. 41:5–15.

Moss, E. H., and J. A. Campbell. 1947. The fescue grassland of Alberta. Can. J. Res., C, 25:209–227.

Nielsen, K. F., R. L. Halstead, A. J. MacLean, R. M. Holmes, and S. J. Bourget. 1960. The influence of soil temperature on the growth and mineral composition of oats. Can. J. Soil Sci. 40:255–263.

Penrod, E. B., J. M. Elliott, and W. K. Brown. 1960. Soil temperature variation (1952–56) at Lexington, Kentucky. Soil Sci. 90:275–283.

Perrier, E. R., C. M. McKell, and J. M. Davidson. 1961. Plant-soil-water relations of two subspecies of orchard grass. Soil Sci. 92:413–420.

Rennie, D. A., and J. S. Clayton. 1960. The significance of local soil types to soil fertility studies. Can. J. Soil Sci. 40:146–156.

Richards, L. A., and R. B. Campbell. 1948a. Use of thermistors for measuring the freezing point of solutions and soils. Soil Sci. 65:429–436.

Richards, L. A., and R. B. Campbell. 1948b. The freezing point of moisture in soil cores. Proc. Soil Sci. Soc. Amer. 13:70–74.

Sampson, H. C. 1921. An ecological survey of the prairie vegetation of Illinois. Ill. Nat. Hist. Surv. Bull. 13:523–577.

Sayegh, A. H., L. A. Alban, and R. G. Petersen. 1958. A sampling study in a saline and alkali area. Proc. Soil Sci. Soc. Amer. 22:252–254.

Simonson, Roy W. 1959. Outline of a generalized theory of soil genesis. Proc. Soil Sci. Soc. Amer. 23:152–156.

Spilsbury, R. H., and E. W. Tisdale. 1944. Soil-plant relationships and vertical zonation in the southern interior of British Columbia. Sci. Agr. 24:395–436.

Staple, W. J., and J. J. Lehane. 1954. Wheat yields and use of moisture on substations in southern Saskatchewan. Can. J. Agr. Sci. 34:460–468.

Veihmeyer, F. J., and A. H. Hendrickson. 1955. Does transpiration decrease as the soil moisture decreases? Trans. Amer. Geophys. Union 36:425–448.

Wadleigh, C. H., and M. Fireman. 1954. Multiple regression analysis of soil data. Soil Sci. 78:127–139.

Weaver, J. E., and T. J. Fitzpatrick. 1934. The Prairie. Ecol. Monogr. 4:109–295.

Welch, C. D., and J. W. Fitts. 1956. Some factors affecting soil sampling. Proc. Soil Sci. Soc. Amer. 20:54–56.

West, E. S., and O. Perkman. 1953. Effect of soil moisture on transpiration. Austral. J. Agr. Res. 4:326–333.

Wilcox, J. C. 1959. Rate of soil drainage following an irrigation. I. Nature of soil drainage curves. Can. J. Soil Sci. 39:107–119.

Wilcox, J. C. 1960. Rate of soil drainage following an irrigation. II. Effects on determination of rate of consumptive use. Can. J. Soil Sci. 40:15–27.

Willis, W. O., C. W. Carlson, J. Alessi, and H. J. Haas. 1961. Depth of freezing and spring run-off as related to fall soil-moisture level. Can. J. Soil Sci. 41:115–123.

Zook, L. L., and H. E. Weakly. 1950. Crop rotation and tillage experiments at the North Platte (Nebraska) Substation 1907-34. U.S. Dep. Agr. Tech. Bull. 1007.

Chapter 5

BREEDING GRASSES AND LEGUMES FOR PASTURE

DAVID H. HEINRICHS
Research Station, Canada Department of Agriculture
Swift Current, Saskatchewan

Only recently has the improvement of forage crops for pasture received much attention from plant breeders in Canada. Earlier breeding programs were concerned mainly with introducing crops from Europe and improving them for better adaptation to the colder climate of Canada and for greater resistance to disease. However, as the need for cultivated forage crops grew and as the demand for improved grasses and legumes increased, it became apparent that plant breeders would have to give more attention to pasture traits of grasses and legumes.

Across Canada the most desirable attribute of plants used for pasture is persistence over a long period. The length of this period varies in different environmental regions, but it is 10 or more years in semiarid regions and 3 or more years in subhumid regions and on irrigated land. In the semiarid prairie region of Canada, good curing qualities are essential in grasses (Pigden, 1953) because most of the growth occurs in May and June. Here, the retention of nutrients in herbage is essential if livestock are to thrive on pasture until late fall. In areas of higher rainfall, curing quality is not as essential, but good recovery after grazing under cool conditions in the spring and fall lengthens the grazing season and is therefore desirable. Palatability is another important attribute; if herbage is palatable, animals eat enough to ensure good gains throughout the entire pasture season. Nutritive value is less important because most of the adapted grasses and legumes are quite acceptable in this regard.

To make rapid progress in improving a particular grass or legume for pasture, a plant breeder must recognize the characteristics of individual plants that are associated with good persistence, curing qualities, recovery, or other characteristics of local importance. Selection during early phases of a breeding program may involve simulated grazing, or actual grazing where animals serve as the mowing machine. In early phases of breeding, animal gains are not a practical yardstick of usefulness because of the high cost involved. Keller (1948), discussing the development of better plants for use on the range, states, "Any attempt to evaluate the products of a grass-breeding program without placing them on the range itself is incomplete and subject to errors of unknown magnitude." This may apply to certain crops but not to others. For instance, alfalfas that recover slowly after cutting are more persistent in dry areas than those that recover rapidly. Thus, slow recovery types

48

can be selected for persistence without actually subjecting plants to grazing pressure. On the other hand, selecting for persistence on the basis of actual grazing only might have detrimental results; plants may persist because they are unpalatable and not eaten, rather than because they are really more persistent under grazing. In the final phase of breeding, when new strains are compared with standard varieties or crops for pasture use, animal gain together with appropriate management techniques must be used as the criteria of evaluation. The best overall progress can be made only when there is close collaboration between pasture researchers and plant breeders.

At the Research Station, Swift Current, Sask., a breeding program for improving alfalfa, *Medicago* sp., has been under way since 1938 with the object of developing persistent strains for the semiarid environment of the Canadian prairies, and more specifically for better persistence under grazing (Heinrichs, 1954). During the entire breeding program, low-crown and creeping-root, known to be associated with winter-hardiness and persistence, have been the prime criteria of selection. Slow recovery after cutting has also been considered to be a desirable characteristic, because of its apparent association with persistence in the local environment. The variety Rambler (Heinrichs and Bolton, 1958) selected in this program is proving useful for both pasture and hay production throughout the prairie region of Canada; plant breeders in many other countries are now breeding for the creeping-root character (Heinrichs, 1963).

Yield is stressed in most forage crop improvement programs, often at the expense of other characteristics that may be more useful in pasture plants. When breeding a plant for pasture, never lose sight of the main weakness of the crop: if it is a low yielder, then improve it for yield; if it lacks persistence, then improve it for persistence; if it is too stemmy, then improve it for leafiness. Attempting to improve a great many characters at one time in a cross-pollinated crop brings results very slowly.

Grass-breeding programs throughout the Prairie Provinces have stressed high seed production. Perhaps this has been overstressed and not enough attention has been given to developing strains with higher leaf-to-stem ratios. The leaves are usually the most nutritive and palatable parts of a plant (Mowat and others, 1965). With crested wheat grass, *Agropyron cristatum* (L.) Gaertn., in particular, more leaf and less stem might well be given priority in selection programs. The tendency of crested wheat grass to go into head makes it a rather unpalatable pasture grass after midsummer. With this crop, selection in the direction of less tendency to head under dry conditions should, therefore, be given consideration.

Agronomic practices conducive to greater seed production could be used to offset the inherent tendency of a pasture strain to produce less seed. In Russian wildrye, a basal-leaf type of grass that cures well, little needs to be done to improve it for pasture, but agronomic characteristics such as seedling vigor need improving before this grass will reach its full agricultural potential.

In Eastern Canada, timothy, orchard grass, and reed canary grass are being improved for pasture use. The criteria for selection have been later maturity, stronger tillering, and rapid recovery after defoliation. Rapid recovery is considered to be very desirable to prevent weeds from invading pastures. Good progress has been made at research institutions in Eastern Canada, and new varieties of brome grass, reed canary grass, meadow fescue, and timothy with improved pasture attributes have been released in the last few years. Cleveland and others (1960) outline a program to improve orchard grass in the northeastern region of the United States, and point out that seasonal management studies are essential.

At the present time there is a general lack of proper animal use in evaluating material for pasture throughout Canada. When persistence or palatability is being assessed, breeding nurseries or test plots can be grazed over by animals at fairly early stages in a breeding program; the use of animals, besides giving a more genuine evaluation, may be cheaper than clipping techniques. In these early stages, animal intake and gain measurements should not be made because too many comparisons would be required and the breeding program would be too costly. Intake and digestibility of forages are important to the growth of animals (Crampton, 1957) and they will have to receive attention in the future.

Basic plant-breeding principles (Hanson and Carnahan, 1956; Heinrichs, Lawrence, and Morley, 1961; Allard and Bradshaw, 1964) apply equally to the improvement of plants for pasture and for hay, but evaluation techniques are more complex. It is, therefore, the techniques that will have to be considered carefully and used judiciously.

References

Allard, R. W., and A. D. Bradshaw. 1964. Implications of genotype–environmental interactions in applied plant breeding. Crop Sci. 4:503–508.

Cleveland, R. W., J. L. Starling, R. P. Murphy, A. A. Hanson, and R. C. Leffel. 1960. Orchard grass breeding in the Northeast. Cornell Exp. Sta. Bull. 955.

Crampton, E. W. 1957. Interactions between digestible nutrients and energy content, voluntary dry matter intake and the overall feeding value of roughages. J. Anim. Sci. 16:546–552.

Hanson, A. A., and H. L. Carnahan. 1956. Breeding perennial forage grasses. U.S. Dep. Agr. Tech. Bull. No. 1145.

Heinrichs, D. H. 1954. Developing creeping-rooted alfalfa for pasture. Can. J. Agr. Sci. 34:269–280.

Heinrichs, D. H. 1963. Creeping alfalfas. Advances in Agron. 15:317–337.

Heinrichs, D. H., and J. L. Bolton. 1958. Rambler alfalfa. Can. Dep. Agr. Pub. 1030.

Heinrichs, D. H., T. Lawrence, and F. H. W. Morley. 1961. Breeding for improvement of quantitative characters in *Agropyron intermedium* (Host) Beauv. by the polycross method. Can. J. Plant Sci. 42:323–338.

Keller, W. 1948. Wanted: A paragon for the range. Grass. U.S. Dep. Agr. Year-book of Agr. p. 347–351.

Mowat, D. N., R. S. Fulkerson, W. E. Tossell, and J. E. Winch. 1965. The in vitro digestibility and protein content of leaf and stem portion of forages. Can. J. Plant Sci. 45:321–333.

Pigden, W. J. 1953. The relation of lignin, cellulose, protein, starch and ether extract to the curing of range grasses. Can. J. Agr. Sci. 33:364–378.

Chapter 6

LABORATORY ANALYSES OF HERBAGE USED TO PREDICT NUTRITIVE VALUE*

WALLACE J. PIGDEN†
Animal Research Institute, Canada Department of Agriculture
Ottawa, Ontario

Estimates of the nutritive value of herbages are based on one or more chemical or microbiological analyses. An analytical method that is relatively exact for one stage of plant growth may give very biased results when used to estimate or predict the nutritive value of the same crop at a different stage of growth. The same applies to different crops. Investigators concerned with plant improvement programs or with feeding herbages in digestibility or metabolism studies should be aware of the advantages and limitations of each technique.

The value of herbage depends on the animal production it will support. Because feeding trials are expensive in terms of animals, labor, equipment, and feed, investigators generally have adopted or are developing laboratory tests to screen potentially valuable livestock feeds. These tests are based on or correlated with animal production characters. They are designed to estimate or to predict:

- Available energy (AE), which is the amount of energy an animal can extract per unit of dry matter (DM) consumed. Though digestible energy (DE) is the preferred unit of measurement, Heaney and Pigden (1963) have shown that it is significantly correlated with other systems of expressing AE, including digestible organic matter (DOM), organic matter digestibility (OMD), digestible dry matter (DDM), dry-matter digestibility (DMD), and total digestible nutrients (TDN)

- Voluntary intake (VI), which is the amount of DM that animals will consume per unit of metabolic body weight ($W^{0.75}$). A highly significant estimate of nutritive value is obtained by multiplying AE by VI

- Nutrient content (NC), which is the concentration of a nutrient in a feed. This is usually expressed as a percentage of DM or of organic matter (OM)

- Net energy (NE), which is the efficiency with which digested nutrients are used for maintenance, growth, milk production, and other animal functions.

---

*Contribution No. 250 from the Animal Research Institute.

†Now Research Coordinator (Animal Nutrition), Research Branch, Canada Department of Agriculture, Ottawa 3, Ontario.

The following discussion considers the value of standard and proposed chemical and microbiological analyses to estimate the nutritive qualities of a feed. Each test is discussed in relation to its prediction value for AE, VI, NE, and NC. In many instances where DOM, OMD, DDM, DMD, or TDN are referred to in the literature, they will be broadly referred to here as AE.

CHEMICAL METHODS

Herbages vary greatly in their nutrient composition, making it necessary to analyze species or even varieties at different growth stages to determine their nutritive value. Notwithstanding proposals for new chemical techniques, the proximate principle analysis for crude protein (CP), Weende crude fiber (WCF), nitrogen-free extract (NFE), and ether extract (EE) is still a recognized standard analysis to estimate the nutritive value of a herbage.

Crude Protein (N x 6.25)

The crude protein (CP) content of herbages ranges from less than 4 to over 35 percent. It is a mixture of true protein and nonprotein nitrogen. There is a general positive association between CP and feeding value, because herbage is higher in CP when young and immature than when it is mature. The decline in CP content coincides with a reduction in the availability of the cell wall constituents (CWC), but this is associative and not causative. Minson and Brown (1957–58) and Raymond (1959) report that CP content is of little value in predicting AE; their association was studied on 264 grass and legume swards throughout Great Britain.

Predicting AE from N. Many formulas have been reported for this purpose. They deal with a wide range of species, varieties, and growth stages, and give correlations that range from near zero to 0.95. This is not surprising, because most of the plant digestible material is made up of carbohydrates and the relationship is incidental. Better CP:AE associations are secured by limiting correlation and regression analyses to grasses or legumes only (Minson and Brown, 1957–58; Kivimäe, 1959). The time of cutting also affects CP:AE ratios, as the slopes of the regression lines are different for early-cut swards and for aftermaths (Minson and Kemp, 1961; Pigden and Heaney, 1962). Reported general relationships between nitrogen (N) and DOM, or OMD are as follows:

Herbage	$Y = a + bx$	SE	r_{xy}	Reference
121 cuts of grasses, legumes, and grass–legume mixtures	DOM $= 48.07 + 5.18$N	± 3.84	0.67	Pigden and Heaney (1962)
291 cuts of grasses	OMD $= 59.7 + 5.20$N	± 6.17		Minson and Kemp (1961)
18 cuts of grasses in April	OMD $= 81.8 + 0.35$N	± 3.56		Minson and Kemp (1961)
12 cuts of grasses in November	OMD $= 41.0 + 8.90$N	± 6.49		Minson and Kemp (1961)

where: N = percentage nitrogen in herbage
DOM = OM digested/100 g DM
OMD = OM digestibility (%).

The available evidence indicates that CP (N $\times$ 6.25) is not the main factor controlling the AE of herbages. With standard errors (SE) as high as 6.5, the regression equations are unsatisfactory for prediction purposes. Even when a restricted population is used (for example, 18 grasses cut in April), the SE of 3.5 is too high for research purposes and is of little value in estimating a significant difference in the AE content of different herbages.

Predicting digestible crude protein (DCP) from N. There is a very significant correlation, usually of the order of $r_{xy} = 0.97$ between the CP content of a herbage and its DCP. This is illustrated below with data from reports by Bell, Bowman, and Coupland (1952), Forbes and Garrigus (1950a, b), and Pigden and Heaney (1962). Because the SE of DCP is only ± 1.30, the CP of a herbage can be used to predict its DCP content. The prediction of DCP will be even more useful when information is available to predict accurately the digestibility of carbohydrates from data provided by carbohydrate analyses.

Prediction of VI and NE from N. There have been very few reports of investigations of the relationship between VI and forage N. Because N is generally positively associated with feeding value, an overall positive relationship would seem likely. However, the N content of a forage may increase or decrease greatly without noticeably affecting VI. Conversely, VI will vary greatly with forages of the same N content. For these reasons the relationship is unreliable for prediction purposes except under very restricted circumstances. For example, Milford and Minson (1964) found that the VI of tropical grasses declined rapidly when their CP content fell below 7 percent. The above statements apply to NE when its prediction is based on the N content of a herbage.

Estimate of NC from N. Crude protein is an extremely important nutrient in ruminant rations. However, even for very high producing dairy cows, the CP requirement does not exceed 12 percent (1.9% N). If an animal is grazing herbage containing more CP than it requires, the excess amino acids are de-aminated, the carbon skeleton is used for energy, and the excess N is excreted in the urine. As long as the CP content does not fall below 12 percent in forages to be fed as the sole feed, the plant breeder should not be very concerned about protein levels. Indeed levels of 10 to 11 percent are adequate for most purposes. However, excess herbage CP is valuable when mixed with high-carbohydrate and low-nitrogen feed such as corn silage (8% CP) or corn grain (8% CP) to bring the CP level up to animal needs. High levels of CP in forages have been advocated chiefly because they are generally associated with high AE content. However, the plant breeder should be concerned about CP level mainly from the viewpoint of nutrient content.

Weende Crude Fiber

The Weende crude fiber (WCF) content of forages varies from about 15 to 45 percent. It is composed of cellulose, lignin, and hemicellulose. There is a negative relationship between WCF and forage quality as plants mature. Not only does the percentage of WCF increase but its digestibility also decreases. There are exceptions to this in tropical grasses where WCF is found to be more digestible than NFE or organic matter (Todd, 1956; Milford, 1957).

Prediction of AE from WCF. Many regressions and correlations based on WCF have been reported. Correlations between WCF and AE range from about $r = -0.50$ to $r = -0.94$. Typical examples are:

Forage	$Y = a + bx$	SE	r_{xy}	Reference
121 grasses, legumes, and mixtures (sheep)	DOM $= 80.8 - 0.778$ WCF	± 4.42	-0.52	Pigden and Heaney (1962)
48 trials with grasses and legumes (sheep)	OMD $= 94 - 1.01$ WCF	± 6.3	-0.64	Forbes and Garrigus (1950a)
50 feeds, mainly forages (ruminants)	OMD $= 92.6 - 0.96$ WCF	± 5.2	-0.94	McMeekan (1943)
R. clover (1st cut) (sheep)	OMD $= 94.3 - 1.01$ WCF	± 2.23	-0.850	Kivimäe (1960)
Timothy (sheep)	OMD $= 117.0 - 1.722$ WCF	± 3.60	-0.919	Kivimäe (1960)

where: WCF $=$ percentage Weende crude fiber in herbage
DOM $=$ OM digested/100 g DM
OMD $=$ OM digestibility (%).

As there is a higher proportion of lignin in the WCF of legumes (Norman, 1935; Van Soest, 1964), the legume content of mixtures is likely to have a marked effect on the slope of the regression line. This has been confirmed by Sullivan (1961), who showed a marked difference between regressions for grasses and alfalfa. Within restricted populations, as in alfalfa hays, Meyer and Lofgreen (1959) have demonstrated a fairly close relationship ($r = 0.87$, SE ± 2.84) between TDN and WCF; this was improved ($r = 0.89$, SE ± 2.52) when a modified high-silica crude fiber analysis was used. Such prediction equations are useful in evaluating hay quality for feeding purposes, but they are of limited value in plant-breeding programs because of the large SE involved.

Prediction of VI from WCF content. There is a relationship between the WCF content of a herbage and its VI. Recently Wilson and McCarrick (1966) have shown quite a good correlation. The association has not received a great deal of attention, so there is relatively little information available.

Prediction of NC from WCF content. The original concept that the WCF technique isolated the indigestible part of a forage has been disproved many times. The alkali digestion process removes much of the lignin (the most indigestible constituent); conversely, much of the fiber isolated from immature forages is highly digestible (Norman, 1935). Moreover, the crude fiber isolated from legumes is much more indigestible than that isolated from grasses. Thus, from a nutrient standpoint, crude fiber may be valuable in some instances but almost useless in others. Digestible crude fiber has a fairly high nutrient value.

Prediction of NE from WCF content. In spite of its deficiencies, WCF is of some value in estimating the net energy value of feeds. Within a restricted population, a fairly close relationship may exist between WCF and NE for alfalfa hay (Meyer and Lofgreen, 1959), and for grasses (Armstrong, Blaxter, and Waite, 1964). Insufficient data are available on this point to enable effective use of the relationship.

Nitrogen-free Extract

The nitrogen-free extract (NFE) fraction represents the difference between 100 and the sum of the CP, WCF, EE, and ash determinations. With forages such as corn silage, containing considerable amounts of starch and fatty acids, it provides a fairly realistic estimate of the soluble or readily digestible portions. While NFE generally contains the more digestible carbohydrates, it also contains some of the lignin and other indigestible materials *plus the errors of the other determinations.* For forages in general, it is not a very reliable or meaningful estimate.

Ether Extract

The ether extract (EE) fraction is of little use in forage evaluation. Much of the EE of young immature forages is in chlorophyll or other pigments and is relatively indigestible. There are some exceptions; for example, some western range grasses tend to be relatively high in true fat at mature growth stages (Pigden, 1953). Ether extract from this type of material provides an estimate of readily available energy, but its application is very limited.

Lignin

Lignin (L) is an aromatic compound which is widely distributed in many woody and herbaceous plants. In common forages it varies from

56

about 1 to 18 percent of DM. Notwithstanding a great deal of research, its exact chemical structure is still in doubt. It occurs in close association with cellulose and hemicellulose and is attached to these carbohydrates by chemical bonding or exists in close physical proximity to them. Its main function appears to be to supply strength and rigidity to plant structures.

Prediction of AE from L. The lignin content of any particular forage species is usually closely related to digestibility. Typical AE–lignin associations are as follows:

Forage	No. of trials	Animals	$Y = a + bx$	SE	$^r xy$	Reference
Grasses, legumes, and mixtures	6	Sheep	OMD $= 94.04 - 2.95$L		-0.978	Lancaster (1943)
Grasses and legumes	22	Steers	OMD $= 100 - 4.71$L	2.4	-0.95	Forbes and Garrigus (1950a)
	488	Sheep	OMD $= 100 - 5.24$L	3.1	-0.93	
Red clover – timothy mixtures	40	Sheep	OMD $= 96.0 - 2.30$L	± 3.17	-0.664	Homb (1953)
Grass samples	35	Sheep	DMD $= 95.6 - 4.02$L	± 2.0	-0.95	Sullivan (1959)

where: OMD $=$ OM digestibility (%)
DMD $=$ digestible DM (%)
L $=$ lignin (%)

The chief problem associated with the use of lignin to predict the AE of forages is that the slope of the regression line is markedly different for grasses and legumes (Sullivan, 1959; Van Soest, 1964) and for different species of grasses (Sullivan, 1959). For these reasons, lignin is a reliable predictor when employed for species or varieties only and not for mixtures. Moreover, there is no standard lignin analysis that is generally accepted, and regressions constructed from the results of one analytical method may not be valid for another. Even if the slope of the regression is unaffected, the constant or intercept value may be. Van Soest (1964) has shown that the WCF digestibility of both grasses and legumes falls on the same regression line, and this relationship may be useful for general prediction of digestibility of the cell wall constituents (CWC).

Prediction of VI from L. Information on this point is very limited. Van Soest (1964) reports a negative relationship between lignin content and intake for several forages, but the association is not consistent enough to be useful. Forbes and Garrigus (1950a) show a reduction of 5.8 to 8.2 percent in intake of OM and DOM respectively for each increase of 1 percent in lignin content of forage grazed by steers.

Prediction of NC from L. Lignin is an indigestible diluent which varies from about 1 to 2 percent of DM in immature herbage, and from

8 to 18 percent in mature forage. At about the flowering stage, the lignin starts to exert an important secondary effect; it encrusts or forms chemical bonds with the cellulose and hemicellulose, and reduces the availability of the CWC (Norman, 1935). This varies with the species. For example, timothy differs from many other forages (Forbes and Garrigus, 1950b). The digestibility of CWC in young plants may approach 90 percent, but it may fall to 35 percent or less after lignification occurs.

There is no doubt that amount and type of lignification are extremely important factors in the utilization of CWC at medium and mature growth stages by ruminants. The chief barrier to the thorough investigation of the factors involved has been lack of an efficient and reliable method for measuring lignin. Recently, improved methods for preparing plant tissue for lignin analysis have placed the lignin determination on a more routine and reliable basis (Van Soest, 1963), and now it appears feasible to introduce studies on lignin into plant-breeding programs. Histological methods (Pigden, 1953; Drapala, Raymond, and Crampton, 1947) are useful in studying seasonal and within-plant lignification patterns as a plant matures. Histology can also contribute to information on the utilization of plant tissue by ruminants, as indicated by the size and lignification of fecal particles. Although such techniques cannot give quantitative data, they provide valuable related information. The most effective approach to the investigation of lignification is to employ histological, chemical, and microbiological methods in parallel studies.

Methoxyl

This is an alternative determination to that of lignin because most of the methoxyl is attached to the lignin molecule. It is a distinct chemical radical which can be determined relatively accurately and routinely. In some cases it gives an estimate of digestibility that is as good as or better than that obtained with lignin (Richards, Weaver, and Connolly, 1958). In other cases the errors are larger than with lignin or crude fiber (Kivimäe, 1960). The main source of these errors appears to be the methoxyl groups attached to nonlignin plant constituents; the degree of interference may vary with the analytical method used (Shearer, 1961). The usefulness of methoxyl to predict AE, VI, NE, or NC content is essentially the same as for lignin.

Hemicellulose

The hemicelluloses are xylans, arabans, and hexosans that are closely associated with lignin and cellulose. Quantitatively, they range from about 5 to 40 percent of the DM (Van Soest, 1964). This fraction can be chemically hydrolyzed more readily than cellulose, and most of it is extractable in 5 percent sulfuric acid over a 4-hour period

(Jarrige, 1960). Grasses are much higher in hemicellulose than legumes; for example, orchard grass contains 40 percent, whereas alfalfa contains only about 6 percent (Van Soest, 1964). This is one of the major chemical differences between grasses and legumes. The various sugars in hemicellulose fiber are available to ruminant microorganisms to a very different extent; glucose, arabinose, and xylose from alfalfa have digestibilities of 86.6, 85.9, and 32.3 percent respectively (Gaillard, 1962).

Prediction of AE from hemicellulose. Burdick and Sullivan (1963) found that the amount of xylose solubilized by dilute acid in 1 hour was closely related ($r = 0.96$) to in vivo digestion coefficients of DM for nine grasses and two alfalfas. The regression was DMD ($\%$) = 44.0 + 1.08 xylose $\pm$ 2.1. Xylose was less rapidly solubilized than other hemicellulose constituents. However, because of the very different amounts and types of hemicellulose present in grasses and legumes, it is unlikely that this method will be useful for mixtures and it is probably applicable only to restricted populations of grasses or legumes.

Prediction of NC from hemicellulose. The quantity of the hemicellulose varies not only between grasses and legumes, but even within a variety. In S23 ryegrass it ranges from 15.8 to 25.7 percent of DM, and in timothy from 24.4 to 29.9 percent (Waite, Johnston, and Armstrong, 1964). Corresponding values for xylan are 6.9 to 14.4 percent and 13.8 to 17.2 percent. Because the digestibility of hemicellulose decreases rapidly with maturity (Waite and others, 1964), and because xylans are the least digestible of the hemicelluloses but quantitatively the most important, it follows that a high xylan content is an undesirable characteristic. Recent developments in analytical methods for estimating xylans (Gaillard, 1962; Waite and Garrod, 1959; Burdick and Sullivan, 1963) make it feasible to employ tests for xylans in plant-breeding programs.

Soluble Carbohydrates

Soluble carbohydrates (SC) are those that are cold water or alcohol soluble. They consist chiefly of monosaccharides, sucrose, and fructosan. The total content varies from very low levels up to 30 percent of the DM in some English ryegrasses. Highest levels normally occur at early growth stages. The SC content can be markedly influenced by nitrogen fertilization, and high plant nitrogen levels are generally associated with low SC. They are of little value as predictors of the digestibility of whole plants (Armstrong and others, 1964).

Prediction of NE from SC. Milford, Minson, and Harris (1959–60) have found that forages high in SC give apparently high NE values when fed to growing lambs. This has been associated with high rumen propionate levels. Thomson (1965), using lambs, found little or no relationship between high SC and NE. Thomson and Terry (1965) have shown that there is little relationship between SC and rumen propionate levels; their work emphasizes the importance of comprehensive rumen sampling because volatile fatty acid (VFA) ratios fluctuate widely, depending on sampling time in relation to feeding time. A very poor correlation between herbage SC content and NE for fattening has been reported by Armstrong and others (1964), and between rumen VFA levels and NE of grasses by Armstrong (1964). The available evidence indicates that high SC values do not necessarily indicate high NE.

Prediction of NC from SC. It is well established that SC are highly digestible and, from this viewpoint, a high level is a very desirable characteristic in herbage to be grazed at an early growth stage or to be ensiled. When hay is harvested under conditions where leaching may occur, or when forages are allowed to mature and are grazed, SC cannot be considered a desirable source of energy. In the former case, leaching of the cold-water-soluble material (monosaccharides, sucrose, and fructosan) may occur, and in the latter case appreciable amounts of SC are not usually found in mature plants. More work is needed on this point to evaluate the cold-water-solubility characteristics of the SC fraction. Plant breeders should conduct routine analyses to relate SC to all stages of plant maturity. The method of Deriaz (1961) can be employed routinely.

Normal-acid Fiber

The analytical method based on normal-acid fiber (NAF) was developed to isolate a more definite ligno-cellulose fraction than WCF, because lignin is not extracted by the acid digestion. But it hydrolyzes most of the hemicelluloses, some of which are relatively indigestible.

Raymond, Jones, and Harris (1956) have shown that in prediction of DOM, quite different DOM–NAF relationships apply to forages grown in summer than to those grown in the fall and winter. Different relationships also apply to different grass species grown during the same period (Raymond and others, 1960). For these reasons and others, NAF has never been widely accepted as an important improvement on WCF; it is useful neither as a predictor of digestibility and intake, nor for the estimation of NAF as a nutrient of significance.

Acid Detergent Fiber (ADF)

Recently Van Soest (1964) developed a new system of analysis based on solubility of forage constituents in detergent solutions. Basically the non-cell wall protein and carbohydrate are isolated in one relatively digestible group, and the less soluble hemicellulose, cellulose, and lignin into another much less digestible cell wall constituent (CWC) fraction known as the acid detergent factor (ADF). Van Soest and Marcus (1964) showed that the relationship between VI and CWC was $r = 0.65$ for 96 samples of grasses and legumes. No significant relation between VI and CWC was found where CWC constituted less than 60 percent of the DM, but above its 60 percent level VI and CWC were fairly closely related.

A further development of the procedure involves dissolving out the hemicelluloses with an acid detergent solution, leaving a ligno-cellulose residue that can be separated readily into lignin and cellulose. This general approach is claimed to provide simpler and more accurate methods of preparing a fibrous residue for lignin analyses with less possibility of creating lignin artifacts. Its superiority over other chemical methods to predict DE and VI, and to isolate nutrients of greater biological significance is not as yet proved; further developmental work is needed.

Solubility Tests

Dehority and Johnson (1963) report correlation coefficients of 0.80 to 0.90 between the solubility of forage cellulose in cupriethylene diamine and in vivo cellulose digestibility, DMD, and nutritive value index (NVI) for samples of four grasses; this method gave low correlations with alfalfa. Donefer and others (1963) have tried numerous other solvents and enzymes, and have correlated the solubility of plant tissue in these with NVI; relatively high correlations were found even with water as a solvent ($r = 0.90$) and with acid pepsin digestions ($r = 0.95$).

The usefulness of these solubility tests is contingent upon the application of NVI, as described below.

MICROBIOLOGICAL METHODS

In Vitro Rumen Systems

These systems involve the digestion of 0.25 to 1 g of ground forage in a flask or tube with a sample of rumen inoculum to obtain an estimate of AE or of cellulose digestion, both of which are highly correlated with pre-determined AE and the intake of the same forage by animals.

Three main variations have been developed: a two-stage DM digestion, the second stage of which involves a digestion with pepsin to give estimates of DM or DOM; a one-stage digestion followed by a cellulose determination of the residue to provide digestible cellulose values correlated with in vivo AE; and a short one-stage digestion followed by a cellulose determination on the residue to provide digestible cellulose values correlated with NVI.

Two-stage in vitro DM digestion. Early in vitro systems used the regression of DM loss in vitro on DM loss in vivo (Walker, 1959; Reid and others, 1959). Tilley, Deriaz, and Terry (1960) have added a second stage to the technique and redigested the residue with pepsin; this brings the in vitro and in vivo DM digestion values essentially in line and obviates the necessity to calculate a regression. The basis for this is the "digestion ceiling" concept. According to this concept, digestion of a forage normally proceeds in vivo until the available cellulose and hemicelluloses of the CWC are essentially exhausted; their availability is determined by the type and extent of lignification (Hale, Duncan, and Huffman, 1947). The same principle holds in the in vitro two-stage DM rumen system. The figure below shows the in vitro DM "digestion ceilings" of four common forages fermented by a modification of the two-stage technique of Tilley and others (1960). Though the digestions were carried to the 72-hour stage, in every instance the curve had leveled off by 48 hours, indicating that most of the available carbohydrate of the CWC had been exhausted. Thus, there is a logical fermentation end point that is essentially the same in vitro and in vivo.

The precision of the method to predict AE is indicated by the high correlation coefficients between in vivo and in vitro digestions ($r = 0.98$, Tilley and others, 1960; $r = 0.97$, Alexander and McGowan, 1961). The variability between duplicates and between runs on standard forages has been reported as $\pm$ 0.38 and $\pm$ 2.05 percent DDM respectively by Pritchard and MacIntosh (1965), and as $\pm$ 0.17 and $\pm$ 1.66 percent DDM respectively by Mowat and others (1965). Since most of the im-

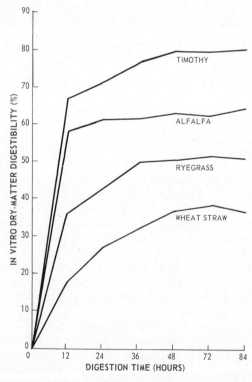

The "digestion ceiling" concept illustrated with forages of different quality in the in vitro rumen system.

portant comparisons are made within runs, the smaller error is generally applicable.

But an estimate of absolute digestibility is not the most important application of this technique. Instead, it is the *relative* digestibility differences between forages that this system can reproduce extremely well, and which are valid and applicable over a considerable range of conditions. It should be kept in mind that in vivo digestibility coefficients are not in themselves constants: they can be varied by changing the physical form of the forage, or the level of intake, or both.

The two-stage technique is unsuitable for estimating the AE of grass, corn, and sorghum silages (Simpkins and Baumgardt, 1962; Tilley, personal communication, 1964) because in vitro values are often lower than in vivo values by as much as 10 digestible units. The same criticism applies to in vitro methods based on cellulose digestion.

In its present form, the two-stage in vitro technique is not adapted for estimating intake. Though there is a close relationship between digestibility and intake with many forages, it is low for others. Nor does the technique measure the content of any one nutrient, but rather the total effect of a number of factors as they affect digestibility. It does, however, give a very valuable estimate of the biological availability of the CWC, a measure that no chemical method can duplicate. Some workers have thought that VFA ratios produced in vitro would be indicative of the net energy value of forages; but because of the tremendous interchanges between acids which occur in such systems and the fact that the importance of VFA ratios to the animal is not well established, the prediction of NE by the two-stage in vitro technique is not very promising.

One-stage in vitro cellulose digestion. Following a one-stage fermentation, the residue is analyzed for cellulose and its percentage digestion is calculated. A regression equation is calculated to establish the relationship between in vitro cellulose digestion and AE in vivo of a representative group of forages. The regression is then used in conjunction with the in vitro system to predict AE.

This technique has several disadvantages as compared with the two-stage system. It has been demonstrated that the regression equations for grasses and legumes give distinctly different slopes when based on cellulose digestion. Hence, the method is unsuitable for mixtures with varying grass:legume ratios, and if employed for mixtures the SE of the prediction equation will be high. Variations of the technique, different digestion times, and different populations of forages may produce different regression equations (Johnson and others, 1962). Thus, there is no standard regression equation, and each investigator must construct one from his own population of forages. When this is done, and restricted forage populations are used, highly accurate predictions of AE can be made. This method is more complicated and less useful for estimating AE than the two-stage in vitro DM digestion method.

Nutritive Value Index (NVI). The NVI concept is based on the hypothesis that total DE intake of forages by ruminants is chiefly controlled by rate of cellulose fermentation in the rumen (Crampton, Donefer, and Lloyd, 1960). The technique gives estimates of total DE intake per unit of metabolic body size ($W^{0.75}$) and is derived by combining separate estimates of AE and VI from animal trials.

In the laboratory procedure, NVI (in vitro) is estimated from a short (12-hour) fermentation of small samples, and a predictive equation is established between digestible cellulose in vitro and NVI (animal) values (Donefer, Crampton, and Lloyd, 1960). Such NVI (in vitro) values are *combined estimates of AE and VI* but do not provide separate estimates of either.

Because NVI (in vitro) is based on a short fermentation period and does not estimate AE, it should not be used in studies where, for example, the availability of CWC is the prime concern. It is not designed to measure VI either, but because VI has such a marked influence on NVI estimates it does provide a general estimate of VI. The main function of NVI (in vitro) is to provide estimates of the production potential of forages when they are fed alone. Application of NVI (in vitro) is limited in research programs because: the prediction error, caused chiefly by animal intake variability, is large (about ± 10 NVI units); it does not measure "palatability factors," which may exert a marked effect on intake of common forages (Reid and others, 1962); and regressions of 12-hour cellulose digestibility on NVI (animal) appear to be different for grasses and legumes (Donefer, 1961). Hence limited regressions should be calculated.

Nylon Bag Technique

From 1 to 5 g of ground forage are placed in a 2- by 4-inch bag made from nylon, silk, or dacron, and suspended in the rumen of a fistulated animal (McAnnally, 1942). After a digestion period varying from 6 to 72 hours, the sample is removed and the loss of dry matter or cellulose determined. These values may then be correlated with in vivo digestion values and a regression equation calculated for prediction purposes. In general, the longer the fermentation period the closer the DM or cellulose digestion of the sample approaches coefficients determined in vivo.

The technique is poorly standardized. Various sizes of cloth mesh from different materials have been used, including parachute cloth and nylon hose. Also, fermentation periods, fineness of grinding, sample size, and other factors influence the results. Animal and day-to-day variations are large. It is less useful and less accurate for most routine evaluation of forages than the two-stage in vitro rumen system, and is not to be recommended for duplicating in vivo digestion coefficients.

The method can be employed in special circumstances. It is useful for following the rate and extent of digestion of specific forages in the rumen of fistulated grazing animals, or for measuring the influence of changes in rumen environment that are brought about by supplements such as nitrogen or minerals. In the latter case, a standard forage can be employed as the test material. Cellulose digestion gives more accurate results than DM digestion. For further details the reader is advised to consult Van Dyne (1962), Hopson, Johnson, and Dehority (1963), Van Keuren and Heinemann (1962), Archibald and others (1961), and Lusk, Browning, and Miles (1962).

A variation of this method involves the use of cellophane sacs instead of tightweave fabrics (Pettyjohn, Leatherhead, and Mochrie, 1964). These sacs are charged with a ground forage sample inoculated with rumen fluid and placed inside a perforated plastic cylinder before being inserted in the rumen. The main advantage over a nylon bag is that small feed particles cannot be lost, but the cellophane sacs may break if the digestion period exceeds 18 to 24 hours. Though animal and day-to-day variations are relatively large, the method shows promise for further development.

OTHER METHODS

Leaf-to-stem Ratios

For many years plant breeders have assumed that leafiness is an index of quality and feeding value. Recent studies by Minson, Raymond, and Harris (1960); Pritchard, Folkins, and Pigden (1963); Bland and Dent (1964); Terry and Tilley (1964); Minson and others (1964); and Mowat and others (1965) have shown that leaf percentage is not a reliable index of digestibility because some grasses with a high proportion of stem may show high digestibilities, especially at early growth stages.

Because of the labor involved in separating leaf from stem, and because percentage leaf is not a very reliable criterion of quality, leaf separations are not recommended as an index of feeding value for grasses. It may be useful for alfalfa where the relationship between percentage leaf and digestibility is quite high (Terry and Tilley, 1964). However, separation of leaf and stem to determine seasonal digestibility patterns in conjunction with the in vitro rumen is a valuable aid to the analysis and pinpointing of factors affecting the availability of the energy in CWC, and it is to be recommended for use in plant-breeding programs.

Date of Cutting

Reid and others (1961) have proposed that date of cutting be used as a basis for estimating the DM digestibility of forages. They report a fairly constant decline of about 0.5 percent digestibility units per day. This relationship may hold generally for mixtures, but it is not reliable for pure species. Minson and others (1960), Pritchard and others

(1963), and Bland and Dent (1964) have shown marked differences in date and rate at which digestibility declines in different species of grasses and legumes. Hence, date of cutting is of little value in estimating AE for plant-breeding studies.

FACTORS TO CONSIDER IN PLANT-BREEDING PROGRAMS

The feeding value of forages is not determined by any single factor, but *is the sum of several that interact during rumen fermentation and in the subsequent metabolism of the fermentation products.* Information on as many factors as possible can help in the appraisal of forage quality. Some are more important than others for certain types of animal production.

Available Energy

The most fundamental nutritional characteristic of a forage is the amount of available energy (AE) per unit DM throughout the growing season; that is, the seasonal available-energy pattern as a plant matures. Differences in AE content between forages are largely controlled by the amount and availability of CWC, and wide differences exist between different plant species or even within a variety. A plant breeder should give high priority to breeding forages with low or highly available CWC. Not only does availability of CWC limit AE per unit of dry matter but it may also have a profound effect on intake. The most suitable way to measure the availability of CWC at present is by the two-stage in vitro rumen method. This technique is more accurate than any chemical method; its procedure is standardized and routine; and it gives satisfactory estimates of the AE of grasses, legumes, and mixed herbages, but not of silage.

Voluntary Intake

Voluntary intake (VI) should be studied whenever possible. This may involve detailed investigations in digestibility cages or many observations on a pasture. VI is important where a forage is to be fed alone and high animal production is required; it is not necessarily important where forage is to be fed with concentrates or where animals are being fed at or near maintenance levels unless the forage is of very low nutritive value. Many nonplant factors affect VI, including environmental temperature when fed, physiological status, and animal age. None of them are related to forage quality. Also, in some cases, forage quality can be profoundly modified by grinding, pelleting, and other forms of processing. Prediction of VI is an extremely active area of research, but although several laboratory methods show promise, none can be recommended at present for estimating intake with accuracy. Thus, the plant

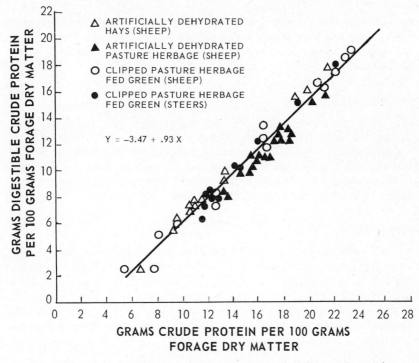

Legend (within figure):
△ ARTIFICIALLY DEHYDRATED HAYS (SHEEP)
▲ ARTIFICIALLY DEHYDRATED PASTURE HERBAGE (SHEEP)
○ CLIPPED PASTURE HERBAGE FED GREEN (SHEEP)
● CLIPPED PASTURE HERBAGE FED GREEN (STEERS)

$Y = -3.47 + .93 X$

Y-axis: GRAMS DIGESTIBLE CRUDE PROTEIN PER 100 GRAMS FORAGE DRY MATTER

X-axis: GRAMS CRUDE PROTEIN PER 100 GRAMS FORAGE DRY MATTER

Relation between forage crude protein content and digestible crude protein.

breeder should be aware of the importance of VI, but he must realize that reliable estimates of this important criterion can be obtained only when sufficient forage is available for animal trials.

Crude Protein

Crude protein (CP) (N × 6.25) is another very important characteristic. It is highly digestible and its digestibility can be predicted accurately from the CP content of a herbage (*see* the above figure). Its level as a nutrient is important, especially at the later stages of plant maturity. The standard Kjeldahl analysis is quite adequate except where a high nitrate-nitrogen level is a problem; then a nitrate-nitrogen determination should be added. In most plant-breeding programs it is important to measure herbage CP content as a routine analysis.

Lignin

Lignin has a profound influence on utilization of CWC. Its effect on energy availability can be measured indirectly by the two-stage in vitro rumen technique. By itself, lignin content is a less accurate and less useful predictor of AE than the two-stage in vitro rumen determinations. Lignin determinations are worthwhile if an investigator is studying the inheritance of lignin and how its concentration affects the availability of CWC, but then they should be employed in conjunction with two-stage in vitro rumen determinations and, possibly, supplemented by histological methods.

Soluble Carbohydrates

Soluble carbohydrates (SC) are highly digestible, and their NE is higher than that of the CWC fraction. Analysis for SC provides very useful information, especially for grasses where large differences in SC are often found. It is less useful for studies with legumes, because their level of SC is usually low. There is normally an inverse relationship between SC and CP (Jones, ap Griffith, and Walters, 1961).

Hemicellulose

Hemicelluloses are readily available and highly digestible during early stages of plant growth, but become less available as plants mature. This is caused by the increase of the xylan fraction. Consequently, a low xylan content in a forage would be a desirable characteristic, and its inheritance should be established. Analytical methods are available. Xylans are much more important in grass- than in legume-breeding programs because of their relatively high levels in grasses.

Mineral Content

The mineral content of forages is important. But routine determinations are generally not worthwhile unless specific problems of deficiency or toxicity are being studied, or unless mineral levels in new varieties or species of crops are being estimated. Some minerals can be readily supplied as low-cost supplements in many animal-production programs.

Vitamins

The vitamin B content of forages is not important because ruminants synthesize their own supply in the rumen. Vitamins A, D, and E are important to ruminants but, because of the loss or destruction of much of these when a plant matures, or during conservation and storage, their content in the original plant is seldom meaningful. Other substances, such as alkaloids and estrogens, which may impair animal health or performance, occur in plants, but they are generally of local importance only.

References

Alexander, R. H., and Mary McGowan. 1961. A filtration procedure for the *in vitro* determination of digestibility of herbage. J. Brit. Grassl. Soc. 16:275–276.

Archibald, J. G., H. Fenner, D. F. Owen, and H. D. Barnes. 1961. Measurement of the nutritive value of alfalfa and timothy hay by varied techniques. J. Dairy Sci. 44:2232–2241.

Armstrong, D. G. 1964. Evaluation of artificially dried grass as a source of energy for sheep. II. The energy value of cocksfoot, timothy and two strains of ryegrass at varying stages of maturity. J. Agr. Sci. 62:399–416.

Armstrong, D. G., K. L. Blaxter, and R. Waite. 1964. The evaluation of artificially dried grass as a source of energy for sheep. III. The prediction of nutritive value from chemical composition. J. Agr. Sci. 62:417–424.

Bell, J. M., C. H. Bowman, and R. T. Coupland. 1952. Chemical composition and digestibility of forage crops grown in Central Saskatchewan with observations on Kochia species. Sci. Agr. 32:463–473.

Bland, B. F., and J. W. Dent. 1964. Animal preference in relation to chemical composition and digestibility of varieties of cocksfoot. J. Brit. Grassl. Soc. 19:306–315.

Burdick, D., and J. T. Sullivan. 1963. Ease of hydrolysis of the hemicelluloses of forage plants in relation to digestibility. J. Anim. Sci. 22:444–447.

Crampton, E. W., E. Donefer, and L. E. Lloyd. 1960. A nutritive value index for forage. J. Anim. Sci. 19:538–544.

Dehority, B. A., and R. R. Johnson. 1963. Cellulose solubility as an estimate of cellulose digestibility and nutritive value of grasses. J. Anim. Sci. 22:222–225.

Deriaz, R. E. 1961. Routine analysis of carbohydrates and lignin in herbage. J. Sci. Food Agr. 12:152–160.

Donefer, E. 1961. The use of an in vitro rumen fermentation procedure to predict the nutritive value of forages. Ph.D. Thesis, McGill Univ., 111 p.

Donefer, E., E. W. Crampton, and L. E. Lloyd. 1960. Prediction of the nutritive value index of a forage from in vitro rumen fermentation data. J. Anim. Sci. 19:545–552.

Donefer, E., P. J. Niemann, E. W. Crampton, and L. E. Lloyd. 1963. Dry matter disappearance by enzyme and aqueous solutions to predict the nutritive value of forages. J. Dairy Sci. 46:965–970.

Drapala, W. J., L. C. Raymond, and E. W. Crampton. 1947. Pasture studies. XXVII. The effects of maturity of the plant and its lignification and subsequent digestibility by animals as indicated by methods of plant histology. Sci. Agr. 27:36–41.

Forbes, R. M., and W. P. Garrigus. 1950a. Some relationships between chemical composition, nutritive value and intake of forages grazed by steers and wethers. J. Anim. Sci. 9:354–362.

Forbes, R. M., and W. P. Garrigus. 1950b. Some effects of forage conservation or its nutritive value when cut and fed green to steers and wethers or determined conventionally and by the lignin ratio. J. Anim. Sci. 9:531–539.

Gaillard, B. D. E. 1962. The relationship between cell wall constituents of roughages and the digestibility of the organic matter. J. Agr. Sci. 59:369–373.

Hale, E. B., C. W. Duncan, and C. F. Huffman. 1947. Rumen digestion studies. 2. Studies in the chemistry of rumen digestion. J. Nutr. 34:747–758.

Heaney, D. P., and W. J. Pigden. 1963. Interrelationships and conversion factors between expressions of the digestible energy of forages. J. Anim. Sci. 22:956–960.

Homb, T. 1953. Chemical composition and digestibility of grassland crops. Acta Agr. Scand. 3:1–32.

Hopson, J. D., R. R. Johnson, and B. A. Dehority. 1963. Evaluation of the dacron bag technique as a method for measuring cellulose digestibility and rate of forage digestion. J. Anim. Sci. 22:448–453.

Jarrige, R. 1960. The membrane constituents of herbage. Proc. 8th Int. Grassl. Congr. 8:628–634.

Johnson, R. R., B. A. Dehority, J. L. Parsons, and H. W. Scott. 1962. Discrepancies between grasses and alfalfa when estimating nutritive value from *in vitro* cellulose digestibility by rumen microorganisms. J. Anim. Sci. 21:892–896.

Jones, D. I. H., G. ap Griffith, and R. J. K. Walters. 1961. Effect of nitrogen fertilizer on the water soluble carbohydrate content of perennial ryegrass and cocksfoot. J. Brit. Grassl. Soc. 16:272–275.

Kivimäe, A. 1959. Chemical composition and digestibility of some grassland crops. Acta Agr. Scand. Suppl. 5.

Kivimäe, A. 1960. Estimation of digestibility of grassland crops from their chemical composition. Proc. 8th Int. Grassl. Congr. 8:466–470.

Lancaster, R. J. 1943. The relative significance of lignin, cellulose and crude fiber in the evaluation of foods. New Zeal. J. Sci. Technol. (A) 25:131–136, 137–151.

Lusk, J. W., C. B. Browning, and J. T. Miles. 1962. Small sample *in vivo* cellulose digestion technique for forage evaluation. J. Dairy Sci. 45:69–73.

McAnnally, R. A. 1942. Digestion of straw by the ruminant. Biochem. J. 36:392–399.

McMeekan, C. P. 1943. A note on the relationship between crude fiber and the digestibility of organic matter. New Zeal. J. Sci. Technol. (A) 25:152–153.

Meyer, J. H., and G. P. Lofgreen. 1959. Evaluation of alfalfa hay by chemical analysis. J. Anim. Sci. 18:1233–1242.

Milford, R. 1957. The values of fecal nitrogen and fecal crude fiber in estimating intake of four sub-tropical plant species. Austral. J. Agr. Res. 8:359–370.

Milford, R., and D. J. Minson. 1964. Intake of tropical pasture species. Proc. 9th Int. Grassl. Congr., Paper 236, 8 p.

Milford, R., D. J. Minson, and C. E. Harris. 1959–60. Measurement of the net retention of energy from herbage. Exp. in Progr., Grassl. Res. Inst., Hurley 13:77–78.

Minson, D. J., and S. A. Brown. 1957–58. Herbage nitrogen as an index of herbage organic matter digestibility. Exp. in Progr., Grassl. Res. Inst., Hurley 11:99.

Minson, D. J., W. F. Raymond, and C. E. Harris. 1960. The digestibility of grass species and varieties. Proc. 8th Int. Grassl. Congr. 8:470–474.

Minson, D. J., and C. D. Kemp. 1961. Studies in the digestibility of herbage. IX. Herbage and fecal nitrogen as indicators of herbage organic matter digestibility. J. Brit. Grassl. Soc. 16:76–79.

Minson, D. J., C. E. Harris, W. F. Raymond, and R. Milford. 1964. The digestibility and voluntary intake of S22 and H.I. ryegrass, S170 tall fescue, S48 timothy, S215 meadow fescue and Germinal cocksfoot. J. Brit. Grassl. Soc. 19:298–305.

Mowat, D. N., R. S. Fulkerson, W. E. Tossell, and J. E. Winch. 1965. The *in vitro* digestibility and protein content of leaf and stem portions of forages. Can. J. Plant Sci. 45:321–331.

Norman, A. G. 1935. The composition of crude fibre. J. Agr. Sci. 25:529–540.

Pettyjohn, J. D., J. M. Leatherwood, and R. D. Mochrie. 1964. Simplified technique for *in vitro* comparison of cellulose and dry matter digestibilities of forages. J. Dairy Sci. 47:1102–1104.

Pigden, W. J. 1953. The relation of lignin, cellulose, protein, starch and ether extract to the "curing" of range grasses. Can. J. Agr. Sci. 33:364–378.

Pigden, W. J., and D. P. Heaney. 1962. Relationship between chemical composition and digestibility of forages. Proc. Can. Soc. Anim. Prod., 73 p.

Pritchard, G. I., L. P. Folkins, and W. J. Pigden. 1963. The *in vitro* digestibility of whole grasses and their parts at progressive stages of maturity. Can. J. Plant Sci. 43:79–87.

Pritchard, G. I., and A. I. MacIntosh. 1965. An in vitro rumen technique for dry matter digestibility and evaluation of forages. Mimeo. Contrib. No. 195, Anim. Res. Inst., Can. Dep. Agr., Ottawa.

70

Raymond, W. F. 1959. The nutritive value of herbage, p. 156–164. *In* J. D. Ivins (ed.) The measurement of grassland productivity. Butterworths Sci. Publications, London.

Raymond, W. F., E. C. Jones, and C. E. Harris. 1956. Normal acid fibre: a proposed method of analysis for evaluation of roughages. Agr. Progr. 30:120–124.

Raymond, W. F., J. M. A. Tilley, R. E. Deriaz, and D. J. Minson. 1960. Herbage composition and feeding value. Chemical aspects of the production and use of grass. Soc. Chem. Ind. Monogr. No. 9, p. 186.

Reid, R. L., D. C. Sheldon, J. A. Welch, and G. A. Jung. 1959. Pasture quality as determined by *in vitro* and *in vivo* techniques. J. Anim. Sci. 18:1537–1538.

Reid, R. L., B. Clark, J. A. Welch, L. Dosza, and C. A. Jung. 1962. Investigation of plant species and maturity stage on forage nutritive value as determined by *in vitro* digestion techniques. U.S. Dep. Agr. Contract No. 12-14-100-4523 (24) West Va. Agr. Exp. Sta. mimeo-report.

Reid, J. T., W. K. Kennedy, K. L. Turk, S. T. Slack, G. W. Trimberger, and R. P. Murphy. 1961. Effect of growth stage, chemical composition and physical properties upon the nutritive value of forages. J. Dairy Sci. 42:567–571.

Richards, C. R., H. G. Weaver, and J. D. Connolly. 1958. Comparison of methoxyl, lignin, crude fibre and crude protein contents of forage and feces as indirect indicators of dry matter digestibility. J. Dairy Sci. 41:956–962.

Shearer, D. A. 1961. Methoxyl analysis of feeds and feces: a comparison of methods. Can. J. Anim. Sci. 41:197–204.

Simpkins, H. L., Jr., and B. R. Baumgardt. 1962. Estimation of silage digestibility by laboratory methods. J. Anim. Sci. 21:1037.

Sullivan, J. T. 1959. A rapid method for the determination of acid insoluble lignin in forages and its relation to digestibility. J. Anim. Sci. 18:1292–1298.

Sullivan, J. T. 1961. The problem of predicting digestibility from chemical composition. Proc. Rumen Function Conf., p. 26–28. (Abstr.)

Terry, R. A., and J. M. A. Tilley. 1964. The digestibility of the leaves and stems of perennial ryegrass, cocksfoot, timothy, tall fescue, lucerne and sainfoin as measured by an *in vitro* procedure. J. Brit. Grassl. Soc. 19:363–372.

Thomson, D. J. 1965. The effect of varying rumen VFA proportions on the energy retention and carcass composition of lambs. Proc. Nutr. Soc. 24:26. (Abstr.)

Thomson, D. J., and R. A. Terry. 1965. Rumen volatile fatty acid proportions and herbage diets. Proc. Nutr. Soc. 24:25–26. (Abstr.)

Tilley, J. M. A., R. E. Deriaz, and R. A. Terry. 1960. The *in vitro* measurement of herbage digestibility and assessment of nutritive value. Proc. 8th Int. Grassl. Congr. 8:533–537.

Todd, J. R. 1956. Investigations into the chemical composition and nutritive value of certain forage plants at medium altitudes in the tropics. II. The digestibility and nutritive value of three grasses at different stages of growth. J. Agr. Sci. 47:36–39.

Van Dyne, G. M. 1962. Micro-methods for nutritive evaluation of range forages. J. Range Manage. 15:303–314.

Van Keuren, R. W., and W. W. Heinemann. 1962. Study of a nylon bag technique for *in vivo* estimation of forage digestibility. J. Anim. Sci. 21:340–345.

Van Soest, P. J. 1963. Use of detergents in the analysis of fibrous feeds. II. A rapid method for the determination of fiber and lignin. J. Ass. Offic. Agr. Chemists 46:829–835.

Van Soest, P. J. 1964. Symposium on nutrition and forage and pastures: New chemical procedures for evaluating forages. J. Anim. Sci. 23:838–845.

Van Soest, P. J., and W. C. Marcus. 1964. A method for the determination of cell wall constituents in forages using detergent and the relation between this fraction and voluntary intake and digestibility. J. Dairy Sci. 47:704. (Abstr.)

Waite, R., and A. R. Garrod. 1959. The comprehensive analysis of grasses. J. Sci. Food Agr. 10:317–326.

Waite, R., M. J. Johnston, and D. G. Armstrong. 1964. The evaluation of artificially dried grasses as a source of energy for sheep. I. The effect of stage of maturity on the apparent digestibility of ryegrasses, cocksfoot and timothy. J. Agr. Sci. 62:391–398.

Walker, D. M. 1959. The *in vitro* digestion of roughage dry matter. J. Agr. Sci. 53:192–197.

Wilson, R. K., and R. B. McCarrick. 1966. Apparent dry matter digestibility, voluntary food intake and yields of dry matter of mixed swards conserved as artificially dried grass and tetrapod hay at progressive stages of maturity. Proc. 10th Int. Grassl. Congr., Section 2:371–379.

Chapter 7

SELECTION OF HERBAGES IN FIELD TESTS

MARK R. KILCHER
Research Station, Canada Department of Agriculture
Swift Current, Saskatchewan

The selection of useful herbages involves a succession of tests that screen breeders' lines, varieties, and exotic and indigenous species for farm use. Preliminary field tests should include a wide range of potential crops. Final field tests may include no more than one or two from the first planting, and it is possible that none will pass critical evaluation.

PRELIMINARY FIELD PLOT EXPERIMENTS

Preliminary field tests provide useful information of stresses on plants caused by environment. A large number of potential crops should be included in these tests, as well as check varieties of known quality. A randomized complete block is recommended with replication at the main planting and additional replication on different soil types (Chamblee, 1962; Chapter 4, Soil–Plant Relationships). Spaced rows, spaced plants, or small plots may be planted, the choice depending on the objectives of the experiment (Green and Eyles, 1960). Most of the data can be obtained by rating crops in a comparative scale and by taking notes for establishment and persistence (Hawkins, 1959). However, much more information should be secured by using other simple techniques, including the determination of leaf:stem ratios (Branson, 1953; Langer, 1954), growth rate and growth patterns (Chamblee, 1962), chemical analyses or in vitro rumen digestion to estimate nutritive qualities at sequential harvests (Davies, 1959), and seasonal production of tillers (Langer, 1958). Glasshouses and growth rooms can be used advantageously to supplement preliminary field observations, particularly to evaluate morphological and physiological characters (see Chapter 1).

Preliminary testing provides an adequate measure of crop adaptation to environmental stresses. Only a few of the crops planted will pass the rigorous selection program, and can be considered worthy to enter the next phase of testing.

ADVANCED FIELD PLOT EXPERIMENTS

The number of crops that will comprise the collection after preliminary testing will be sufficiently small to permit an increased number of imposed management and agronomic treatments in later experiments.

The number and range of factors that can be studied and measured in advanced field plot tests is governed by the limitations of space, staff, equipment, and problem priority. A field plot test can conceivably be designed to measure a number of factors, such as yield, compatibility of species in mixtures, nutritive quality, and other related unknowns. However, it is at this stage that a decisive and deliberate stand should be taken. The introduction of one too many splits in an experiment is like adding the straw that breaks the camel's back. Excessive imposition of treatments and measurements results in a conglomeration of interactions that tend to mask specific factors and prevent valid interpretations. It is advisable, therefore, to plant two or more specific experiments designed to provide for no more than two or three measurable factors. This is particularly important for determining such things as methods of seeding, fertilizer response, irrigation practices, companion crop influences, and other cultural effects.

Other important considerations in advanced field plot experimentation are the number of plots and the size of each plot. Relatively small plots of 20 to 100 square feet are adequate for simple and easily controlled tests on individual plots of single species or for tests conducted in a stable microclimate (irrigated). On the other hand, more replication or larger plots are necessary when an experiment includes a number of multiple mixtures, or when herbage is grown in a highly variable environment, as on dryland sites. Wallace and Chapman (1956) describe an 18-square-foot plot as minimum for oat variety comparisons; Brim and Mason (1959) recommended a 400-square-foot plot to compare check-row crops; Wassom and Kalton (1953) suggest other plot sizes and shapes for bromegrass uniformity trials. Where possible, it is desirable to use experimental plot layouts that provide for uniformity in plot length. This greatly improves the organization of experimental space for good accessibility, easy maintenance, limited plot equipment, and the use of standard conversion factors.

SIMULATED GRAZING

Scheijgrond and Vos (1960) point out the importance of good management and carefully executed work, but emphasize that only a limited amount of reliable evaluation data can be accumulated even when recommended simulated grazing techniques are used. Too often simulated grazing comprises a mowed swath at some arbitrarily predetermined growth stage. At best this method may simulate a "daily-break" system of complete defoliation within a 2-day period. A better simulation of grazing is to remove daily cuttings across a plot width, making each subsequent daily cutting adjacent to that of the previous day. The second go-around should not normally start before a time lapse of 25 to 30 days. Though this system is better than the daily-break one, it is not true simulation of actual grazing. The resulting dry-matter (DM) yield will be 20 to 30 percent greater than could be obtained by a grazing animal, while the total digestible nutrient (TDN) or digestible energy (DE) content will be slightly less than for herbage selected by animals.

A similar mowing practice whereby adjacent cuts are taken each 5 to 10 days is used to simulate four- to eight-paddock rotations. This system may be acceptable if it is remembered that the yield obtained is greater than in a grazing rotation using animals. The mechanically measured yields will probably be 25 to 40 percent greater.

Two recently devised harvesting systems more closely approach actual continuous grazing. In the first system, herbage is cut each few days to one-half the height of the existing sward. This system provides individual harvesting yields, which are about 20 to 30 percent of the potential yield of the entire stand were it completely removed (Hunt, 1960). This method of mechanical defoliation is time-consuming and requires a mower with a wide range of cutting heights. Further, the machine must have a reel and a collection basket.

The second system involves the sequential removal of a prede-termined weight of dry matter at each of 8 to 12 cuttings during a sea-son. It is important to be able to forecast expected yield in order to determine the amount of herbage to remove at each cutting. For ex-ample, a plot measuring 11 by 40 feet with a forecast yield of 2000 pounds per acre would require a harvest removal of about 2 pounds once every 2 weeks for 20 weeks. Since the growth rate varies during a season, being slow at first, then rapid, and finally slow again, the system may sometimes necessitate removal of all top growth or adjust-ment in late-season cutting schedules.

When obtaining simulated grazing yields, workers should not feel completely bound to predetermined methods of cutting schedules (Reid, 1967). They will often need to adapt schedules to inclement weather, climatic fluctuations, and other adverse influences. The advantages of replication will be evident to the reader by this time. On dryland test sites where yields are low—less than 1000 pounds of dry matter per acre —it is important to increase replication six or even eight times, to use small subplots (1 by 2 square yards or meters), and to use hand shears instead of a clipping machine.

Simulated grazing by almost any method gives a more reliable measure of grazing than techniques that measure hay yields. Simulated grazing is particularly useful for comparing crops (Linehan, 1952), even if it does not measure absolute values. When compared with actual graz-ing, however, any simulated procedure has some defects. It overesti-mates the amount of herbage available to grazing livestock and does not indicate the stability of the flora making up the sward. It does not necessarily indicate potential livestock gains and does not indicate animal acceptability of the herbage.

References

Branson, F. A. 1953. Two new factors affecting resistance of grasses to grazing. J. Range Manage. 6:165–171.

Brim, C. A., and D. D. Mason. 1959. Estimates of optimum plot size for soybean yield trials. Agron. J. 51:331–334.

Chamblee, D. S. 1962. Small-plot experiments, p. 147–164. Pasture and Range Res. Tech. Comstock Publishing Ass., Ithaca, New York.

Davies, Wm. 1959. The evaluation of grassland research techniques, p. 3–9. *In* J. D. Ivins (ed.) The measurement of grassland productivity. Butterworths Sci. Publications, London.

Green, J. O., and Jean C. Eyles. 1960. A study in methods of grass variety testing. J. Brit. Grassl. Soc. 15:124–132.

Hawkins, R. P. 1959. The preliminary classification of herbage varieties, p. 29–33. *In* J. D. Ivins (ed.) The measurement of grassland productivity. Butterworths Sci. Publications, London.

Hunt, I. V. 1960. Spatial limits to grass production. Proc. 8th Int. Grassl. Congr. 8:273–275.

Langer, R. H. M. 1954. A study of leaf growth in timothy *Phleum pratense*. J. Brit. Grassl. Soc. 9:275–284.

Langer, R. H. M. 1958. Changes in the tiller population of grass swards. Nature (London) 182:1817–1818.

Linehan, P. A. 1952. Use of the cage and mower-strip methods for measuring the forage consumed by grazing animals. Proc. 6th Int. Grassl. Congr. 6:1328–1333.

Reid, D. 1967. Studies on the cutting management of grass–clover swards. V. The effect of changes in the closeness of cutting at different times in the season on the yield and quality of herbage from a perennial ryegrass – white clover sward. J. Agr. Sci. 68:249–254.

Scheijgrond, W., and H. Vos. 1960. Method of appraisal of herbage species and varieties. Proc. 8th Int. Grassl. Congr. 8:118–122.

Wallace, A. T., and W. H. Chapman. 1956. Studies in plot technique for oat clipping experiments. Agron. J. 48:32–35.

Wassom, C. E., and R. R. Kalton. 1953. Estimation of optimum plot size using data from bromegrass, *Bromus inermis*, uniformity trials. Iowa Agr. Exp. Sta. Bull. 396:296–320.

Chapter 8

INSULATED PLYWOOD SILOS FOR STORAGE OF EXPERIMENTAL FORAGES*

GRANT M. CARMAN
Information Division, Canada Department of Agriculture
Ottawa, Ontario

WALLACE J. PIGDEN† and KARL A. WINTER‡
Animal Research Institute, Canada Department of Agriculture
Ottawa, Ontario

The insulated plywood silos described below are of a convenient size for moderate-scale animal studies; they can be built from readily available materials, and they provide good insulation against winter temperatures. Four of the silos at the Animal Research Institute, Ottawa, have been in continuous use since 1957 for winter feeding trials with cattle and sheep and they have performed very satisfactorily.

The silos are 16 feet high and have a 6-foot inside diameter. Each is capable of storing 6 to 9 tons of grass silage.

The silo walls have interior and exterior shells nailed to a frame of 2- by 3-inch uprights placed 16 inches apart (outside-center) between the shells. The inside shell consists of a *double* layer of ¼-inch, 4- by 16-foot marine-grade plywood placed vertically with the seams completely overlapped. Alternate sheets of the interior plywood are pressure treated with creosote, and the whole interior is sealed with several coats of paraffin dissolved in petroleum spirits. The outer shell is ¼-inch tempered masonite painted on the exterior. Three metal rings, each 2 inches wide and ¼ inch thick, placed around the exterior, provide additional strength. Standard fiber glass batts, 3 inches thick, placed between the 2- by 3-inch uprights, provide insulation.

Each silo has a metal bottom with an exterior flange seated between the two plywood layers. A center drain, and a pipe leading from this drain to one side of the silo, provide drainage so that effluent may be collected if desired. Drainage is facilitated by several inches of 1-inch stone on the bottom and an ordinary wash basin inverted over the center drain hole.

The roofs are of galvanized metal and are removable for filling. They are wired in place.

Each silo is equipped with a feed-out chute about 4 feet wide and

---

*Contribution No. 276, Animal Research Institute.

†Now Research Coordinator (Animal Nutrition), Research Branch, Canada Department of Agriculture, Ottawa 3, Ontario.

‡Present address: Research Station, Research Branch, Canada Department of Agriculture, Charlottetown, Prince Edward Island.

Bank of four insulated plywood silos for storing experimental silage at the Animal Research Institute, Ottawa.

2 feet deep connecting the silo to the barn. Four doors are cut in the side of each silo in the feed-out chute for removing silage. A narrow ladder in the chute provides access to the doors. A double electrical outlet near the top of the chute serves as a connection for lights and heat lamps.

The base of each silo is constructed of 2- by 10-inch planks placed on three 6- by 6-inch sills, to facilitate moving the silos as desired.

Forage should be cut in 1-inch lengths or less when ensiling so that it can be well packed. Packing is more important in these small silos than in larger units.

In winter, when small quantities (2 to 6 inches) are being fed out daily, it is necessary to suspend one or two heat lamps over the silage to prevent freezing. This is unnecessary if larger quantities are fed out regularly. At Ottawa, no freezing has occurred around the inside walls prior to opening the silos, even in the most severe winter weather.

After ten winters, the silos at the Animal Research Institute still have some of the original paraffin coating, and little or no deterioration of the plywood lining has occurred.

Plans for both small and large silos are available from the Institute.

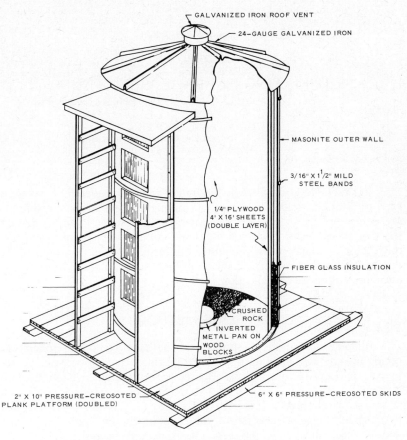

GALVANIZED IRON ROOF VENT

24–GAUGE GALVANIZED IRON

MASONITE OUTER WALL

3/16" X 1 1/2" MILD
STEEL BANDS

1/4" PLYWOOD
4' X 16' SHEETS
(DOUBLE LAYER)

FIBER GLASS INSULATION

CRUSHED
ROCK
INVERTED
METAL PAN ON
WOOD
BLOCKS

2" X 10" PRESSURE–CREOSOTED
PLANK PLATFORM (DOUBLED)

6" X 6" PRESSURE–CREOSOTED SKIDS

Details of construction of insulated plywood silos.

Chapter 9

ESTIMATING HERBAGE YIELD FROM SIMULATED GRAZING TRIALS

DOUGLAS A. COOKE
Research Station, Canada Department of Agriculture
Melfort, Saskatchewan

In simulated grazing trials, the total weight of sequential harvests is used to estimate yield. This simple technique is particularly valuable for preliminary studies with a large number of treatments, as in adaptation trials of species, varieties, seed mixtures, cultural experiments, and fertility trials. Though much preliminary information can be obtained by this method with considerable saving in time, labor, and land, the results have limited practical application.

SAMPLING METHODS

Reliable quantitative estimates of herbage yield are difficult to obtain in simulated grazing trials. Once grazing begins, it becomes necessary to consider factors such as apparent consumption, palatability, and grazing patterns. Because grazing habits vary between breeds of animals as well as within breeds, it is impossible to duplicate the grazing complex by mechanical means. Therefore, the capabilities and limitations of the various mechanical sampling techniques that have been devised must be appreciated to obtain the best possible estimates.

Mower-strip Method

The mower-strip method, which involves harvesting forage just before and immediately after grazing, is useful for a short-cycle grazing system. However, if the grazing period exceeds 1 week, forage production is underestimated because of the growth occurring within the period. During seasons of rapid growth, this method is useless if the grazing period exceeds 2 days. With experiments having longer grazing periods, it is necessary to protect sample plots with cages or other types of exclosures.

Pasture cages are used to estimate the relationships between production and consumption. Unfortunately, the microclimate within a pasture cage differs from that of an unprotected area (Williams, 1951). This problem is intensified in small cages (particularly along the sides and ends) and in those covered with a fine mesh (Cowlishaw, 1951). To minimize this difficulty, cages should be covered with the largest mesh that will protect the herbage, and should be large enough to permit sampling free of border effect. Campbell and Lodge (1955) used 3- by 7-foot cages with an open mesh and found them superior, in most respects, to conventional 4- by 4-foot cages; they harvested 2- by 6-foot plots. Prendergast and Brady (1955) designed a rectangular open-frame cage carrying four electrified wires that protected a 3- by 11-foot area from both sheep and cattle; they report that the error associated with conventional cages was reduced greatly by their design. Such factors as the method of sampling, the size and type of pasture, the kind of grazing animal, and the frequency of cutting and relocating cages, affect the choice of pasture cage.

Direct and Difference Methods

There are "Direct" and "Difference" Methods for estimating yield and consumption (Linehan, 1952; Carter, 1962; Carter, Bolin, and Erickson, 1960). With the Direct Method, sites that are permanently established and protected by cages are not moved throughout a season. Only the herbage within the cage is harvested and measured periodically to estimate production. However, the yield estimates obtained are of doubtful value because the method does not simulate grazing and usually overestimates production.

The Difference Method requires twice as much sampling as the Direct Method but provides estimates of both yield and consumption. It differs from the Direct Method in that an outfield sample from a grazed area adjacent to each pasture cage is harvested also. The caged sample indicates production, and the difference between the yield from it and from its associated equal-sized outfield sample provides a measure of the amount of herbage consumed, trampled, or otherwise destroyed. After each harvest the cage is moved to a new location. The amount of herbage covered by the cage in its new location is assumed to equal that measured by the outfield sample adjacent to the previous cage location. This amount subtracted from the cage yield on the next harvest date gives a measure of herbage production for the second period. Summation of the appropriate series of differences throughout a season represents total production and consumption.

Provided sampling is adequate, the Difference Method gives estimates of consumption and production that are theoretically sound. In practice, however, the unprotected vegetation is subject to grazing and trampling, and because its capacity to carry on normal photosynthesis is reduced thereby, it does not grow as rapidly as the undisturbed caged vegetation. See Chapter 23 for the procedure to record data and to calculate yields.

Number of Sample Plots per Treatment

When the Difference Method is used to test pasture cultivars, alone or in mixtures, it is recommended that 20 to 24 caged plots and an equal

81

number of outfield plots be sampled. This number of plots is sufficient to sample high-yielding, relatively uniform swards and lower-yielding pastures sown in spaced rows. Twice as many or more are needed when sampling low-yielding grasslands. The plots should be distributed equally between replicates.

A paired-plot technique is recommended when the Difference Method is used. That is, the cages and outfield plot areas should be selected for relative uniformity, and a coin flipped to decide which is to be caged. This procedure does not interfere with randomization if all pairs are located at random relative to one point. The following is recommended as an empirical guide to the number of caged plots required with different replications for an expected coefficient of variability of 20 percent:

	Number of caged plots per replicate	
Number of replicates	Dense swards and spaced rows	Natural grasslands
8	3	6
5 or 6	4	8
3 or 4	6	12
2	10	20
None	20	40

SAMPLING EQUIPMENT

Hand Shears

Hand-operated or power-driven sheep shears are excellent implements for harvesting areas up to 1 square meter. Brown (1954) reports that it is normal to cut 80 to 100 square-meter plots per man-day on a 10-acre pasture. Shears are especially useful for sampling low-yielding swards, and sheep pastures where it is necessary to cut closer to the ground than is possible with a plot mower. Nevens and Kuhlman (1935) have proposed the use of a frame with a movable bar to guide the shears accurately over the plot area. Nevens (1945) has shown that without such a guide yield estimates for a given period can vary as much as 50 percent. At the Grassland Research Institute, Hurley, England, improved models of power-driven sheep shears and hedge trimmers are used. These machines are of interest because they permit sampling at or near ground level, and because narrow sampling units have a relatively low coefficient of variability (Green, Langer, and Williams, 1952).

Power Mowers

For harvesting upright growth grazed by cattle, a plot tractor equipped with a sickle-bar mower is recommended. The cutting bar is mounted on the front of the tractor and is fitted with a detachable collection pan. Metal runners, attached to both ends of the sickle bar, allow mowing at a uniform height of 2.5 to 10 cm above ground level.

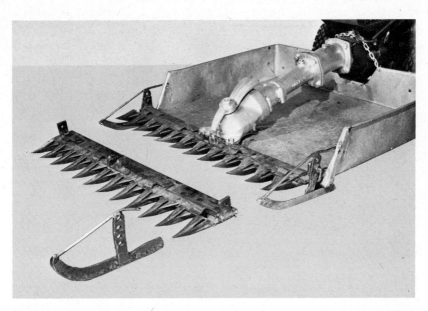

Close-up of pan assembly and cutting height adjustment on a sickle-bar mower.

This type of mower is suitable for sampling cattle pastures where the herbage has a fairly upright growth. If growth is very short or if there is a high percentage of brittle stubble, yields may be underestimated because herbage may be flicked off the knife. Since these machines are unable to cut lower than 1 inch, they are not suitable for sampling sheep pastures.

Plot mowers with a horizontal rotary cutting mechanism have been developed (Page, Jackson, and Hunter, 1957; Kemp and Kalbfleisch, 1957; McGinnies, 1959; Miltimore, McMechan, and Wilcox, 1961). These machines have two common faults: the chopped herbage cannot be hand separated easily for species identification, and as rotary mowers rely on forced air or suction to deliver the chopped forage to a collection point, the sample may be contaminated by debris.

Thompson and Heinrichs (1963), and Thompson (1967) have described a flail-type plot harvester that cuts the herbage with an anti-clockwise rotation. This machine is ideal for harvesting hay plots or high-yielding pasture swards if separations are unnecessary. Its limitations are the same as those for rotary mowers when close grazing is simulated.

A plot mower designed to cut a narrow swath has been developed by the Engineering Research Service, Canada Department of Agriculture (Kemp, 1965). It has a front-mounted sickle bar, moving fingers that gather lodged stems and leaves, and a belt to move the herbage to a collection box.

Swift Current plot harvester, Model No. 2, described by Thompson and Heinrichs (1963).

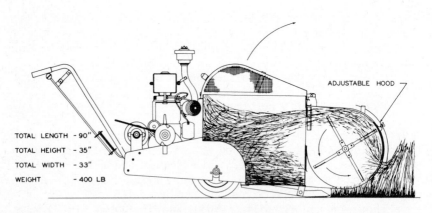

ADJUSTABLE HOOD

TOTAL LENGTH - 90"
TOTAL HEIGHT - 35"
TOTAL WIDTH - 33"
WEIGHT - 400 LB

Swift Current plot harvester, Model No. 2. The harvesting action and the collection box are illustrated.

DRY-MATTER DETERMINATION

The determination of dry matter in herbages must involve compromise regardless of the drying method used. No exact determination is possible because of the complicated physical and chemical properties of the moisture fraction of plants.

84

Left: Side view of a narrow-swath mower. *Right:* Front view of narrow-swath mower. The fingers can be seen, but the sickle bar is partially hidden below the rollers.

Drying Techniques

Of the various techniques used for dry-matter estimates, heat drying is the most important. This is especially true when a large number of dry-matter determinations are required. Modern drying ovens are capable of providing results well within the limits of error considered satisfactory. If greater precision is required, more refined techniques, including radio-frequency dielectric heating (Merridrew and Raymond, 1953), freeze-drying (Bath and Budd, 1961), and dehydrating compounds in conjunction with heat (Greenhill, 1960) are recommended.

Factors contributing to error have been reported (Davies, Evans, and Evans, 1948; Raymond and Harris, 1954; Hesse and Kennedy, 1956; Walker, 1959; McDonald and Dewar, 1960). Based on the findings and experience of these and other authors, the following procedure is suggested:

- Dry samples as soon after harvest as possible. Tissue decomposition is rapid, especially in lush samples, and a delay of only a few hours between harvesting and drying may result in a considerable loss of dry matter. If immediate drying is impractical, samples should be frozen until drying facilities are available
- Maintain the drying oven at a uniform temperature throughout the drying period. Though a constant temperature between 100 and 105 C is satisfactory for most dry-matter determinations, drying at 80 to 90 C is better for samples to be analyzed chemically. There will be some destruction of heat-labile substances even at these lower temperatures, but the traditional "proximate" analyses will not be affected unduly

85

- Preheat the oven to the desired drying temperature before loading with samples. Do not overload the oven as this will lengthen the drying time. Do not add fresh samples to a batch of partly dried samples
- Subdivide large samples before drying them. Large tightly packed samples dry slowly and are subject to losses caused by the differential between surface and inner temperatures
- Do not dry fresh and frozen material at the same time. Frozen samples will dry to constant weight much quicker than fresh samples of equal weight and bulk.

Weighing Oven-dried Samples

When a sample is weighed immediately on removal from a drying oven operating at or near 100 C, the superheated sample sets up convection currents that may result in an underestimation of weight. However, if a dried sample is allowed to cool before it is weighed, it will rapidly absorb atmospheric moisture and the dry weight will be overestimated, as indicated in the accompanying graph. For example, an empty 1400-g drying tray will vary in weight from 1387 to 1402 g as it cools to room temperature when the relative humidity is 50 percent or

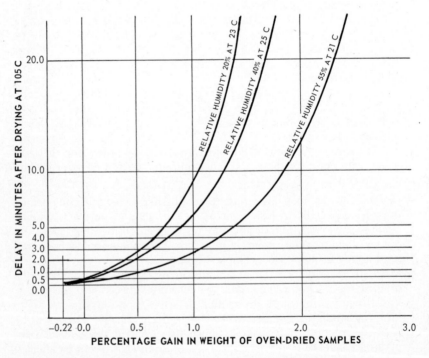

Effect of relative humidity on the weight of oven-dried herbage.

higher. For this reason the technique of standardizing the weights of drying trays and determining sample dry weight by subtraction is not reliable. Variations of 4 to 6 percent may occur when samples of 200 to 250 g dry weight are handled in this manner.

A recommended procedure is to place dried material in a weighing pan resting on a scale that is accurate to within 0.2 g and that has a taring device so that the sample weight can be read directly from the dial. Using this procedure, a sample can be removed from the oven, and its weight determined (within 0.5 percent of that determined by cooling over a desiccant) and recorded in less than 30 seconds.

The weighing pan (illustrated below) should be large enough to allow rapid emptying of the drying tray and it should have sufficient capacity to hold at least 500 g of dried material.

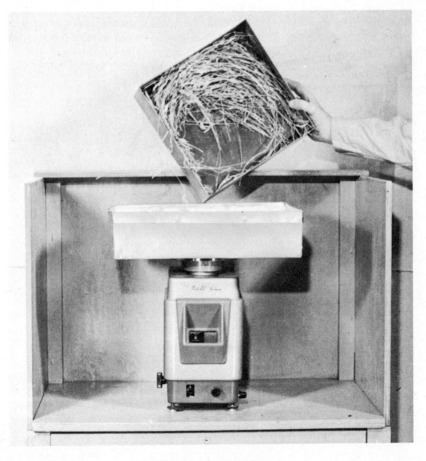

Scale with sample weighing pan.

Conversion Factors for Dry-matter Yields

The factors used to convert herbage yields from grams of dry matter per plot to pounds per acre or kilograms per hectare are:

Size and shape of plot	Conversion factors to lb/acre	to kg/ha
1 yd², or ½ × 2 yd	10.67	11.96
½ × 2.13 yd	10.0	11.21
1 m², or ½ × 2.4 yd	8.91	10.0
2 yd², or 1 × 2 yd	5.33	5.97
1 × 2.13, or ½ × 4.25 yd	5.0	5.60
2 m², or 1 × 2.4 yd	4.46	5.0

Preparing Oven-dried Samples for Chemical Analysis

A dried sample must be ground before being subsampled for chemical analysis. The grinding should be done as soon after drying as possible since freshly dried material pulverizes readily and provides a more uniform sample. If at all possible, the entire sample should be milled and stored in moisture-proof containers. The machine and collection box or bag should be cleaned carefully after each sample is ground.

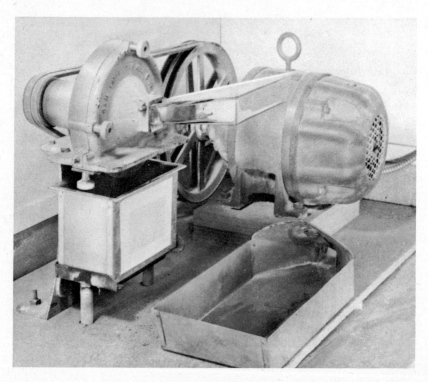

Hammer mill equipped with collection box.

Subsampling ground material is difficult and may result in serious sub-sampling errors because, during storage, fine particles may settle, and leave a layer of coarse material on top. Each ground sample should be stirred gently before subsampling for chemical analysis.

The most common laboratory mills are of the hammer-mill or shear-mill type. Hammer mills are fast and have good capacity. But because air pressure is built up within a hammer mill, minute particles may be lost through air leaks around it or through the cloth filter or collection bag. Shear mills are slower and usually more expensive than hammer mills of comparable capacity. The ground material is collected in an airtight container but in a shear mill part of the sample may be left inside the mill. Cleaning a shear mill is tedious, but it is necessary if contamination is to be avoided.

A satisfactory grinding unit is shown below. The collection box is raised or lowered by means of a cam lever operated by a foot pedal under the bench. The collection box is fitted with a heavy nylon panel that permits sufficient air flow to facilitate collection but reduces the loss of fine material to a minimum. Details of an excellent grinding, collection, and dust extraction system, developed at the Grassland Research Institute, Hurley, may be found in Bulletin 45 of the Commonwealth Bureau of Pasture and Field Crops, Hurley, Berkshire, England.

References

Bath, I. H., and R. T. Budd. 1961. A laboratory apparatus for freeze-drying herbage samples. J. Brit. Grassl. Soc. 16:278–280.

Brown, D. 1954. Methods of surveying and measuring vegetation. Commonwealth Agr. Bur., Farnham Royal, Bucks. Bull. 42.

Campbell, J. B., and R. W. Lodge. 1955. Sturdy cage for range and pasture studies. J. Range Manage. 8:128.

Carter, J. F. 1962. Herbage sampling for yield: Tame pastures, p. 90–101. Pastures and range research techniques. Cornell Univ. Press, Ithaca, N.Y.

Carter, J. F., D. W. Bolin, and D. O. Erickson. 1960. The evaluation of forage by the agronomic difference method and the chromogen – chromic oxide indicator technique. N. Dak. Tech. Bull. 426.

Cowlishaw, S. J. 1951. The effect of sampling cages on the yields of herbage. J. Brit. Grassl. Soc. 6:179–182.

Davies, A. W., R. A. Evans, and W. C. Evans. 1948. A new technique for the preparation and preservation of herbage samples. J. Brit. Grassl. Soc. 3:153–158.

Green, J. O., H. J. Langer, and T. E. Williams. 1952. Sources and magnitudes of experimental errors in grazing trials. Proc. 6th Int. Grassl. Congr. 6:1374–1379.

Greenhill, W. L. 1960. Determination of the dry weight of herbage by drying methods. J. Brit. Grassl. Soc. 15:48–54.

Hesse, W. H., and W. K. Kennedy. 1956. Factors causing errors in the determination of dry matter and nitrogen in forage crops. Agron. J. 48:204–207.

Kemp, J. C. 1965. Harvesters for grain test plots. News, Can. Dep. Agr. 1105:2, 7.

Kemp, J. C., and William Kalbfleisch. 1957. A crop harvester for forage plots. Can. J. Plant Sci. 37:418–422.

Linehan, P. A. 1952. Use of cage and mower-strip methods for measuring the forage consumed by grazing animals. Proc. 6th Int. Grassl. Congr. 6:1328–1333.

McDonald, P., and W. A. Dewar. 1960. Determination of dry matter and volatiles in silage. J. Sci. Food Agr. 11:566–570.

McGinnies, W. J. 1959. A rotary lawn mower for sampling range herbage. J. Range Manage. 12:203–204.

Merridrew, J. N., and W. F. Raymond. 1953. Laboratory drying of herbage by radio-frequency dielectric heating. Brit. J. Appl. Phys. 4:37.

Miltimore, J. E., A. D. McMechan, and J. C. Wilcox. 1961. A self-propelled plot forage harvester. Agron. J. 53:206–207.

Nevens, W. B. 1945. A comparison of sampling procedures in making pasture yield determinations. J. Dairy Sci. 28:171–185.

Nevens, W. B., and A. F. Kuhlman. 1935. A method of harvesting samples of pasture forage. J. Dairy Sci. 18:793–794.

Page, G. E., T. L. Jackson, and A. S. Hunter. 1957. A self-propelled forage plot harvester. Agron. J. 49:56–57.

Prendergast, J. J., and J. J. Brady. 1955. Improved moveable cage for use in grassland research. J. Brit. Grassl. Soc. 10:189–190.

Raymond, W. F., and C. E. Harris. 1954. The laboratory drying of herbage and faeces and dry matter losses possible during drying. J. Brit. Grassl. Soc. 9:119–130.

Thompson, J. L. 1967. Modifications of the Swift Current forage harvester II. Can. J. Plant Sci. 47:459.

Thompson, J. L., and D. H. Heinrichs. 1963. Note on the Swift Current forage plot harvester. Can. J. Plant Sci. 43:602–604.

Walker, D. M. 1959. The in vitro digestion of roughage dry matter. J. Agr. Sci. 53:192–197.

Williams, Stella S. 1951. Microenvironment in relation to experimental techniques. J. Brit. Grassl. Soc. 6:207–217.

Chapter 10
DESIGN OF EXPERIMENTS WITH PLOTS GRAZED BY LIVESTOCK

SYLVESTER SMOLIAK
Research Station, Canada Department of Agriculture
Lethbridge, Alberta

This stage of testing introduces the animal factor. It represents the transition from purely agronomic problems to those in which animal responses are the important measurements.

There are two general methods of experimental organization. In the first, several replicated crops are enclosed by one fence and are grazed by one unit of livestock throughout the summer. The main objective is to find out the acceptability of different crops at different seasons.

The second method is based on individual treatments or crops. A livestock unit is assigned to each treatment being tested. The replicates are grazed in succession. This latter method should be used when the following are of prime importance:

- The rate of recovery and persistence of swards after different intensities of defoliation (Whyte, Nilsson-Leissner, and Trumble, 1953)
- The resistance of a herbage to trampling (Edmund, 1966), and soil compaction (Tanner and Maramil, 1959), and its response to feces and urine deposits
- The nutrient status of the same crop or mixture from grazed and mowed plots
- An indication of the grazing capacity of two or more crops, or an indication of the best management practice on one crop.

METHOD NO. 1

Simple experimental designs are recommended. A Latin square design is practical if no more than six treatments are included in one test, but a randomized complete block design simplifies the work when more treatments are being compared. Four replicates are necessary for all studies, but six or more may be advisable if the soil is variable in texture and nutrient availability. No livestock measurements are recorded.

A test can be fenced as a unit and grazed by one herd or flock. Or each replicate can be fenced separately, and grazed in succession by one livestock unit or simultaneously by a livestock unit on each replicate. It is not necessary for all replicates to be adjacent. If they are not, however, labor and supplies will cost more. Wagner and others (1950) and

Wagner (1952) recommend the mower-strip sampling technique to estimate yield and apparent consumption. But Green, Langer, and Williams (1952), and Linehan (1952) suggest pregrazing and postgrazing randomized subsamples from plots 1 by 3 or ½ by 6 feet in size.

An alternative procedure involves haying and grazing. Each year half the replicates are grazed, and the other half cut for hay (McIntyre and Davies, 1952); the order is reversed in alternate years. Postgrazing cuts are taken from the grazed plots, but no pregrazing sampling is necessary.

Plots measuring 1500 to 3000 square feet are recommended, though larger areas may be necessary in arid locations. When plots are smaller, the livestock congregate on the most palatable crops, causing excessive damage by trampling and heavy grazing. If larger plots are used, herbage selection is more evident (Arnold, 1960).

One limitation of this method is the uneven distribution of dung and urine between plots. Cattle will defecate and urinate three to five times during both the morning and late afternoon grazing periods and six to eight times during lounging hours. Thus, there is a concentration of fertility in the lounging area, in addition to its uneven distribution. In part, this unevenness can be overcome by applying fertilizers at rates somewhat greater than those determined in other plot trials.

Cattle will graze over a test or a replicate without being unduly attracted by herds in adjacent paddocks, though they will congregate while lounging. Sheep need to be isolated from other flocks, and when this is done reasonably good utilization will be obtained. When isolation is not possible, the use of a decoy flock in a perimeter paddock is recommended. Locating shelter, water, and mineral supplements in the center of the paddock is also effective for obtaining uniform distribution.

Selection of herbage should not be based entirely on its apparent acceptability at any one season, because animals may prefer a crop in the fall that was their second or third choice earlier in the year. Also, a herbage should be grazed by both cattle and sheep, because they may differ considerably in their preference.

This testing method should be introduced early in a selection program. If possible, it should be undertaken in conjunction with preliminary field-plot studies, and no later than when advanced field-plot work is started. A simple method of organization is to have two or three replicates fenced, and grazed according to a simulated grazing schedule. This achieves a rapid selection of valuable pasture plants.

METHOD NO. 2

This method of testing is based on treatments or crops. It is used to compare the effects of livestock pressure on different herbage by different management practices. Because it is flexible and adaptable to many situations, it is a valuable tool in the selection of useful herbages.

In many instances, the results can be applied directly to farm practice.

Each treatment or crop is assigned a livestock unit that grazes that particular treatment or crop throughout the grazing season. The replicates are grazed progressively. Unless animals have been trained to graze on a tether, it is well to fence each treatment-replicate and use a small herd or flock as the livestock complement. Three yearling steers or their equivalent in animal units are recommended as a minimum-sized herd; more might be used when rapid defoliation is an objective of a test.

A simple experimental design suffices because relatively few treatments are included. A randomized block design usually controls soil variability, and is recommended because of its flexibility. Incomplete block designs may be used where the response differs from group to group. A split-plot design can be superimposed without affecting the basic design or the primary objective. Plot size ranges from a few square rods to several acres, depending on the following conditions:

- The local environment. The larger-sized plots are necessary in semi-arid and arid regions
- The length of the grazing period. Small plots usually suffice with intermittent grazing, but larger plots are needed if the objective is to provide season-long pasturage
- The size of herd or flock superimposed as the livestock complement
- The estimated yield per unit of land and the desired degree of utilization.

This method of testing is adaptable to many situations. Experiments can be undertaken to observe and measure the effects of trampling and soil compaction (Tanner and Maramil, 1959), the influence of urine and feces deposits (Weeda, 1967), the rate and recovery of swards under different intensities of grazing, the incidence of selective grazing within a mixture, and the compatibility of species comprising a mixture (Ahlgren, 1947; Brown, 1954; Castle, 1955; Wagner and others, 1950; Wagner, 1952).

This method should not be overlooked when an indication of grazing capacity or management practices is desired. Moving livestock daily from replicate to replicate is comparable to continuous grazing; rotations can be introduced by alternate grazing and resting; repeated-seasonal and deferred-rotations can be simulated by seasonal use of successive replicates; grazing capacity can be indicated by different levels of stocking or by resting different treatments for different periods of time. Though livestock measurements should be recorded, they will indicate the expected animal production of one treatment rather than show how treatments compare (Linehan, 1952). Spedding (1965) points out the unreliability of animal-days per unit of land unless wide differences occur between treatments, though these data may be useful when correlated with liveweight gain or other plant and animal measurements. Grazing activity studies are not particularly valuable unless the natural grazing patterns of livestock are observed (*see* Chapter 12).

Various sampling techniques used to estimate dry-matter yield and apparent consumption are discussed in Chapters 2 and 9. Green and others (1952) mention a point of considerable interest that applies when their subsample technique is used. They point out that the sampling error of a plot should approximate the sampling error of a treatment; they describe the simple calculations required to obtain comparable plot and treatment errors.

Many sampling techniques are not practicable under extensive grazing management practices because the dry-matter yield is often less than 500 pounds per acre. Green and others (1952) state that sampling intensity should be inversely related to dry-matter yield, but that there is a limit beyond which more sampling will not add much precision. On high-yielding swards the treatment-replicate error is a useful statistic. But on low-yielding swards it is better to grid a paddock and sample according to a random pattern within the grid.

No method of testing measurement or technique is perfect (McMeekan, 1960). The method described here has limitations. The first is the transfer of fertility from replicate to replicate on high-yielding swards. This problem can be overcome by starting each go-around or each season's grazing on different replicates. It is not a serious limitation on low-yielding swards. Nor is it serious when continuous grazing is practiced by moving livestock from replicate to replicate each day.

A second limitation is the lack of reliable livestock data (Spedding, Large, and Kydd, 1966). As indicated in Chapter 15, it is necessary that grazing be continuous for 3 months or more for a small herd to show a low coefficient of variability. When intermittent grazing is practiced, liveweight gains or other animal measurements have little or no reliability. Further, no error estimate can be established because only one herd is used per treatment.

The third limiting factor is the cost of an experiment in relation to the information obtained. Fences, corrals, shelter, and water installations can be expensive unless they are provided as part of an overall program that includes other studies. On the other hand, the investment in livestock is relatively small.

References

Ahlgren, H. L. 1947. A comparison of methods used in evaluating the results of pasture research. J. Amer. Soc. Agron. 39:240–259.

Arnold, G. A. W. 1960. Selective grazing by sheep of two forages at different stages of growth. Austral. J. Agr. Res. 11:1026–1033.

Brown, D. 1954. Methods of surveying and measuring vegetation. Commonwealth Bur. of Pasture and Field Crops. Bull. 42:1–223. Hurley, Berks.

Castle, M. E. 1955. Methods of evaluating grassland production in temperate zones. Herb. Abstr. 25:1–9.

Edmund, D. B. 1966. The influence of animal treading on pasture growth. Proc. 10th Int. Grassl. Congr. 2:453–458.

Green, J. O., H. J. Langer, and T. E. Williams. 1952. Sources and magnitude of experimental errors in grazing trials. Proc. 6th Int. Grassl. Congr. 6:1374–1379.

Linehan, P. A. 1952. Use of cage and mower-strip methods for measuring the forage consumed by grazing animals. Proc. 6th Int. Grassl. Congr. 6:1328–1333.

McIntyre, G. A., and J. G. Davies. 1952. Small plot studies in the evaluation of pasture intended for grazing. Proc. 6th Int. Grassl. Congr. 6:1361–1366.

McMeekan, C. P. 1960. Grazing management. Proc. 8th Int. Grassl. Congr. 8:21–26.

Spedding, C. R. W. 1965. Grazing management for sheep. Herb. Abstr. 35:77–84.

Spedding, C. R. W., R. V. Large, and D. D. Kydd. 1966. The evaluation of herbage by grazing animals. Proc. 10th Int. Grassl. Congr. 2:479–483.

Tanner, C. B., and C. P. Maramil. 1959. Pasture soil compaction by animal traffic. Agron. J. 51:329–331.

Wagner, R. E. 1952. Weight estimation and other procedures for measuring the botanical composition of pastures. Proc. 6th Int. Grassl. Congr. 6:1315–1321.

Wagner, R. E., M. A. Hein, J. B. Shepherd, and R. E. Ely. 1950. A comparison of cage and mower-strip methods with grazing results in determining production of dairy pastures. Agron. J. 42:487–491.

Weeda, W. C. 1967. The effect of cattle dung patches on pasture growth, botanical composition, and pasture utilization. New Zeal. J. Agr. Res. 10:150–159.

Whyte, R. O., G. Nilsson-Leissner, and H. C. Trumble. 1953. Legumes in agriculture, FAO Agr. Studies, 21:225–232. Rome, Italy.

Chapter 11

REPLICATED ANIMAL AND PADDOCK
EXPERIMENTS

DONALD B. WILSON
Research Station, Canada Department of Agriculture
Lethbridge, Alberta

Replicated animal experiments are the best devised so far to evaluate a group of treatments. The results may be expressed in terms of the output of any livestock product per acre, and the influence of the animal and the herbage on each other can be assessed. The cost is high because good land, labor, and physical facilities are necessary.

Mower-strip and cage techniques can be used to measure herbage yields and consumption by animals. Evaluation of a group of treatments requires understanding of the limitations of each sampling method and a high level of competence in executing it.

Replicated animal and paddock experiments require a livestock complement for each replicate of a treatment. The design permits critical evaluation of a group of treatments because livestock performance gives direct measures of animal production from each replicate. Transference of fertility and the complication of grazing each replicate when plants are at different growth stages are avoided. The main problem is to express livestock response in unbiased terms. There are four possible sources of bias:

- Differences in the ability of individual animals to convert herbage to measurable livestock products
- The reaction of a herd or flock to physical or biotic factors of the environment
- The effect of grazing pressure on herbage growth
- The efficiency of harvesting.

Replicated plot and animal experiments require good physical facilities and may be costly to operate. Relatively large acreages are needed to balance livestock numbers with forage production, and compensate for the variability between animals by using large populations. Plot size may vary from less than half an acre on irrigated land to several hundred acres on range. The acreage available often dictates the class of livestock to be used, the treatments to be studied, and the intensity of replication. The degree of compromise necessary is an index of the desirability of choosing a completely replicated design.

There is no single criterion for comparing one treatment in comparison with a second, but many different measurements will provide a broad basis for assessment. Weight gains are practical but vary with the age, condition, and individual characteristics of an animal; total digestible nutrients (TDN) and digestible energy (DE) estimates are objective but are based on averages that are not always applicable; grazing days are informative but insufficient; herbage yields can be precise but require interpretation. Whatever measures of production are recorded, they are valid only in terms of the management imposed. Thus a management scheme should be planned carefully, adhered to rigidly, and changed only for good reason.

MANAGEMENT

First decide whether production per unit of land or per animal is to be a basic criterion. This must be done before the conditions of management can be established. From the agronomic viewpoint, the choice is usually the former, but from an animal husbandry viewpoint it may be the latter. A light stocking rate underestimates the productivity of a sward, but permits maximum performance of each animal. Too heavy a rate gives a temporary overestimate of herbage productivity followed by an overgrazed condition, and poor performance of individual animals.

Usually it is necessary to adjust stocking rates during a season. The more animals a plot can accommodate the more efficiently an adjustment can be made. Theoretically, by the addition or removal of one animal, forage consumption can be controlled within 12.5 percent with a basic number of four animals on each plot, within 5 percent with 10 animals, and within 1 percent with 50 animals.

Good management requires an accurate estimate of the amount of forage available and a prediction of animal intake. A rough guide to daily intake of dry matter (DM) is 2 percent of body weight for cattle (McCarrick, 1947), and 3 percent for sheep. The available forage can be determined by estimation, or by clipping and weighing sample areas. A simple method for estimating yields has been described by Alexander, Sullivan, and McCloud (1962), who found that, by dropping a 2-foot-square piece of cardboard onto the grass from a constant height and measuring the distance the board was held off the ground by the grass, they could estimate relative yield of standing forage with considerable reliability.

Plot size is dictated by the type of animals used, the magnitude of the differences to be measured, and the extent of the facilities available. A minimum paddock size of 1/6 acre for cattle and 1/20 acre for sheep has been suggested (Grassland Research Institute, 1961). The total area required is a function of the number of paddocks per plot. If a daily rotation is used, each treatment plot will have to be 30 to 40 times the minimum paddock area to provide time for regrowth after grazing. Unnatural grazing habits need to be avoided. One cow or steer may behave nearly normally, but five sheep are needed for a socially stable flock (Crofton, 1958).

Small differences due to treatments are hard to detect. In a comparison between two groups of steers, to be 80 percent certain that a 5 percent difference in liveweight is significant at the 5 percent level, one would need 8 pairs of animals with a coefficient of variation of 3 percent or 65 pairs with a coefficient of variation of 10 percent (Alder, 1959). It is not uncommon for weight gains of steers on the same pasture during a season to differ by 100 pounds. Tables or formulas that permit estimation of feed consumption from weight gains and maintenance requirements help to overcome these differences (*see* Chapter 17).

Sheep are convenient animals to use because their numbers can be adjusted readily and they require less land than cattle. From tables, TDN and DE equivalents can be estimated on the basis of weight changes in the sheep, and the probable response of various classes of cattle can be predicted. Complete substitution is undesirable because of differences in palatability preferences, closeness of bite, bedding habits, nutritional requirements, effects of treading, and fertilizing value of excreta. The effects of one or more of these factors must be considered before deciding on the kind of livestock to use.

Because herbage is not produced at a uniform rate during the growing season, feed surpluses and shortages occur. It is not possible to get good utilization of feed without adjusting the grazing routine during the season. On high-producing pastures, it is best to vary the stocking rate with "put-and-take animals," or to harvest the surplus spring herbage and feed it back in the fall. The latter procedure is hampered by small paddocks, and this should be considered in designing fences and gates. A combination of the two methods is often the most practical solution. All treatments should be managed in a similar manner, although small variations in technique to bring out the best features of each treatment are permissible. The practical application of results should always be considered when deciding on management techniques.

HERBAGE EVALUATION

Mower-strip and cage techniques are used extensively to estimate herbage yields. With the mower-strip technique, strips of herbage are mowed and gathered for weighing before the animals are turned into the pasture. With cage techniques, sample areas that are protected by wire cages are mowed and weighed after fields have been grazed. The Difference Method may be used with either harvesting technique by cutting a sample of the herbage remaining on the grazed portion of the field at the end of the grazing period and subtracting its weight from that of the ungrazed sample. This permits estimation of both production and consumption (*see* Chapters 9 and 23).

The mower-strip method is best applied on rotation pastures that are grazed for short periods. It underestimates yields because no account is taken of growth that occurs during the grazing period. The degree of underestimation varies with the number of days each paddock is grazed. With a four-field rotation each paddock will be occupied for 25 percent of the grazing season, and the growth that occurs during that time will not be recorded. An approximate correction can be made by arithmetically increasing the measured yields in proportion to the length of time each paddock is occupied during the grazing season (Freer, 1960), or by estimating growth on the basis of a previous grazing period (Campbell, 1966).

The yield from the strip measures apparent consumption within the limits noted if the height to which animals will graze can be predicted. The alternative is to use the Difference Method, but here it should be recognized that the postgrazing sample includes herbage that grew during the grazing period, and its weight will be subtracted from the pregrazing yield and not added to it as it should be. Error can be minimized by providing a maximum number of rotation fields and keeping the grazing periods short.

If there are several rotation fields (six or more), all of similar productivity, it is not essential that all of them be sampled. For any given number of sampling sites, almost as good an estimate of yield is obtained if only half the rotation fields are sampled, but at double the intensity. This procedure will sometimes effect a reduction in labor. It is best to sample alternate fields in a rotation, starting with either the first or the second (Wilson, 1966).

Cage techniques should be used when the grazing period lasts for several days. Cage techniques permit flexibility in the time of harvest, as it is often possible to harvest a day or two after animals are moved if inclement weather prevails. Late in the season, when daily growth is slow, caged areas may be left for several days and harvested when it is convenient. This is not possible with a mower-strip procedure, which necessitates removal of the herbage before grazing starts.

The number of cages required depends on the precision desired, the type and uniformity of the herbage, and the size of each cage. Green, Langer, and Williams (1952) have reported that with a sampling unit of 1 or 2 square yards, the coefficient of variation between sample yields was 20 to 35 percent when the yield was 1000 to 2500 pounds of DM per acre, and between 60 and 80 percent when the yield was 500 pounds. This means that sampling precision will vary during the season if the number of sampling units remains the same. At Lethbridge, Alberta, the coefficient of variation was about 25 percent for the accumulated seasonal yields (four or five grazings) from 1- by 2-yard cages on irrigated grass–legume pastures yielding about 6000 pounds of DM per acre (Wilson and Clark, 1961).

Klingman, Miles, and Mott (1943) investigated the number of 4- by 4-foot cages necessary for various levels of precision of yield estimation on a 12-acre grass–clover pasture sustaining about 700 pounds of DM per acre. For the 5 percent level of probability they found the requirements to be:

Precision desired		Number of cages required		
lb DM/acre	%	Singly	In pairs	In threes
700 ± 50	7	308	502	696
700 ± 100	14	77	126	174
700 ± 150	21	34	56	78
700 ± 200	28	19	32	45
700 ± 250	36	12	20	30
700 ± 300	43	9	14	21
700 ± 400	57	5	8	12
700 ± 500	71	3	6	9

Klingman and co-workers have pointed out that the number of cages does not necessarily increase in proportion to plot size. Approximately the same number of cages would be required on a 2-acre plot as on a 12-acre plot if variability was similar on both areas. It is evident from the above data that it is more efficient to place cages singly than in groups.

For the same reasons several small cages give a better estimate of yield than larger cages covering the same sampling area. Green and others (1952) report the relationship of the coefficient of variation in yield to the logarithm of sampling unit size to be almost linear. They emphasize the advantage of sampling units of 3 to 6 square feet rather than the more common units of 9 to 18 square feet, and suggest that long strips 4 to 6 inches wide would be even better. The cage method becomes impractical as the sampling unit size is decreased or its shape elongated, but the mower-strip method could well be used where the duration of grazing is short.

Harvesting technique also has a bearing on the size and number of cages used. For example, one 3- by 3-foot cage might give as accurate an estimate as four 1- by 1-foot cages, but the former would be easier to harvest with a power mower and the latter with hand shears.

Under continuous grazing, each cage should be relocated during the season rather than left in one place. The procedure is to choose a cage location in the spring, remove and weigh the existing herbage to a predetermined stubble height, and place the cage. After a predetermined period the herbage under the cage is harvested and a new cage location is selected; the existing herbage is removed and discarded and the cage placed. This sequence is repeated until the end of the season. The total weight of herbage harvested from under the cages, plus the initial harvest, represents the yield for the season.

When the Difference Method is used to measure consumption, a good procedure is to enter a pasture before it has been grazed and locate one sampling site at random and then select another site that appears similar to it. By random choice, one can decide which site to cage and which to postharvest. Klingman and others (1943) have found that this was more efficient than choosing both sites at random. Animals may loiter near the cages, so the postgrazing harvest site should be far enough away to avoid the unnatural conditions that result from heavy traffic.

100

The height of cutting of both samples should be only as low as necessary to reach the lowest grazing height and to recover trampled grass. It is not desirable to denude the ground because a considerable amount of litter, which is unevenly deposited over the pasture, may be picked up and the sampling error increased. Poor technique may result in the grazed site yielding more than the ungrazed one. Better results are often obtained by expressing the yield as organic matter instead of dry matter.

Herbage that grows during a long grazing period should have special consideration. Linehan, Lowe, and Stewart (1947) point out that it is neither proper to ignore it (as with pregrazing sampling) nor to consider it completely available (as with cage sampling). They propose an alternative formula to estimate consumption through x days by y animals on z units of land:

$$\text{Consumption} = c - f\,\frac{\log d - \log f}{\log c - \log f}$$

where $c =$ the pregrazing yield,
$d =$ the cage yield at the end of the grazing period,
$f =$ the uneaten herbage remaining on the grazed field.

This scheme requires an extra sample, but it gives a closer approximation of consumption than the standard method.

If the height of grazing can be simulated when caged areas are mowed, it is not necessary to use the Difference Method. Grazing should be managed with the sampling procedure in mind. A common mistake is to permit animals to graze closer than the mower will cut. This leads to underestimation of consumption.

Power mowers, hand shears, scythes, and hand plucking have been used to harvest herbage for this type of experiment. The diversity of methods has arisen partly because of a desire to make yield estimates completely objective. Objectivity eliminates personal bias and makes it possible to make more use of semiskilled labor. However, because pasture conditions vary with location, season, and year, a subjective approach to yield determination is often necessary.

RELATING HERBAGE CONSUMPTION AND ANIMAL DATA

Herbage consumption in relation to the liveweight change of an animal is an index to herbage quality, but it is not infallible. The relationship between herbage consumption and individual animal production is curved, rather than linear. If feed is plentiful, the last unit of intake does not produce the same response as an earlier one. A comparison between pastures is not really valid unless the degree of utilization is the same on all of them.

Utilization varies with the palatability, digestibility, and availability of herbage. These aspects are all part of the larger consideration of general suitability, but each is also important in itself. For example, a species with a low palatability index but a high yield might be unsatisfactory for production but excellent for maintenance. A species having a low nutritive value for one kind of stock might provide adequate nutrition for another. Herbage grazed with difficulty by cattle might be available to sheep.

Palatability is indicated by animal-grazing-days per unit of forage consumed, although it is affected by rate of digestion. Digestion can be measured by indicator methods discussed elsewhere in this book. Availability can be measured by stand density and by observation.

Changes in the species composition of a herbage mixture should be studied in conjunction with animal observations. Unpalatable species may quickly dominate a sward and this will be reflected in animal performance.

The seasonal production trend of a mixture might indicate the desirability of an alternative type of management. A mixture that does not produce uniformly throughout a season might be useful for one kind of stock early in the year and for a different kind later, or it might be suitable for a hay–pasture combination. The value of a treatment for a variety of purposes can be estimated, and the objectives of an experiment should be flexible enough to make use of many different kinds of observations.

SAMPLE EXPERIMENT

An irrigated pasture study conducted by Wilson and Clark (1961) illustrates the observations recorded in a replicated plot and animal experiment. They compared two fertilizer treatments (blocks) on four herbage mixtures (plots), replicated three times. Six 2-acre blocks were established, three of which were topdressed while the other three were left as controls. Each block was then subdivided into four ½-acre plots on which four herbage mixtures were seeded at random. Each plot was subdivided into four 1/8-acre paddocks to permit rotational grazing. The test comprised 96 individual paddocks, each measuring 64 by 85 feet. The area, including roadways and holding pasture, occupied 15 acres.

The year following seeding, grazing began with 24 flocks of white-faced yearling ewes. Stocking rates were commensurate with estimated herbage yields so that all mixtures would have near equal grazing seasons and utilization. An attempt was made to maintain the same animals on a plot for an entire season, but adjustments in stocking rates were often necessary to balance sheep numbers with herbage supply. In the spring, for example, a temporary surplus of herbage occurred because growth began on all paddocks of a plot at the same time. Stocking rates were increased temporarily, but still complete utilization of the herbage was not possible. Following removal of the sheep, the rejected growth was sampled for yield and then mowed. An alternative would have been to harvest the spring surplus as hay for feeding later in the year, but this was impractical because of the number and size of paddocks. The average length of a rotation cycle was 1 month, with 1 week of grazing and 3 weeks of recovery for each paddock, but this varied with the season.

Two 3- by 6-foot protective cages were used in each paddock. Forage yields were measured by mowing the herbage on the caged areas after a field had been grazed. The herbage was placed in paper bags, oven-dried, and weighed. Subsamples were retained for chemical analysis. The cages were relocated at random in the next paddock of the plot and the sheep moved. The Difference Method was used to estimate production and consumption in the late spring and early summer when a considerable amount of herbage was left uneaten. The practice was to harvest the caged area and then cut a 3- by 6-foot strip about 6 feet away. The dried weight of the material harvested outside the cage was subsequently subtracted from the weight of that inside. In the early spring and late summer, utilization of the herbage was more complete, and sampling of the uncaged area was unnecessary. The practice then was to mow the herbage on the caged area to the same stubble height as the grazed portion.

Botanical compositions were determined every June and September by hand separation of a composite sample of green herbage weighing about 300 grams. Only one of the four paddocks of each plot was sampled but it was the same paddock each year. In addition, visual estimates of botanical composition were made during the season.

The ewes were held on pasture similar to that in the test plot for 10 days before the test began. During this time they were shorn, and treated for keds and internal parasites. Treatment for parasites was repeated during the season when necessary.

The sheep were weighed on 2 consecutive days before the test began and at 2-week intervals during the season. Initial weights were about 90 pounds. Grazing was permitted at all times but water was withheld for 12 to 15 hours before weighing. The weighings were done during the morning. No weight records were kept of animals that were added to a plot for only a few days. They were assumed to have converted herbage to energy at the same rate as those that had been grazing continuously. A mineral mixture of salt and bonemeal was available. Final evaluation of the mixtures was based on DM and TDN yields, changes in botanical composition, animal weight gains, grazing days, and management required by both herbage and animals.

References

Alder, F. E. 1959. Animal production from grassland, p. 109–118. *In* J. D. Ivins (ed.) The measurement of grassland productivity. Butterworths Sci. Publications, London.

Alexander, C. W., J. T. Sullivan, and D. E. McCloud. 1962. A method for estimating forage yields. Agron. J. 54:468–469.

Campbell, A. G. 1966. Grazed pasture parameters. 1. Pasture dry-matter production and availability in a stocking rate and grazing experiment with dairy cows. J. Agr. Sci. 67:199–210.

Crofton, H. D. 1958. Nematode parasite populations in sheep on lowland farms. VI. Sheep behavior and nematode infections. Parasitology 48:251–260.

Freer, M. 1960. The utilization of irrigated pasture by dairy cows. 2. The effect of stocking rate. J. Agr. Sci. 54:243–256.

Grassland Research Institute. 1961. Research techniques in use at the Grassland Research Institute, Hurley, Berks. Bull. 45. Comonw. Agr. Bur., Farnham Royal, Bucks. 166 p.

Green, J. O., H. J. Langer, and T. E. Williams. 1952. Sources and magnitudes of experimental errors in grazing trials. Proc. 6th Int. Grassl. Congr. 6:1374–1379.

Klingman, D. L., S. R. Miles, and G. O. Mott. 1943. The cage method for determining consumption and yield of pasture herbage. J. Amer. Soc. Agr. 35:739–746.

Linehan, P. A., J. Lowe, and R. H. Stewart. 1947. The output of pasture and its measurement. Part II. J. Brit. Grassl. Soc. 2:145–168.

McCarrick, R. B. 1967. The growth and body composition of cattle fed conserved fodders, p. 121–129. In R. J. Wilkins (ed.) Fodder conservation. The Brit. Grassl. Soc., Hurley, nr. Maidenhead, Berkshire.

Wilson, D. B. 1966. Variability in herbage yields from caged areas in a pasture experiment. Can. J. Plant Sci. 46:249–255.

Wilson, D. B., and R. D. Clark. 1961. Performance of four irrigated pasture mixtures under grazing by sheep. Can. J. Plant Sci. 41:533–543.

104

Chapter 12

PASTURE ACTIVITIES OF CATTLE AND SHEEP

J. BADEN CAMPBELL
Research Station, Canada Department of Agriculture
Swift Current, Saskatchewan

ELWOOD STRINGAM
Head and Professor, Division of Animal Science
University of Manitoba, Winnipeg, Manitoba

PAUL GERVAIS
Professor of Field Crops, Laval University
Quebec, Quebec

This summer I continued my investigations as to which plants are consumed by cattle, which are ignored, and which are avoided; this work
in my opinion, is of fundamental importance both for private owners of
cattle and animal husbandry as a whole.

C. Linnaeus

A ruminant divides its pasture day among three main activities: grazing, ruminating, and idling. The time spent in each indicates the availability of a herbage or its nutritive status. By itself, a
pasture activity study may be of greater academic interest than of practical value. But, when considered with other criteria, it may explain
anomalies in herbage utilization or help to improve the management of
experimental swards.

Pasture activities of ruminants comprise grazing, traveling, drinking
water, eating supplements, and ruminating or idling while standing or
lying down (Cory, 1927). These activities are nearly uniform from day
to day in near-constant environments. But stress caused by heat, cold,
rain, humidity, insects, sward condition, size of pasture, and the number
in a herd or flock may change a daily routine considerably. Domestic
animals adjust their routines quickly to compensate for some of the
adverse effects of these discomforts. The adjustments, unless known,
may be great enough to affect the interpretation of experimental data
(Hafez and Schein, 1962; Hafez and Scott, 1962; Hancock, 1953;
Tribe, 1955).

CATTLE

Cattle graze 6 to 8 hours each day when herbage is abundant and
nutritious but up to 12 hours when herbage is short or sparse. In temperate environments they graze intensively in the early morning and
late afternoon, and lightly near noon and midnight and at other times
of the day. The morning period starts before sunrise, or after the morn-

105

ing milking, and lasts for 3 or 4 hours; intensive grazing resumes in the late afternoon, or after milking, and ends an hour or two after sunset (Hancock, 1953; Harker, Taylor, and Rollinson, 1954; Hughes and Reid, 1951; Johnstone-Wallace and Kennedy, 1944; Wilson, 1961). Cattle eat avidly at the start of the morning and afternoon grazing periods, but more slowly as they become filled. In the tropics and sub-tropics and during prolonged periods of hot weather in temperate zones, night grazing may account for 80 percent of the total grazing time, starting about 6 p.m. and ending near midnight (Lampkin and Quarter-main, 1962; Larkin, 1954). There are no great differences in the pasture routines of different breeds of *Bos taurus*. *Bos indicus* animals graze longer and idle less than *B. taurus* (Lampkin and Quartermain, 1962). Species, breed, and individual differences may be particularly striking under stress.

More time is spent grazing and less resting as stocking rates increase (Arnold, 1962; Kromann, Meyer, and Hull, 1961), when pastures are naturally short or eaten down (Lofgreen, Meyer, and Hull, 1957; Peterson and Woolfolk, 1955), as the nutritive value of a sward declines (Duckworth and Shirlaw, 1958; Hancock, 1954; Taylor, Rollinson, and Harker, 1955), and on swards comprising species of different quality or growth habit (Hancock, 1958; Larkin, 1954). Under one or more of these stresses cattle may graze up to 12 hours daily. Grazing time increases and idling time decreases when the available dry matter drops below about 1000 pounds per acre in dense swards, and below about 500 pounds per acre in spaced rows or open stands (Arnold and Dudzinski, 1967; Campbell, 1963; Semple, 1951). Grazing time increases also on high-yielding, coarse-herbage pastures because of the extra time taken to select desirable fodder (Holder, 1960; Smith, 1959, 1961). In all these cases more energy is used for work and less for production.

Pasture routines of *B. taurus* breeds are nearly constant when mean daily temperatures range from 35 to 70 F, or when the ambient temperature is less than 70 F for several hours each day (Hancock, 1954; McDaniel and Roark, 1956), though pyrexia and anorexia may be apparent when mean daily temperatures rise above 70 F (Arrillaga, Henning, and Millar, 1952; Worstell and Brody, 1953). More time is spent standing than lying down when ambient temperatures are less than 35 F or when the ground is wet (Larkin, 1954; MacDonald and Bell, 1958). Breeds of *B. indicus* have a greater tolerance to heat than those of *B. taurus* (Worstell and Brody, 1953), but less to cold because their thermoneutral zone is between 50 and 80 F (Harker and others, 1954). Both species react adversely to high humidity (Johnson and others, 1962; Larkin, 1954). Decreasing milk production has been associated with an increasing temperature–humidity index (THI), which is calculated from the following equation: $THI = 0.55 D.B + 0.2 D.P + 17.5$ (Johnson and others, 1962). Pasture routine is affected by THI also.

Cattle ruminate for 4 to 8 hours daily, about 70 percent of this time occurring during the night. Although more time is spent ruminating as grazing time increases, neither can be expressed directly in terms of the other. The fiber content of herbage appears to be closely related to ruminating time (Duckworth and Shirlaw, 1959), though McCullough (1956) suggests that ruminating time is a function of several factors including DM intake, DM digestibility, and the species comprising a sward. There is no apparent association between ruminating time and ambient temperature.

Idling is a general term for resting, and accounts for 20 to over 50 percent of a 24-hour day. It is an important activity, because the longer the time spent idling the better the pasture and the fewer the stresses. Idling time is divided equally between standing and lying down during daylight hours, but the ratio of time spent standing to time spent lying is about 1:5 at night. Relationships between idling and energy-consuming activities of cattle on different quality swards are given below as percentages of a 24-hour day:

Herbage		Percentage of a 24-hour day		
Quantity	Quality	Grazing	Ruminating	Idling
Sufficient	Lush	30 to 35	20 to 25	40 to 50
Abundant	High	25 to 30	20 to 25	45 to 55
Abundant	Low	30 to 35	20 to 30	35 to 50
Sparse	High	30 to 40	30 to 35	30 to 35
Sparse	Low	35 to 50	30 to 35	20 to 30

Size of herd does not influence pasture activities greatly if the previously mentioned stresses are not excessive. At least two cattle are needed for pasture activity studies to avoid isolation influencing the grazing–ruminating–idling pattern. When only two animals are observed per treatment, replication is necessary.

Cattle show heat stress by panting, reduced rumination time, frequent drinking, excessive walking, standing instead of lying, and irritation. They will lie down in the late afternoon when they would usually be grazing. All visual symptoms of heat stress are more pronounced during the late spring, supporting the theory that a rapid increase in ambient temperature increases heat production and pulse rate in ruminants (Kibler and Brody, 1956; McDaniel and Roark, 1956). Shade of any kind promotes liveweight gains during hot weather, and natural shade is better than artificial. On moderately hot days, cattle often lie at the edge of a shaded area while ruminating or idling. It is best to allow 40 to 60 square feet of artificial shade with a 10-foot clearance per animal unit (McDaniel and Roark, 1956).

SHEEP

In temperate environments, sheep graze for 8 to 9 hours daily on good pasture, up to 12 hours when herbage is short or a pasture is overstocked, but less than 6 hours when social stresses increase aimless travel (Arnold, 1962; Campbell, 1963; Hughes and Reid, 1951; Lofgreen and others, 1957; Southcott, Roe, and Turner, 1962). Sheep ruminate about 3½ hours each day when they are on good pasture, but this activity decreases linearly as grazing time increases. Sheep select or reject herbage more critically than cattle, and they masticate more before swallowing.

Sheep begin grazing shortly before sunrise and feed for 3 or 4 hours. They idle until early afternoon and then graze intensively until sunset. If corralled at night they idle less during midday. When left on pasture, they graze considerably at night during the fall but very seldom throughout the spring or summer (Arnold, 1962). Willoughby (1959) has shown that the daily intake of sheep was reduced after herbage dry-matter content dropped below 1400 pounds per acre.

The thermoneutral zone for sheep carrying a 2-inch fleece is estimated at 30 to 85 F at the grazing level (Blaxter, Graham, and Wainman, 1959; Carter, Bolin and Erickson, 1960). Within this range they can conserve or disperse energy to maintain a near-constant body temperature. Stress caused by cold or wet weather is indicated by grazing in a compact flock. Heat stress occurs when ambient temperatures at the grazing level rise above the thermoneutral zone, and is shown by open grazing, spreading of hind legs, greater water intake, rapid breathing, less daytime grazing, and reduced rate of gain or even liveweight loss. On bright midsummer days, heat stress may start as early as 9 a.m. and continue until 3 or 4 p.m. even in temperate environments. Natural or artificial shade reduces heat stress.

A flock of at least five sheep is needed to study pasture routines (Southcott and others, 1962). While grazing, sheep orient themselves by reference to two other animals or points (Crofton, 1958), and when these are not available a social stress is shown by aimless travel and decreased grazing time. Shaded sites and decoys in a perimeter paddock reduce social stress. They also help to attract test animals to all points in an experimental field. To reduce traffic distractions, experimental paddocks should be at least 50 yards from a public road.

DAY AND NIGHT GRAZING

Theoretically, ruminants graze the same herbage at night as they do throughout the day. During daylight, because animals can see, they may choose to graze a particular area in a field, but it is doubtful if sight plays a significant role in herbage selection. Likewise, each of the other senses, by itself, may not affect selection materially. Because ruminants generally have limited ability to distinguish colors, and do not necessarily select herbage according to nutritional need (Gordon and Tribe, 1951; Tribe, 1955), herbage eaten or avoided is probably evaluated by several or all senses. Also, it is a recognized fact that animals become

108

accustomed to an odor if they live with it day after day, and so a herbage grazed continuously would not be rejected because of its scent, whereas plants with different or unusual scents might be avoided unless another sense assured their acceptability. This suggests that acceptability of herbage by ruminants is a negative and not a positive response. In other words, rejection is positive, whereas acceptance is the result of satisfactory experiences and thus a negative reaction. If this hypothesis is valid, ruminants will graze the same herbage during daylight and darkness.

SAMPLING TECHNIQUES

There are no recognized standards or techniques for pasture activity studies, and this chapter does not attempt to establish any. However, it does present a few details of the procedures used by several investigators, and recommends some of them. In future work the infrared ray equipment of Burton and Castle (1950), the rangemeter of Cresswell and Harris (1959), and light meters to standardize day and night grazing periods will probably be used.

Herds of cattle and flocks of sheep generally behave as units and not as collections of individuals, although differences in degree are observed. Some take larger bites, others graze or ruminate faster, and a few start or finish grazing before their companions. To understand pasture routines, careful recording of the activities of several animals over a period of days is necessary.

Observations of each animal should be made continuously or at regular intervals. Hancock (1952) has reported continuous observation of several pairs of monozygotic twins (cattle) for a fortnight during successive months, whereas others have reported the activities of only one or two animals for a single day. Satisfactory patterns can be obtained by taking observations between these two extremes. Observations every 5 minutes are advised when there is a choice of sward (Joplin, 1962), if the times spent ruminating, or idling or for other activities of short duration when standing or lying down are to be separated. Hull, Lofgreen, and Meyer (1960) made 5-, 15-, and 30-minute observations, but were unable to show significant differences in total grazing time per day between the different intervals. However, when the activities of five or fewer animals are being recorded, it is recommended that observations be made at 5-minute intervals. Recordings at 10-minute intervals are suggested when more animals are being observed, unless two or more observers are employed.

The duration of observations depends on the objective of a study. One day's observations may suffice in some instances. In others, observations may be necessary for 1 or more days during successive weeks. It is recommended that observations be recorded for 5 successive days when only one period is of concern. If a knowledge of changing pasture routines throughout an entire grazing season is desired, then 1 or 2 days' observations per week should be recorded.

A herd of two cattle or a flock of five sheep is needed to prevent social stress. However, these numbers are insufficient to study pasture routines. For this latter purpose, at least five cattle or ten sheep should be used, and twice as many is better.

Distance traveled per day and size of pasture are related. Each day cattle walk about 1.25 miles on small, highly productive paddocks, but over 6 miles on open range (Hancock, 1953). Sheep travel about 1.25 miles daily when herbage is abundant, 1.75 miles on moderately good pasture, but over 3 miles when herbage is sparse. The surest way to reduce aimless traveling is to stock experimental paddocks at their grazing capacity, unless a study is designed to over- or under-graze.

The daily routines of lactating cows are determined by their milking times; their day and night periods are therefore set artificially. When beef, dry dairy cattle, and sheep are on pasture 24 hours each day, it is necessary to set the day and night periods arbitrarily. Because of variations caused by a pasture or an environmental stress, the best division between day and night is based on sunrise and sunset. One procedure is to divide the day into equal periods beginning at 6 a.m. and 6 p.m.

Binoculars, a watch with a sweep second hand, shelter for observers, and forms to record activities are sufficient equipment for day observations. A strong flashlight is necessary for night work; it should not be focused on an animal for more than 10 seconds at a time. Standard meteorological records should be obtained (*see* Chapter 3), together with records of temperature and humidity at the grazing level.

There are social pressures other than isolation and outside distractions that affect pasture routines. One is herd or flock leadership. When two or more animals are together, one will dominate, and will assert its authority by forcing its way to a feeder, a favored grazing spot, or a water trough. When two groups of cattle are thrown together, the dominant individuals from each will try to establish authority by butting and shoving. In turn, each animal in a herd or flock will accept a relative position in the "butting order" (Hafez and Schein, 1962; Hafez and Scott, 1962). The determination of social position may require only a few minutes or several days, but pasture routines will not follow a regular pattern until the hegemony is established. The acceptance of this social system is seen in the sexual abberations of groups of bulls or rams, and the authority of individual cows or steers in feedlots and pastures.

Extremes of understocking or overstocking should be avoided. Both influence pasture routines. When understocking is practiced, herbage matures and is not eaten readily. With cattle, grazing and ruminating time increases; with sheep, grazing time increases and ruminating time decreases. When a pasture is overstocked its growth is retarded and its yield reduced; then animals need more grazing time to obtain a fill.

Pasture activity studies only complement other pasture investigations. By themselves, they seldom lead to improved animal and pasture management practices, and in many cases they may be of greater academic interest than of practical importance. However, they add to our knowledge of the how, when, and where of grazing, and thus to our understanding of the pasture complex relative to livestock response.

References

Arnold, G. W. 1962. The influence of several factors in determining the grazing behavior of Border Leicester × Merino sheep. J. Brit. Grassl. Soc. 17:41–47.

Arnold, G. W., and M. L. Dudzinski. 1967. Studies on the diet of grazing animals. II. The effect of physiological status in ewes and pasture availability on herbage intake. Austral. J. Agr. Res. 18:349–359.

Arrillaga, C. G., W. L. Henning, and R. C. Millar. 1952. The effects of environmental temperature and relative humidity on the acclimation of cattle to the tropics. J. Anim. Sci. 11:50–60.

Blaxter, K. L., N. McC. Graham, and F. W. Wainman. 1959. Environmental temperature, energy metabolism and heat regulation in sheep, III. J. Agr. Sci. 52:41–49.

Burton, H., and M. E. Castle. 1950. A description of the construction and use of portable infra-red ray equipment for animal observations in the field. J. Dairy Sci. 17:229–230.

Campbell, J. B. 1963. Grass–alfalfa vs. grass-alone pastures grazed in repeated-seasonal pattern. J. Range Manage. 16:78–81.

Carter, J. F., D. W. Bolin, and D. Erickson. 1960. The evaluation of forages by the agronomic "difference" method and the chromogen–chromic oxide "indicator" technique. N. Dak. Agr. Exp. Sta. Bull. 426.

Cory, V. L. 1927. Activities of livestock on the range. Texas Agr. Exp. Sta. Bull. 367.

Cresswell, E., and L. E. Harris. 1959. An improved rangemeter for sheep. J. Anim. Sci. 18:1447–1451.

Crofton, H. D. 1958. Nematode parasite populations in sheep on lowland farms. Parasitology 48:251–260.

Duckworth, J. E., and D. W. Shirlaw. 1958. The value of animal behavior records in pasture evaluation studies. Anim. Behav. 6:139–146.

Gordon, J. G., and D. E. Tribe. 1951. The self-selection of diet by pregnant ewes. J. Agr. Sci. 41:187–190.

Hafez, E. S. E., and M. W. Schein. 1962. The behavior of cattle, p. 247–296. In E. S. E. Hafez (ed.) The behavior of domestic animals. Bailliere, Tindall and Cox, London.

Hafez, E. S. E., and J. P. Scott. 1962. The behavior of sheep and goats, p. 297–333. In E. S. E. Hafez (ed.) The behavior of domestic animals. Bailliere, Tindall and Cox, London.

Hancock, J. 1952. Grazing behavior of identical twins in relation to pasture type, intake and production of dairy cattle. Proc. 6th Int. Grassl. Congr. 6:1339–1407.

Hancock, J. 1953. Grazing behavior of cattle. Anim. Breed. Abstr. 21:11–13.

Hancock, J. 1954. Studies of grazing behavior in relation to grassland management. J. Agr. Sci. 44:420–433.

Hancock, J. 1958. The effect of stocking rate and concentrate feeding. J. Agr. Sci. 50:284–296.

Harker, K. W., J. I. Taylor, and D. H. K. Rollinson. 1954. Studies on the habits of Zebu cattle. J. Agr. Sci. 44:193–198.

111

Holder, J. M. 1960. Observations on the grazing behavior of lactating cows in a sub-tropical environment. J. Agr. Sci. 55:261–268.

Hughes, G. P., and D. Reid. 1951. Studies on the behavior of cattle and sheep to the utilization of grass. J. Agr. Sci. 41:350–366.

Hull, J. L., G. P. Lofgreen, and J. H. Meyer. 1960. Continuous versus intermittent observations in behavior studies with grazing cattle. J. Anim. Sci. 19:1204–1207.

Johnson, H. D., A. C. Ragsdale, I. L. Berry, and M. D. Shanklin. 1962. Effect of various temperature–humidity combinations on milk production of Holstein cattle. Univ. Missouri Res. Bull. 791.

Johnstone-Wallace, D. B., and K. Kennedy. 1944. Grazing management practices and their relationship to the behavior and grazing habits of cattle. J. Agr. Sci. 34:190–197.

Joplin, A. D. H. 1962. The use of grazing animal observations in the early stages of pasture evaluation in the tropics. J. Brit. Grassl. Soc. 17:171–177.

Kibler, H. H., and S. Brody. 1956. Influence of diurnal temperature cycles on heat production and cardiorespiratory activities in Holstein and Jersey cows. Univ. Missouri Res. Bull. 601.

Kromann, R. P., J. H. Meyer, and J. W. Hull. 1961. Energy requirements of grazing steers. J. Anim. Sci. 20:450–453.

Lampkin, G. H., and J. Quartermain. 1962. Observations of the grazing habits of grade and Zebu cattle, II. J. Agr. Sci. 59:119–124.

Larkin, R. M. 1954. Observations on the grazing behavior of beef cattle in tropical Queensland. Queensland J. Agr. Sci. 11:114–141.

Lofgreen, G. P., J. H. Meyer, and J. L. Hull. 1957. Behavior patterns of cattle and sheep being fed pasture or soilage. J. Anim. Sci. 16:773–780.

MacDonald, M. A., and J. M. Bell. 1958. Effects of low fluctuating temperature on farm animals, IV. Can. J. Anim. Sci. 38:160–170.

McCullough, M. E. 1956. Univ. Georgia Tech. Bull. 4.

McDaniel, A. H., and C. B. Roark. 1956. Performance and grazing habits of Hereford and Hereford–Angus cows and calves on improved pasture as related to types of shade. J. Anim. Sci. 15:59–63.

Peterson, R. A., and E. J. Woolfolk. 1955. Behavior of cows and calves on short grass range. J. Range Manage. 8:51–57.

Semple, A. T. 1951. Improving the world's grasslands. University Press, Aberdeen. FAO Agr. Studies 16, xiii and 147 p.

Smith, C. A. 1959. Studies on the Northern Rhodesia *Hyparrhenia* veld. J. Agr. Sci. 52:369–375.

Smith, C. A. 1961. Studies on the Northern Rhodesia *Hyparrhenia* veld. J. Agr. Sci. 56:243–247.

Southcott, W. H., R. Roe, and H. N. Turner. 1962. Grazing management of native pastures, II. Austral. J. Agr. Res. 13:880–893.

Taylor, J. I., D. H. L. Rollinson, and K. W. Harker. 1955. Studies on the habits of Zebu cattle, II. J. Agr. Sci. 45:257–263.

Tribe, D. E. 1955. The behavior of grazing animals, II, p. 585–602. *In* J. Hammond (ed.) Progress in the physiology of farm animals. Butterworths Sci. Publications, London.

Willoughby, W. M. 1959. Limitations to animal production imposed by seasonal fluctuations in pasture and by management practices. Austral. J. Agr. Res. 10:248–268.

Wilson, P. N. 1961. Grazing behavior and free-water intake of East African shorthorned Zebu heifers at Serere, Uganda. J. Agr. Sci. 56:351–364.

Worstell, D. M., and S. Brody. 1953. Comparative physiological reaction of European and Indian cattle to a changing environment. Univ. Missouri Res. Bull. 515.

Chapter 13

GRAZING SYSTEMS

L. A. CHARETTE
Animal Science Department, Laval University
Quebec, Quebec

VAUGHN S. LOGAN
Animal Research Institute, Canada Department of Agriculture
Ottawa, Ontario

J. BADEN CAMPBELL
Research Station, Canada Department of Agriculture
Swift Current, Saskatchewan

The advantages of one grazing system over another can seldom be measured by one simple criterion. Measurements of the yield and quality of herbages by plot and laboratory studies often show a significant advantage for one system over another. But this advantage may not be realized when the animal factor is added. Continuous grazing usually produces more livestock products on low-yielding pastures. But with high-yielding herbages, rotational or soiling systems are necessary to maintain a healthy stand and to use the greater yield efficiently.

Grazing systems can be classed in three groups: continuous, rotational, and soiling. The same measurement techniques to estimate herbage production are useful for all, though certain techniques may be more reliable for one than for the others.

CONTINUOUS GRAZING

Continuous grazing is also known as *set-stocking*, and *free* or *uncontrolled grazing*. Livestock are placed on pasture as early as possible and remain there until the environment or a failing grass supply forces their removal. The season of use may be only 2 or 3 months or the entire year, depending on latitude and altitude. The system is based on two opposing attitudes, that of the stockman desiring cheap gains, and that of the pasture manager anxious to maintain a productive sward. A system that balances inexpensive gains against a productive sward ensures the best results. It is a fallacy that continuous grazing always means complete defoliation, because fields can be understocked when growth is rapid and the herbage that is not grazed, or the carry-over, used when growth ceases.

Continuous grazing has advantages from both theoretical and practical viewpoints. Compared with other systems, it requires smaller investments in fencing, stock-watering facilities, and shelter; and less labor for management and supervision. Further, the animals appear to be more contented. Another advantage is that the digestibility of the herbage being grazed changes only slightly from day to day.

113

The system also has limitations. A careful forecast of grazing capacity is necessary to prevent bias caused by overstocking or under-stocking, by selective grazing, and by the need for carry-over. A sward complex may change rapidly, with grazing-resistant and light-stimulated plants becoming dominant. Large numbers of samples are needed to measure a sward, though differences in production between treatments can be measured equally well by the energy output of animals (*see* Chapter 17).

Reports by Sarvis (1941), Hubbard (1951), and Campbell (1961*b*) show that continuous grazing produces more liveweight gain per acre than other systems on low-yielding pastures where only one plant community is grazed and where the grazing season is two to five times as long as the period of plant growth.

ROTATIONAL GRAZING

There are several variations of rotational grazing: daily-strip, deferred-rotational, complementary, repeated-seasonal, and simple rotations of three to eight paddocks. In rotations, a sward is defoliated rather rapidly and then rested. Defoliation may take 1 hour, 1 day, 1 week, or longer. The resting period depends on the growth pattern of the sward and the experimental design. Rotationally grazed high-yielding swards may or may not produce more animal products than similar swards grazed continuously. Freer (1959*a*) has reviewed 15 major studies comparing continuous and rotational practices. In two cases the rotationally managed pastures produced more than continuous grazing, but in two others the reverse was true. The systems differed little in the other 11 investigations. Evidently the age of the stand, the species in the sward, the intensity of defoliation, and the design of the experiment affect results. McMeekan (1960) has pointed out that well-managed, continuously grazed pastures often produce more herbage than poorly managed or poorly designed rotations, particularly if the design ignores basic biological principles of plant and animal growth.

A study conducted at Swift Current substantiates some of the above findings (unpublished data). An irrigated sward was sown there in 1955 to the following mixture: intermediate wheatgrass, *Agropyron intermedium* (Host) Beauv.; timothy, *Phleum pratense* L.; alsike clover, *Trifolium* spp.; and alfalfa, *Medicago* spp. The wheatgrass was the main component of the seed mixture, and produced most of the herbage in 1956 and 1957. The numbers of sheep-days of grazing per acre for five treatments during four seasons were:

Grazing treatment	Grazings per year	Sheep-days per acre				
		1956	1957	1958	1959	Average
4-week rest	5	1710	1620	1870	1630	1710
4-paddock rotation	4	1650	1560	1550	1520	1570
5-week rest	3	1580	1470	1580	1410	1510
3-week rest	6	1310	1460	1460	1170	1450
Continuous	1	1730	1685	1150	865	1360

Certain management principles are indicated by the above data. Intermediate wheatgrass is not a pasture species; it is stemmy, it recovers slowly after defoliation, and when heavily grazed it dies out quickly on both dry and irrigated pastures (Campbell, 1961b). When continuously grazed, it is soon depleted, as is shown for 1958 and 1959. In the experiment a 3-week rest was insufficient for the sward to recover to a high grazing capacity, whereas a 5-week rest allowed the intermediate wheatgrass to mature to a point where it recovered slowly after the second grazing or go-around. The 4-week rest period allowed enough regrowth for a relatively high grazing capacity, but was not long enough for maturity to greatly reduce regrowth. The weed cover increased under continuous use, because the associated species did not grow quickly enough to fill the bare spots left by the dying intermediate wheatgrass.

Rotational grazing is not advantageous unless it allows a higher carrying capacity than continuous grazing. Experimental design must recognize this factor. Increasing the animal load often reduces the gain per animal, but the return per acre is greater up to a point (McMeekan, 1960). As stocking rates are increased an animal may not obtain enough nutrients in a normal grazing day (See Chapter 17), then the law of diminishing returns may apply because more of the energy intake is used for work and maintenance instead of for production.

Rotations are not successful unless the species in a sward are adapted to the management practice used. Grasses that recover slowly after defoliation, or produce more flowering than vegetative tillers, or mature early in the season, are seldom satisfactory. Langer (1956, 1958) points out the importance of tiller formation and the regular emergence of leaves if rotational practices are to be successful. He shows that tillers of timothy are both annual and biennial and that the survival of a plant depends on a continuous production of both types. Branson (1953, 1956) suggests that two factors influence new growth: the site of the growing point of a leaf, and the ratio of vegetative to flowering tillers. His first factor may not be valid because meristematic tissue appears to be inactive after the leaf unfolds; his second may be valid because he shows wide ratios of vegetative to flowering tillers for grasses known to be good pasture species.

Leaves regenerate from lateral buds on basal stem nodes (Cook and Stoddard, 1953; Langer, 1954; Lawrence and Ashford, 1964). The buds emerge as leaves in 10 to 12 days and usually mature within a month after bud initiation. Though the number of living tillers, and consequently the number of mature leaves, varies from month to month (Langer, 1958), leaf growth is usually fairly far advanced after 4 weeks of rest. A rotation has the advantage of using mature leaves, whereas continuous pasturing removes many leaves before they complete their growth. The term "leaf maturity" is used in the sense that growth has ended but senescence has not halted photosynthesis or lowered nutritive qualities.

Milk production declines as a rotationally grazed paddock is eaten

115

down. In a report from Iceland, Pall Sveinsson (personal communication) shows milk production dropping sharply after animals had grazed for 3 days on rotation paddocks. Carter, Bolin, and Erickson (1960) report that herbage digestibility is lower on the third than on the first day of pasturing. Increased grazing time on irrigated rotated paddocks has been noted by the fifth day (Lofgreen, Meyer, and Hull, 1957), indicating either insufficient readily available forage or more time spent selecting herbage. On rotation treatments, Line (1960) has noted reduced milk yield after the fifth day of use. The appreciable daily change in herbage quality in a conventional four- to six-paddock rotation may limit the value of its somewhat greater yield of dry matter.

Daily-strip, daily-break, ration grazing, and close-folding are synonyms for an intensive form of rotational grazing. It is a method that harvests herbage in 1 day or part of 1 day. Depending on the composition of a sward and the experimental design used, it takes 20 to 30 days to complete a go-around. Movable front and back fences divide long strips into small paddocks to ensure complete harvesting, greater control of sward and livestock, and small changes in the nutrient levels of herbage from day to day. The costs of replication, supervision, and services are high, and greater stress may be evident in the livestock because they are enclosed in small areas. A variation provides a common lounging area and water supply; this reduces stress but upsets the balance of fertility (Sears and Newbold, 1942). Animals graze longer on strip-grazed areas than in rotationally grazed paddocks, but they consume less herbage (Waite, Macdonald, and Holmes, 1951). There is, however, greater consumption of TDN by cows on strip-grazed swards than on continuously grazed ones (Logan and Miles, 1958).

Milk yield is recognized as the best animal measurement to compare the value of any two grazing practices. Logan and Miles (1958) show 22 percent more TDN from lactating cows under strip-grazing than under continuous-grazing, but 70 percent of the increase was credited to feeding back silage harvested during the flush growth period. Freer (1959b) was unable to show differences in milk yield or liveweight gain per acre between rotational and daily-strip methods, but the swards he compared were comprised of species of *Lolium, Dactylis,* and *Trifolium,* all of which are adapted to grazing. Because of a higher grazing capacity, Hereford steers (800 lb) have produced 12 percent more liveweight gain per acre on a strip-grazed irrigated sward than on a three-paddock rotation (Campbell, 1961a). McMeekan (1960) states that a delicate balance exists between grazing capacity and production, because a slight over-stocking will "bust" any management system. This was observed by Campbell (1961a) when a 12 percent increase in stocking with yearling Hereford steers on a strip-grazed sward reduced the liveweight gain by 19 percent per acre. Alder and others (1967) report a 25 percent decline in liveweight gain per hectare with a 30 percent increase in stocking rate above maximum grazing capacity.

A modified strip-grazing system uses lactating and dry herds. The

116

lactating cows go ahead and consume the top growth, then the dry cattle follow to mow the herbage to the desired level (Blaser and others, 1960). Another variation provides a side creep for lambs; the creep area is kept mowed to provide highly nutritious new growth for the lambs, but the ewes remain on more mature forage (Spedding and Large, 1959).

Deferred-rotation methods use two or three equal-sized fields that are grazed for equal periods each year. When three fields are used, each is grazed twice in successive years during a 6-year period. Theoretically, the method encourages more seed setting and natural seeding. The system has been compared with continuous grazing on low-producing natural grasslands; better grass covers result but there is less liveweight gain per animal and per acre (Thomson, 1938; Hargrave, 1949). There are two main reasons for the poorer performance of the "deferred and rotation fields" (Thomson, 1938): herbage is insufficient for a full feed during the early season because of slow spring growth, and crude protein in deferred herbage during the late summer and autumn is less.

Smoliak (1960) has reported production from two equal-sized fields from 1949 through 1956. One field was grazed continuously. The other was divided into two paddocks and managed in a deferred-rotated system. One paddock was grazed in the spring and fall, the other during the summer. The procedure was reversed in consecutive years. No significant differences were shown in grass cover, yield of herbage, or gain per animal or per acre. Klipple (1964) reports similar results.

The repeated-seasonal method (Campbell, 1961b) is a rotation using the same field during the same season for successive years. It assumes that certain cultivars will produce more energy during a particular season because of their growth characters. The method has produced neither more dry matter nor more liveweight gain than the continuous use of a perennial sward adapted to the environment. However, it is a useful method to employ when perennial and annual crops are used in rotations, because the grazing readiness of annuals can be controlled by staggering seeding dates.

An important rotation practice is known as *complementary* (Gregor, 1946). It is concerned with two types of herbage growth. Gregor, working in the Highlands of Scotland, used 1 acre of heavily fertilized pasture composed of *Lolium* sp. and *Trifolium* sp. and 50 acres of unfertilized rough grazing for a daily ration for cattle. His design attempted to balance nutrient intake. Campbell and others (1962) describe a complementary method using crested wheatgrass, *Agropyron cristatum* (L.) Gaertn., as an early-season pasture, and native grass for the balance of the year in a 1:4 ratio. This combination produced 75 percent more liveweight gain than an equal area of native grass only. Variations of the complementary system can be used to increase the nutrient supply or to provide more total energy to animals.

Any advantage of rotational over continuous grazing depends on the adaptability of a herbage to rotational practices. In many cases, the

117

advantages of a rotational method reported from herbage data cannot be reproduced by livestock production measurements, because grazing management techniques are not sufficiently critical to measure small significant differences in milk production or liveweight gain (McMeekan, 1952).

SOILING

Soiling is the feeding of herbage that is cut and fed fresh in a feed-lot. The system has no standard name because soiling, green chopping, zero grazing, and mechanical grazing are synonymous. Three factors need to be considered when comparing this with other management systems: response of swards harvested by machinery; effects on livestock production; and economics in terms of investment in equipment.

The Sward

Arnon (1960) points out that grazing utilizes pasture better than soiling if herbage has a high leaf:stem ratio, a regular production of tillers, and considerable leafage below the grazing line to maintain photosynthesis. When herbages have one or more of these characters, better grazing management is recommended rather than soiling. Leafy strains of *Lolium, Festuca, Poa, Dactylis, Elymus, Medicago,* and *Trifolium* possess characters that produce high yields under good grazing management.

Cultivars that yield more as hay than as pasture often produce more livestock products under soiling (Mather, Bartlett, and Cason, 1959). Tall-growing varieties of *Bromus, Sorghum, Agropyron, Elymus, Phleum, Phalaris, Medicago, Trifolium,* and many others usually yield more dry matter per acre with soiling. In part, this may be related to the wastage of dry matter on pasture (Arnon, 1960), though waste of nutrients may be less than expected because grazing animals select leafy varieties (Lofgreen, Meyer, and Peterson, 1956).

There is no natural return of dung and urine with soiling, although both can be collected and spread where needed. Chemical fertilizers can replace natural sources, but Arnon (1960) questions whether pasture yields can be maintained with chemical fertilizers only.

The Livestock

McMeekan (1952) suggests that two principles govern the measurement of sward production by animal response: under good management, production per animal will not vary, no matter what grazing method is used; greater yield of animal products per acre can be obtained only by using more animals.

These principles have been proved with experiments conducted by Logan and others (1960), Ittner, Lofgreen, and Meyer (1954), and

118

Lofgreen and others (1956). Logan and his associates report that equal milk flows per cow can be obtained from 0.84 soiling acres and 1.21 strip-grazed acres; their results were obtained on a sward composed of timothy, cocksfoot, alfalfa, and alsike clover. Ittner and others (1954), and Lofgreen and others (1956) compared soiling and strip-grazing of alfalfa; they showed that soiling produced 200 more pounds of live-weight gain per acre with similar gains per animal. An interesting point was observed by Runcie (1960), who reports a higher first service conception for dairy cows on soiling than on strip-grazing.

Cattle eat more on soiling than on continuous or strip-grazed pastures (Lofgreen and others, 1956), yet individual animals do not produce more animal products. This is hard to understand when the exercise factor on pasture is considered (*see* Chapter 17). Two reasons are suggested to explain this anomaly: cattle on pasture select their fodder, and there are psychological and physiological benefits on pastures that are not experienced in feedlots.

Economics

A herd of at least 30 lactating cows has been suggested as a minimum for efficient soiling practice. About 400 more pounds of milk or over 100 more pounds of liveweight gain per acre are needed to pay extra production costs.

GENERAL CONSIDERATIONS

Pasture research workers are often confronted with the decision of whether to use a constant acreage with variable numbers of animals (put-and-take) or a constant herd on different-sized paddocks. Each system has proponents. Work reported by Logan and others (1960) supports the second concept. They compared two systems of management by maintaining near-equal milk production per animal from unequal acreages. This procedure is recommended by Blaser and others (1960) and appears to be the better technique to evaluate swards and management. It may require mechanical harvesting during periods of lush growth. Any extra production can be stored or fed as hay or silage when pasture growth slows down in the fall.

Ruminants utilize herbage more efficiently on reduced rations than on full feed. Harkness (1963), who has reviewed the literature on this subject, reports that cattle and sheep react similarly.

References

Alder, F. E., S. J. Cowlishaw, J. E. Newton, and D. T. Chambers. 1967. The effect of level of nitrogen fertilizer on beef production from grazed perennial ryegrass/white clover pasture. J. Brit. Grassl. Soc. 22:230–238.

Arnon, I. 1960. Grazing versus feeding cut forage crops. Proc. 8th Int. Grassl. Congr. 8:648–652.

Blaser, R. E., C. Hammes, Jr., H. T. Bryant, W. A. Hardison, J. P. Fontenot, and R. W. Engel. 1960. The effect of selective grazing on animal output. Proc. 8th Int. Grassl. Congr. 8:601–606.

Branson, F. A. 1953. Two new factors affecting resistance of grasses to grazing. J. Range Manage. 6:165–171.

Branson, F. A. 1956. Quantitative effect of clipping on five range grasses. J. Range Manage. 9:86–88.

Campbell, J. B. 1961a. Annual report. Experimental Farm, Swift Current, Sask.

Campbell, J. B. 1961b. Continuous versus repeated-seasonal grazing on grass–alfalfa mixtures at Swift Current, Sask. J. Range Manage. 14:72–77.

Campbell, J. B., R. W. Lodge, A. Johnston, and S. Smoliak. 1962. Range management of grasslands and adjacent parklands in the Prairie Provinces. Can. Dep. Agr. Pub. 1133.

Carter, J. F., D. W. Bolin, and D. Erickson. 1960. The evaluation of forages by the agronomic "Difference" method and the chromogen–chromic oxide "Indicator" technique. N. Dak. Exp. Sta. Bull. 426.

Cook, C. W., and L. A. Stoddard. 1953. Some growth responses of crested wheatgrass following herbage removal. J. Range Manage. 6:267–270.

Freer, M. 1959a. Thesis. University of Melbourne, Australia.

Freer, M. 1959b. The utilization of irrigated pastures by dairy cows. 1. A comparison of rotational and strip grazing. J. Agr. Sci. 52:129–136.

Gregor, J. W. 1946. The use of complementary grassland. Scot. Agr. 26:1–6.

Hargrave, H. J. 1949. Progress report 1937–1947. Dom. Range Exp. Sta., Manyberries, Alta.

Harkness, R. D. 1963. Studies in herbage digestibility. J. Brit. Grassl. Soc. 18:62–68.

Hubbard, W. A. 1951. Rotational grazing studies in Western Canada. J. Range Manage. 4:25–29.

Ittner, N. R., G. P. Lofgreen, and J. H. Meyer. 1954. A study of pasturing and soiling alfalfa with beef cattle. J. Anim. Sci. 13:37–43.

Klipple, G. E. 1964. Early- and late-season grazing versus season-long grazing of short-grass vegetation on the Central Great Plains. U.S. Forest Service Research Paper RM-11. Rocky Mountain Forest and Range Exp. Sta., Fort Collins, Colo.

Langer, R. H. 1954. A study of leaf growth in timothy, *Phleum pratense*. J. Brit. Grassl. Soc. 9:275–284.

Langer, R. H. 1956. Growth and nutrition of timothy, *Phleum pratense*. 1. The life history of individual tillers. Ann. Appl. Biol. 44:166–187.

Langer, R. H. 1958. Changes in the tiller population of grass swards. Nature (London) 182:1817–1818.

Lawrence, T., and R. Ashford. 1964. Seed yield and morphological development of Russian wild rye grass, *Elymus junceus* Fisch., as influenced by grazing. Can. J. Plant Sci. 44:301–310.

Line, C. 1960. Maximum milk production from pasture. Proc. 8th Int. Grassl. Congr. 8:598–601.

Lofgreen, G. P., J. H. Meyer, and J. L. Hull. 1957. Behavior patterns of sheep and cattle being fed pasture and soilage. J. Anim. Sci. 16:773–780.

Lofgreen, G. P., J. H. Meyer, and M. L. Peterson. 1956. Nutrient consumption and utilization from alfalfa pasture, soilage and hay. J. Anim. Sci. 15:1158–1165.

Logan, V. S., and Vern Miles. 1958. Pasture management studies. I. Daily strip grazing versus free range grazing of dairy cattle on cultivated pasture. Can. J. Anim. Sci. 38:133–144.

Logan, V. S., W. J. Pigden, V. J. Miles, G. J. Brisson, A. I. Magee, and K. Rasmussen. 1960. Mechanical versus daily or strip grazing for lactating cows. Proc. 8th Int. Grassl. Congr. 8:652–655.

120

Mather, R. E., J. W. Bartlett, and J. L. Cason. 1959. Different methods of utilizing forages in dairy cattle nutrition—pasture vs. soiling vs. hay vs. silage, p. 161–172. *In* H. E. Sprague (ed.) Grasslands. Pub. 53, Amer. Ass. Advance. Sci., Washington, D.C.

McKeekan, C. P. 1952. Interdependence of grassland and livestock in agricultural production. Proc. 6th Int. Grassl. Congr. 6:149–161.

McMeekan, C. P. 1960. Grazing management. Proc. 8th Int. Grassl. Congr. 21–26.

Runcie, K. V. 1960. The utilization of grass by strip-grazing and zero grazing with dairy cows. Proc. 8th Int. Grassl. Congr. 8:644–648.

Sarvis, J. T. 1941. Grazing investigations of the Northern Great Plains. N. Dak. Agr. Exp. Sta. Bull. 308.

Sears, P. D., and R. P. Newbold. 1942. The effect of sheep droppings on yield, botanical composition and chemical composition of pasture. New Zeal. J. Sci. Technol. 24:36*a*–61*a*.

Smoliak, S. 1960. Effects of deferred-rotation and continuous grazing on yearling steer gains and shortgrass prairie vegetation of southeastern Alberta. J. Range Manage. 13:239–243.

Spedding, C. R. W., and R. V. Large. 1959. Sideway creep grazing for intensive lamb production. J. Brit. Grassl. Soc. 14:17–28.

Thomson, L. B. 1938. Results of experiments 1927 to 1936. Dom. Range Exp. Sta., Manyberries, Alta.

Waite, R., W. B. Macdonald, and W. Holmes. 1951. Studies in grazing management. J. Agr. Sci. 41:163–173.

Chapter 14

ESTIMATING LIVEWEIGHT GAINS

R. DAVID CLARK
Research Station, Canada Department of Agriculture
Lethbridge, Alberta

J. BADEN CAMPBELL
Research Station, Canada Department of Agriculture
Swift Current, Saskatchewan

Liveweight gains or losses between weighings are a useful indication of an animal's response to its environment. As relative measures, they indicate the quality and the abundance of a herbage, the efficiency of management, the health of the animal, the ability of the animal to convert herbage to useful livestock products, and the effects of stress.

Liveweight is a relative measure. Accurate weights are rarely attainable and even the most accurate are relative as indicated by the graph below. An 800-pound steer can gain or lose 20 pounds in 24 hours without apparent reason, and the same steer may weigh less on a given day than it did 2 weeks previously, even when gaining over 1 pound daily (Campbell, 1955). These changes are caused by increases or decreases in fill, which are related either to environmental influences or to an irregular cyclic weight pattern (Baker and Guilbert, 1942; Campbell, 1955; Maymone and Sircana, 1930). Also, rate of gain may change without apparent changes in herbage quality or consumption. This change in rate may be caused by a change in the ratio of muscle to fat deposition.

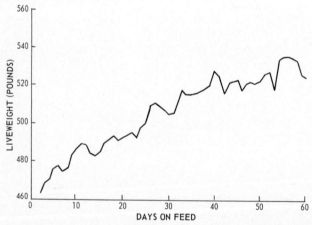

Average daily weights of 18 steer calves on a mixture of oats, barley, and alfalfa hay, Nov. 21, 1953, to Jan. 20, 1954 (Campbell, 1955).

There may be an irregular cyclic growth pattern when weights are recorded at the same hour on successive days. Day-to-day variations in cattle weights are of two types: one is caused by environment, the other is cyclic and is caused by characteristics of the animals. The variation caused by environment can be obviated if conditions can be made sufficiently uniform, but cyclic variations cannot be obviated by controlled environmental conditions. Both variations are correlated between members of a herd; that is, the response to environment is shown by the majority of the animals, whereas the cyclic nature of growth—when environment is uniform—follows a similar course for all animals of the same sex and age on the same feed (Campbell, 1955). A similar observation has been reported by Harker (1963): "Factors affecting variations in weight may have been affecting all the animals in the same direction."

When daily weights are analyzed by the least-squares method to estimate rate of gain, they indicate that 15 regularly spaced weighings are required to reduce the standard error of the regression to an acceptable level (Campbell, 1953), and that a grazing study should be conducted for at least 54 days (Harker, 1963). This intensity of weighing is impractical for many experiments, and modifications are necessary.

Techniques have been proposed for in vivo estimates of muscle, fat, mineral, and water components of animals (Reid, Wellington, and Dunn, 1955). A promising procedure uses liveweight and total body water, which is estimated by injection of tritiated water (Panaretto, 1963). As yet this technique has not been applied to estimate change in the ratio of muscle to fat as an animal ages. It may have an application in the more precise evaluation of herbages.

Among the management practices that add precision to liveweight data are the following:

- A regular weighing schedule
- Preselection of experimental animals to rid a herd of extremely nervous or otherwise undesirable individuals
- Pregrazing on herbage comparable to that being tested in an experiment
- The provision of good facilities to reduce stress when animals are being weighed.

WEIGHING SCHEDULES

Weight variations caused by fill can be reduced by holding animals off feed and water for 12 hours before weighing them (Harker, 1963). When this procedure is impractical, livestock should be weighed about 2 to 3 hours after sunrise, when hunger is appeased and before the first big drink of the day (Hughes and Harker, 1950). Select weigh days with comparable weather—calm or windy, bright or dull, hot or cool.

123

Do not weigh animals immediately after a severe storm, particularly when they are being removed from pasture in the fall.

The most important weights are taken at the beginning and end of an experiment. In some studies, these may be all that are needed or that can be obtained. More frequent weighings are desirable, and as mentioned above, 15 or more regularly spaced weighings are recommended when rate of gain is estimated by regression analysis. Some schedule between these extremes suffices when midseason weights are required to facilitate interpretation of data rather than to calculate rate of gain or total gain. Monthly weighings are recommended for range studies and where scales are not located near pastures. Weighings once every 2 weeks are recommended on continuously grazed fields close to scale facilities; the frequency should be increased to weekly weighings toward the end of the pasture season when growth is slow. On-and-off weighings are recommended when livestock are moved from paddock to paddock in a rotation, although the gains on any one paddock may show no relationship to apparent consumption or to seasonal gain (Mott, 1959). Daily weighings are suggested when a study involves 30 or fewer days (Harker, 1963). In all cases, a pre-experimental weight should be obtained as a basis for grouping and as a check on subsequent weights.

Little precision has been attained by averaging three successive-day weights at the beginning and end of a grazing test to estimate total gain (Bean, 1948; Dembiczek and others, 1957; Hughes and Harker, 1950; Lush and Black, 1925–26; Patterson, 1947). Single-day weights are equally satisfactory; they cause less stress to animals and reduce the labor and time needed to handle large numbers of livestock.

SELECTION AND TRAINING OF EXPERIMENTAL ANIMALS

Experimental animals that are comparable in age and gaining ability should be selected to form a group. Those that are nervous, timid, and extremely aggressive should be culled. The following procedure is suggested:

- Three to five months before grazing begins, obtain about twice the number of animals needed. Place the herd or flock on a self-fed ration that provides sufficient nutrients and energy to produce a predetermined rate of gain
- After the animals have settled in the new environment, begin a selection program based on daily, twice-weekly, or weekly weighings. Nervous and otherwise undesirable animals will be recognized readily and can be culled. Continue the weighing schedule for 8 to 10 weeks. Daily weighings are recommended. When less than 30 animals are used this is possible, but twice-weekly weighings are more practicable with larger herds or flocks
- Weights of individual animals should be studied at the end of the 8- to 10-week period. Rate of gain can be estimated by regression analysis,

by subtraction and division, or by plotting gain against original weight. With all procedures, the animals can be grouped and randomized to pasture treatments and replicates.

The above procedure provides a background knowledge of test animals that is quite comparable to the background knowledge of the herbages to be studied—a factor as important as the expected association of $r = 0.45$ between winter feedlot and summer pasture gains (Koger and Knox, 1951; Urick and others, 1957). Furthermore, the animals quickly become accustomed to entering chutes and scales and they accept this phase of management as part of their daily activities.

The above procedure for selecting grazing animals is not always practicable. Where large numbers or special types of animals are required, they should be allowed to become acclimatized on pretest pasture. More animals than are required for the experiment should be secured about a month before the actual test is to start. They should be chosen from one source or from sources that have a similar environment, and should be uniform in breeding, weight, age, and sex. During the acclimatization or adjustment period, the animals should be pastured or fed so that they will be as uniform as possible at the start of the trial. Preliminary weighings and all preliminary treatments common to all animals, such as branding, dehorning, vaccinating, and identifying, should be carried out during the adjustment period. Nervous or otherwise undesirable animals should be culled. The rest of them will become fairly well accustomed to handling before the trial starts.

PRETEST GRAZING AND TRAINING

Livestock usually lose weight when moved from dry feed to fresh herbage. As shown in the graph below yearling steers lost an average

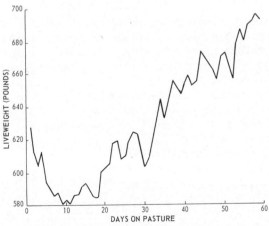

Average daily weights of 18 Hereford steers on irrigated grass and legume pasture, May 8 to July 7, 1954 (Campbell, 1955).

125

of 50 pounds within 5 days when moved from dry feed to irrigated pasture, and 4 weeks elapsed before the loss was regained. A weight loss of this kind is largely caused by a loss of fill and does not affect the health or strength of an animal. However, it must be considered when estimating the total liveweight gain from a pasture (Mott, 1959).

There are management practices that reduce the drop in weight and shorten the recovery period. If animals are placed on a pretest or holding pasture containing a considerable amount of old growth, the loss will be reduced considerably, unless adverse weather interferes. Also, animals moved from a winter ration containing a moderate amount of grain lose less weight than other animals and recover the loss quickly (*see* Chapter 16); this feeding technique is useful when no pretest pasture can be provided.

During the pretest period, animals should be trained to the test routine. Weighings need to be regular. Where it is necessary to use horses or dogs to drive cattle and sheep to a weighing center, the animals should be trained to accept this stress. In fact, any great change in management routine should be practiced during the pretest period.

Allow 2 weeks on a holding pasture before moving animals to test fields; a longer period may be needed in some cases. It is preferable, though not absolutely necessary, that holding and test swards contain the same herbage mixture; but it is important that both swards be at the same stage of growth.

FIELD FACILITIES

The holding or pretest pasture should be in the general area of the test fields. It needs to be large enough to accommodate both the test animals and the put-and-take animals. A point to remember is that put-and-take animals should be weighed according to the schedule of the test animals.

Good corral arrangements facilitate the weighing and managing of cattle. Allow approximately 80 square feet per animal to provide for holding and separating pens, chute, scale, squeeze, and other necessary equipment. Because it may be necessary to work from both sides of a scale or a squeeze, place gates so that they are easily accessible to herdsmen. One strong chute is sufficient, but it is necessary to provide separate entries for the squeeze and scale, either by off-setting or by construction that permits animals to move through the chute in both directions. A circular chute that narrows towards the scale end, helps to keep animals moving forward. When weighing sheep on pasture, it is often easier to build temporary pens in their paddocks and move the scale as needed.

References

Baker, G. A., and H. R. Guilbert. 1942. Non-randomness of variations in daily weights of cattle. J. Anim. Sci. 1:293–299.

Bean, H. W. 1948. Single weight versus a three-day average weight for sheep. J. Anim. Sci. 7:50–54.

Campbell, J. B. 1953. A technique to estimate the reliability of weights of livestock used in experiments. Rep. Western Forage Crop Comm., Can. Dep. Agr. 106–122.

Campbell, J. B. 1955. The weigh scales mystery. Can. Cattleman 10:11, 25–28.

Dembiczek, Cecelia M., H. D. Eaton, Geoffrey Beall, and H. J. Lucas, Jr. 1957. Design and conduct of calf nutrition studies. 1. One- vs. two- and three-day growth measurements. J. Dairy Sci. 9:1133–1151.

Harker, K. W. 1963. The weighing of Zebu bullocks in grazing experiments. Empire J. Exp. Agr. 31:311–316.

Hughes, G. P., and K. W. Harker. 1950. The technique of weighing bullocks on summer grass. J. Agr. Sci. 40:403–409.

Koger, Marvin, and J. H. Knox. 1951. The correlation between gains made at different periods by cattle. J. Anim. Sci. 10:760–767.

Lush, J. L., and W. H. Black. 1925–26. How much accuracy is gained by weighing cattle three days instead of one at the beginning and end of the feeding experiment? Proc. Amer. Sci. Anim. Prod.: 206–210.

Maymone, B., and C. Sircana. 1930. Die Normalen Lebendgewishtsvariationen bei Rindern. Z. Zücht. Reihe B. 18:63–108.

Mott, G. O. 1959. Animal variations and measurement of forage quality. Agron. J. 51:223–226.

Panaretto, B. A. 1963. Body composition in vivo. III. The composition of living ruminants and its relation to tritiated water spaces. Austral. J. Agr. Res. 14:594–601.

Patterson, R. E. 1947. The comparative efficiency of single versus three-day weights of steers. J. Anim. Sci. 6:237–246.

Reid, J. T., G. H. Wellington, and H. O. Dunn. 1955. Some relationships among the major chemical components of the bovine body and their application to nutritional investigations. J. Dairy Sci. 38:1344–1359.

Urick, J., A. E. Flower, F. S. Willson, and C. E. Shelby. 1957. A genetic study of steer progeny groups during successive growth periods. J. Anim. Sci. 18:217–223.

127

Chapter 15

NUMBERS OF ANIMALS AND OF REPLICATIONS NEEDED FOR ESTIMATING LIVEWEIGHT GAINS

WILLIAM A. HUBBARD
Research Station, Canada Department of Agriculture
Kamloops, British Columbia

J. BADEN CAMPBELL
Research Station, Canada Department of Agriculture
Swift Current, Saskatchewan

ALEXANDER JOHNSTON
Research Station, Canada Department of Agriculture
Lethbridge, Alberta

Liveweight gains or losses of grazing ruminants are useful for estimating pasture productivity, although they do have limitations (Alder, 1959; Ivins, 1959; Spedding, 1965). When herds or flocks are of sufficient size and suitable quality, and when tests are replicated in space and time, they are among the best means of comparing swards and management practices. Other useful animal measurements are: differences in animal-days per unit of land, and equal daily liveweight gains or milk flow from unequal acreages (Henderson, Cobble, and Cook, 1959; Pigden and Greenshields, 1960).

SIZE OF HERD OR FLOCK

Cattle

The liveweight gains or losses of three cattle per replicate provide a low error of estimate when the grazing season is 3 or more months long, when there are at least three replications per treatment (Petersen and Lucas, 1960), when the animals used have a high production potential and are uniform in breeding and age (Alder, 1965), and when a grazing test is conducted over a period of years (Hilmon, Clutter, and Cable, 1963).

More than three animals or more than three replications are needed when the grazing season is shorter than 3 months. For a 2-month pasture period, it is necessary to triple the number of cattle if only three replications are employed, or to double the number of replications of three cattle to obtain comparable estimates of error.

More cattle are required when there is no replication or when only one herd grazes two or more separately fenced replications of a pasture treatment during successive fortnightly, monthly, or longer periods. McMeekan (1960) has observed that 40 lactating cows per herd would be needed to establish differences between grazing methods in the 10 to 15 percent range. Harker (1963) reports that the liveweight gain of 10 beef-type cattle for 54 days was a minimum herd-period; however, he used mature animals and suggests that a larger herd or a longer period would be necessary when young fast-growing cattle or a mixed-age herd comprise the livestock load.

Federer (1955) states, "Several readings on a single plot (or pen) do not result in replication on a treatment which is subject to environmental variation but merely result in decreasing variance due to measuring or technique errors; the plot to plot or pen to pen variation has not been reduced." Thus, when herd replication is not provided, it is important to use a sufficient number of cattle for several readings to be obtained. Though McMeekan (1960) and Harker (1963) estimate the number of cattle required to compare treatments, neither indicates the variance expected when different numbers of cattle are grazed for different periods of time. To illustrate these conditions, the liveweight gains of 36 yearling Hereford steers have been analyzed (authors' unpublished data). These steers were uniform in age, weight, and breeding. For 180 days before the beginning of the grazing period they had been self-fed on a ration that produced an average gain of 1.2 pounds per day. On pasture, individual daily gains ranged from 1.63 to 2.17 pounds; the herd average was 1.87 pounds per day. They were weighed at 8 a.m. once every 2 weeks during a 112-day grazing period. The results were as follows:

Grazing period (days)	Number of steers	Mean gain (lb)	Standard deviation (%)	Coefficient of variation* (%)	Level of probability† (%)
56‡	9	105	21	20	17
14	36	26	17	65	28
28	36	41	15	37	16
56	36	107	18	17	8
112	36	210	24	11	5
112	3	205	47	23	35
112	9	208	29	24	13
112	18	210	27	13	10

$$*CV = \frac{\sigma}{M} 100$$

$$\dagger p = \sqrt{\frac{t^2 C^2}{N}},\text{ where } p = \text{level of probability, } t = 2.6$$

$$C = CV, \text{ and } N = \text{number of animals}$$

‡Comparable to the report by Harker (1963)

Assuming that a coefficient of variation of 15 percent at the 90 percent level of probability is desired, only two of the eight analyses meet the requirements. The herd-period that Harker (1963) suggests is too short to provide liveweight gain data of acceptable precision. McMeekan's (1960) concept of herd numbers is more realistic.

No specific number of cattle is necessary when livestock are used as defoliants in an experiment comparing several herbages within one paddock. The only considerations are to balance numbers with the time expected for defoliation, and to have a herd large enough to ensure normal behavior. Liveweight gain or animal-days per unit of land have no meaning in this situation. It may be profitable to record pasture routines to determine the most acceptable species or varieties, or the changes in daily grazing patterns as defoliation progresses (*see* Chapter 10). A "lounging area" with water and shelter must be provided.

Sheep

In experiments where there is a separate flock for each replication of a treatment, the general considerations described for cattle apply for sheep, but more animals are necessary per replication. Southcott, Roe, and Turner (1962) state that five head is a minimum size of flock to prevent social stresses, but data from a more recent study (authors' unpublished data) suggest that six yearling ewes should be grazed for at least 100 days to reduce the level of probability to less than 10 percent when there are only three replications per treatment. More animals should be used during shorter grazing periods.

Even more animals are required when only one flock grazes several replications of a treatment or when treatments are not replicated. Under these conditions, the liveweight gains of flocks of up to 200 head have been used to compare treatments, and the use of 50 head is not uncommon. It is feasible to graze experimental flocks of these sizes where the grazing capacity is ten or more sheep per acre. But smaller flocks are more likely to be used where up to 1 acre of pasture is needed per animal. With this level of production, it is recommended that a minimum flock comprise 25 head, whether or not the pastures are replicated; this recommendation is based on the results of one experiment where 18 head were used to compare treatments, and where the probability level of each flock was 15 percent.

REPLICATION

Federer (1955) states that the number of replications of an experiment are determined by four considerations:

- Degree of precision desired; that is, variance of the treatment mean
- Amount of variability present in the experimental material
- Available resources, including personnel and equipment
- Size and shape of experimental unit.

Because the liveweight gains of cattle and sheep are the difference between two measurements that are subject to considerable error, an investigator may have to accept less precision than desirable. Also, individual animals in a herd or flock are not replicates but only separate units whose measurements contribute to the yield of a replication mean. Larger numbers of animals per replication necessitate larger paddocks, which, in turn, may increase the error within a block. When liveweight gain is the criterion used to estimate treatment differences, the least variance of a treatment mean is associated with small herds or flocks in more replications, rather than with large herds in a few replications. This procedure is practical in most cases, because few field experiments compare more than three treatments. Thus, with limited personnel, equipment, and land, an investigator should plan for as many replications as possible. It is not necessary for replications to be adjacent. In fact, replications on different soil types are recommended for both yield and management studies.

The number of replications needed for a given level of precision can be calculated if an estimate of variance is available (Federer, 1955). When the number of animals and the duration of the grazing season can be gauged, the experimental error per paddock can be estimated for average daily-gain per animal from the equation reported by Petersen and Lucas (1960) and by Lucas and Mott (1962):

$$C_R = \sqrt{\frac{(157.2)^2}{t} + \frac{(17.3)^2}{a} + \frac{(225.4)^2}{d}} \tag{1}$$

where C_R = error of a paddock mean expressed as a coefficient of variation
t = grazing period in days
a = number of animals per paddock
d = animal days per paddock.

In turn, the variance of a treatment mean of a replicated test can be estimated from the equation:

$$C_T = \frac{\Sigma C_R}{R\sqrt{R-1}} \tag{2}$$

where C_T = error for treatment as a CV
R = the number of replications per treatment.

The figures given below, which illustrate Equations 1 and 2, have been calculated from actual liveweight gain data of yearling Hereford steers (authors' unpublished data). The average weight of the steers was 640 pounds when moved to pasture, where their average gain was 1.87 pounds per day. The C_T estimate of three and nine head replicated two, three, and four times for 14, 28, 56, and 112 days is as follows:

131

Days of grazing	Number of steers per replication	C_T estimates as percentage variance with 2, 3, and 4 replications		
		2	3	4
14	3	55	39	32
14	9	46	33	27
28	3	40	28	23
28	9	33	23	19
56	3	29	20	17
56	9	24	17	14
112	3	22	15	13
112	9	17	12	10

These results support previous statements about the advantage of having long grazing periods and several replications. Two replications do not increase the precision provided by a single herd, but for all grazing periods, four replications of three steers provide data as precise as three replications of nine steers. Additional replication means more fencing, labor, and accounting, but less land and fewer cattle are needed to reduce variance within a treatment to a probability level in the 10 to 15 percent range.

GENERAL CONSIDERATIONS

The objectives of an experiment should indicate the area where the results will apply. This often determines the class of animals to be used, as well as the number of units of livestock per replication and the number of replications per treatment. Mixed-age herds or flocks have greater variability than those of one age and sex, but the results may apply to a wider range of conditions. To a limited degree, the liveweight gains of mixed-age herds can be applied within a breed by calculating liveweight in terms of metabolic body size ($W^{0.75}$) and making comparisons on that basis (see Chapter 17), though the results will be indicative only. Where the local livestock economy is on a cow–calf or ewe–lamb basis, it is often advisable to use these units for production experiments. Johnson and Laycock (1963) discuss these and other factors relative to type and numbers of animals for experimental herds and flocks.

According to Federer (1955), "In perennial pasture experiments, years do not represent true replications for perennial pastures grown on the same plot, whereas in annual pastures which are reseeded and reallocated every year the years constitute replication." Although the year-to-year yields of stands of perennial herbages are not replicates, the animals grazing thereon represent yearly replications when different animals are used each pasture season. Then a 4-year test comparing three treatments that are replicated four times would have only 11 degrees of freedom for perennial herbages, but 47 degrees of freedom for annual crops and for the livestock.

References

Alder, F. E. 1959. Pasture experiments with animals, p. 109–118. *In* J. D. Ivins (ed.) The measurement of grassland productivity. Butterworths Sci. Publications, London.

Alder, F. E. 1965. Aspects of the evaluation of herbage species and varieties in animal production experiments. Proc. 9th Int. Grassl. Congr. 2:1477–1481.

Federer, W. T. 1955. Experimental design. The Macmillan Company, New York, 544 p.

Harker, K. W. 1963. The weighing of Zebu bullocks in grazing experiments. Empire J. Exp. Agr. 31:311–316.

Henderson, B. W., J. W. Cobble, and H. J. Cook. 1959. Soilage feeding of dairy cattle. Rhode Island Agr. Exp. Sta. Bull. 336.

Hilmon, J. B., J. L. Clutter, and D. R. Cable. 1963. Design and conduct of grazing experiments, p. 124–131. *In* Range research methods. Misc. Pub. 940. U.S. Dep. Agr. Forest Serv., Washington, D.C.

Ivins, J. D. 1959. The interpretation of animal production data in grassland evaluation, p. 148–155. *In* J. D. Ivins (ed.) The measurement of grassland productivity. Butterworths Sci. Publications, London.

Johnson, W. M., and W. A. Laycock. 1963. Kind, number, and selection of livestock for grazing studies, and animal measurements most suited for evaluating results, p. 137–142. *In* Range research methods. Misc. Pub. 940. U. S. Dep. Agr. Forest Serv., Washington, D.C.

Lucas, H. L., and G. O. Mott. 1962. Size and number of pastures, number of animals, and length of grazing period, p. 7–10. *In* Pasture and range research techniques. Comstock Publishing Associates, Ithaca, N.Y.

McMeekan, C. P. 1960. Grazing management. Proc. 8th Int. Grassl. Congr. 8:21–26.

Petersen, R. G., and H. L. Lucas. 1960. Experimental errors in grazing trials. Proc. 8th Int. Grassl. Congr. 8:747–750.

Pigden, W. J., and J. E. R. Greenshields. 1960. Interaction of design, sward and management on yield and utilization of herbage in Canadian grazing trials. Proc. 8th Int. Grassl. Congr. 8:594–597.

Southcott, W. H., R. Roe, and H. N. Turner. 1962. Grazing management of native pastures. Austral. J. Agr. Res. 13:880–893.

Spedding, C. R. W. 1965. The physiological basis of grazing management. J. Brit. Grassl. Soc. 20:7–14.

Chapter 16

EFFECT OF PREPASTURE TREATMENTS ON LIVEWEIGHT GAINS

STANLEY E. BEACOM
Research Station, Canada Department of Agriculture
Melfort, Saskatchewan

When liveweight gain per acre is used as a criterion of the relative yield and quality of herbage, it is necessary to stock experimental paddocks with animals of comparable gain potential. Gain potential is influenced by many factors, but an important one is the carry-over of prepasture treatments.

NUTRITIONAL VALUE OF PREPASTURE RATIONS

Cattle fed for a high daily gain during the winter, do not gain as fast on pasture as do comparable cattle fed for a low daily prepasture gain. This is shown by the figures below, which come from four studies in which the nutritional level of the rations fed to cattle was controlled.

Reference	Length of pre-pasture period (days)	Prepasture gain (lb/day)	Length of pasture period (days)	Pasture gain (lb/day)
Embray and others (1958)	153	0.31	157	1.73
		1.03		1.41
Heinemann and Van Keuren (1956)	155	0.33	155	2.45
		1.01		1.91
		1.29		1.89
McVey and others (1956)	140	0.55	159	1.21
		0.86		1.08
		1.54		0.83
		1.96		0.66
Sylvestre and Jordan (Private communication)	140	0.20	150	1.89
		0.86		1.50
		1.19		1.27
		1.57		1.16

The above results show that for every extra pound of gain made during the winter, cattle on a high-plane prepasture ration gained 0.2 to 0.6 pound less on pasture than those fed a lower-plane prepasture ration. Similar observations have been reported by McCampbell (1922), Potter and Withycomb (1926), Guilbert and others (1944), Kincaid, Litton, and Hunt (1945), Beeson, Perry, and Mott (1949), Johnson, Rinehart, and Hickman (1952), Mott and others (1953), Winchester and Howe (1954), Bohman (1955), and Bohman and Torell (1956).

134

Alder (1959) reports that two lots of 1000-pound cattle fed high-and low-plane winter rations from January through April gained 240 and 133 pounds, but that after 6 weeks on pasture their carcass gains were 46 and 74 pounds respectively. Alder (1959) also reports that steers whose winter gain is retarded gain faster on pasture, because they eat more than those fed for a high rate of winter gain. His experiments showed that fecal output on pasture was of similar composition regardless of the nutritional level of the winter ration, but was 11 percent greater in volume for cattle from low-plane rations than for those from high-plane rations. This observation suggests a partial explanation for the greater pasture gains made by cattle fed a low-plane ration during the winter.

However, in none of the reports cited above was prepasture gain regulated by varying the amount of a single winter ration. Thus, the differences in pasture gain cannot all be attributed to the rate of prepasture gain; differences in the bulk and composition of winter rations may also influence pasture performance.

COMPOSITION AND BULK OF PREPASTURE RATIONS

Alder (1959) states: "It is possible that cattle reared at pasture, where rumen and other development is encouraged, may have bigger capacities for grass in later life and may utilize it more efficiently than cattle reared indoors until six months or one year old." Balch and others (1960) investigated the effect of two levels of hay (in a rearing diet of hay and concentrates) on the appetite and digestive efficiency of five pairs of identical twin heifers. The diets were fed from weaning until 6 months before calving. One member of each pair received hay to capacity plus 2 pounds of grain daily; its twin was fed 40 percent as much hay plus sufficient grain to provide an equal rate of gain. In the digestion trials that followed, each heifer was fed (a) the diet on which it had been reared, (b) the diet on which its sister had been reared, and (c) an all-hay diet. These tests showed that the method of rearing had no subsequent effect either on the appetite of the animals for hay, or on the digestibility of the components of their rations.

In a study at the Research Station, Melfort, Saskatchewan, the effects of hay:grain ratios in winter rations on the subsequent pasture performance of yearling steers, were as follows:

Winter feeding period—180 days; steers individually fed

Approximate hay:grain ratio	90:10	70:30	40:60
Number of steers	7	7	7
Average initial weight (lb)	412	413	414
Average daily gain (lb)	1.1	1.0	1.0
Hay eaten (lb/day)	11.4	7.6	3.8
Grain eaten (lb/day)	1.2	3.2	6.0
Increase in heart girth (inches)	5.88	6.6	6.7
Increase in paunch girth (inches)	5.5	4.4	3.4

135

Pasture period—90 days; all steers on one pasture

Average change during adjustment			
period (lb)	−18	9	5
Average gain during test period (lb)	195	182	166
Average overall gain on pasture (lb)	177	191	171

During the 10-day adjustment period, the steers fed the 90:10 hay:grain ration lost weight after being moved to pasture. This is a common occurrence. But the interesting point is the increase in weight during the adjustment period made by the two lots fed rations that contained more grain. The results of this study show that a prepasture ration containing a large proportion of hay affects subsequent pasture gains, but the effect is less obvious when the change in weight during the adjustment period is added to or subtracted from the total pasture gain. Thus, even when winter gains are controlled, the composition and bulk of the winter ration affect the pasture response.

Bohman and Torell (1956) suggest that the protein supplement fed during the winter affects summer gains on pasture. However, the long-term studies of Brouse (1955) fail to show differences in summer gain caused by different protein supplements in winter rations, because differences in summer gains could be related to differences in rate of winter gain. Johnson, Rinehart, and Hickman (1952) report that moderate levels of grain or alfalfa supplements in winter rations result in equal gains on pasture the following summer. Differences in gain on either dryland or irrigated pastures can be attributed to factors other than different protein supplements fed in prepasture rations (Mott and others, 1953; Heinemann and Van Keuren, 1956).

GROUP FEEDING

When cattle are placed on pasture in the spring, those that have been fed individually during the previous winter usually gain more than those that have been group-fed. Bohman and Torell (1956) found equal winter gains of about 0.45 pound per day on 400-pound Hereford calves, whether they were fed as individuals or in groups of 18. But on pasture the individually fed and group-fed calves gained 1.30 and 1.15 pounds per day respectively.

The effect of making animals spend an adjustment period on a conditioning pasture between prepasture and pasture seasons is shown by data from a study conducted from 1955 through 1961 at the Research Station, Melfort, Saskatchewan (unpublished data). The 450-pound steers were group-fed a hay and grain prepasture ration that provided sufficient energy for an average liveweight gain of about 1 pound per day. The steers were studied for 190 days during the winter, then transferred to a conditioning sward for a 5- to 14-day adjustment period before being put on pasture for a 50-day test period. Because the gains of individual steers varied considerably during the prepasture period, the herd was divided each year into three weight lots whose average prepasture gains were 220, 191, and 165 pounds. Pasture gains were studied for (*a*) gain or loss during the adjustment period, (*b*) 50-day gains plus gain or loss during the adjustment period, and (*c*) 50-day gains after the adjustment period. Significant findings are summarized below:

	Prepasture period gain (lb) 7-yr av.	Average weight change (lb)							
		1955	*1956*	*1957*	*1958*	*1959*	*1960*	*1961*	*Av.*
Adjustment period	220	50	−24	−26	−5	−7	−9	13	−1
gain or loss	191	49	−20	−19	−6	2	−10	11	1
	165	54	−14	−11	−4	4	−1	16	6
50-day gain plus	220	138	103	88	116	113	125	121	115
adjustment period	191	134	102	84	117	120	123	123	115
gain or loss	165	132	105	95	125	124	128	126	119
50-day gain excluding	220	88	127	114	121	120	134	108	116
adjustment period gain	191	85	122	103	123	118	133	112	114
or loss	165	78	119	106	129	120	129	110	113
Adjustment period (days)		14	14	5	13	9	6	12	
Number of steers (each lot)		18	12	15	15	15	12	18	

There were differences between years in liveweight changes during the adjustment period. But whether or not the gains or losses during the adjustment period were added to the pasture period gains, there were no significant differences in average gain between lots for any one year or for the 7 years averaged together. No definite explanation for these results can be given. Perhaps the differences in winter gain were not great enough to have an important influence on pasture gains. Undoubtedly, group feeding affects the inherent gaining ability of individual steers. It is also possible that stresses caused by group feeding during the winter, such as crowding or butting order, may not be effective on pasture. However, the results suggest that the use of an adjustment period between the prepasture season and the pasture season may not be warranted.

DIFFERENT CROPS IN RELATION TO AN ADJUSTMENT PERIOD

When cattle of any age or body condition are turned out to pasture after being on dry feed, they invariably show an appreciable loss in liveweight. The loss may be 12 to 16 percent (Morgan, 1948). Ivins and Morgan (1957) presented carcass yield data on two sets of identical twin calves, and showed that most of the loss could be attributed to a loss in fill. They cite the theory that loss in liveweight is caused mainly by the laxative nature of spring grass, and suggest that kind of pasture probably influences the degree of such losses. This has been borne out at the Research Station, Melfort, Saskatchewan, where steers used on implant tests and placed on a brome grass–alfalfa sward for a 13-day adjustment period gained about 26 pounds each, whereas those on a crested wheat grass–alfalfa stand gained an average of 14 pounds during the same period. To check this observation, dry-fed steers from the same prepasture treatment were placed on three different pastures. The 1964 and 1965 results are averaged below:

Pasture	Number of steers	Average initial weight (lb)	Gain or loss (lb) at			
			1 day	4 days	10 days	16 days
Brome grass	12	604	1	−6	26	50
Crested wheat grass	12	605	−4	−10	20	44
Russian wildrye	8	606	−7	−24	11	40

The main argument for using an adjustment period is to avoid a negative feed efficiency during the first few days on pasture. But the above figures show that an adjustment period may not accomplish this because animals adjust more readily on one grass than on another. Further, unless animals are weighed at frequent intervals during the adjustment period, they may gain considerably before going on test pastures; this reduces the apparent length of the grazing season and the apparent gain per acre. Because of differences in fill, cattle coming off conditioning pasture at an average weight below their initial weight are likely to show greater pasture gains than those that increase their weight during the adjustment period. This is borne out by the results presented above, which demonstrate that both negative and positive feed efficiency effects may occur on different kinds of herbage. Thus, a conditioning period on an adjustment sward appears to be of little value, and may introduce more errors than it can correct.

It is apparent that much more information is needed about the effects of prepasture rations, adjustment periods on conditioning pasture, and different types of herbages before the interrelationships of these factors can be adequately explained.

References

Alder, F. E. 1959. Pasture experiments with animals, p. 109–118. *In* J. D. Ivins (ed.) The measurement of grassland productivity. Butterworths Sci. Publications, London.

Balch, C. C., R. C. Campling, V. W. Johnson, and Jill Roy. 1960. The effect of the level of roughage during the rearing period on the utilization of food by adult cattle. Brit. J. Nutr. 14:379–390.

Beeson, W. M., T. W. Perry, and G. O. Mott. 1949. The influence of wintering rations and gain prior to and during pasturing on growth and fattening of calves. Indiana Agr. Exp. Sta., 62nd Annu. Rep., p. 13.

Bohman, V. R. 1955. Compensatory growth of beef cattle. The effect of hay maturity. J. Anim. Sci. 14:249–255.

Bohman, V. R., and C. Torell. 1956. Compensatory growth of beef cattle. The effect of protein supplements. J. Anim. Sci. 15:1089–1096.

Brouse, E. M. 1955. Wintering calves in the Nebraska Sandhills. Nebr. Agr. Exp. Sta. Bull. 356 (revised).

Embray, L. B., A. C. Dittman, and G. F. Gastler. 1958. Wintering calves with alfalfa hay or prairie hay. S. Dak. Agr. Exp. Sta. Bull. 466.

Guilbert, H. R., S. H. Hart, K. A. Wagnon, and H. Goss. 1944. The importance of continuous growth in beef cattle. Calif. Agr. Exp. Sta. Bull. 688.

Heinemann, W. W., and R. W. Van Keuren. 1956. The effect of wintering plane of nutrition on subsequent gains of beef yearling steers on irrigated pastures. J. Anim. Sci. 15:1097–1102.

Ivins, J. D., and J. T. Morgan. 1957. Note on the extent and significance of losses in liveweight of in-wintered cattle on turning out to grass in spring. J. Brit. Grassl. Soc. 12:19–21.

Johnson, R. F., E. F. Rinehart, and C. W. Hickman. 1952. A system of wintering, pasturing, and finishing beef calves for Idaho. Idaho Agr. Exp. Sta. Bull. 292.

Kincaid, C. M., G. W. Litton, and R. E. Hunt. 1945. Some factors that influence the production of steers from pasture. J. Anim. Sci. 4:164–173.

McCampbell, C. W. 1922. The effect of winter rations on summer pasture gains of cattle. Proc. Amer. Soc. Anim. Prod. 77 p.

McVey, W. M., R. E. Smith, H. N. Wheaton, and G. O. Mott. 1956. Beef production from alfalfa–grass pastures when grazed by steers wintered at four levels of nutrition. Purdue Univ., Agr. Ext. Serv., Lafayette, Indiana. Mimeo AY-147.

Morgan, J. T. 1948. The milk production, milk composition and certain other physiological characters of dairy cows in relation to winter feeding and a system of rotational grazing. M.Sc. Thesis. Univ. Wales.

Mott, G. O., R. E. Smith, W. M. McVey, and W. M. Beeson. 1953. Grazing trials with beef cattle. Purdue Agr. Exp. Sta. Bull. 581.

Potter, E. L., and R. Withycomb. 1926. Wintering stock steers. Oregon Exp. Sta. Bull. 224.

Winchester, C. F., and P. E. Howe. 1954. Some effects on beef cattle of interrupted growth. 1. Results of the 1950–51 identical twin steer trials. U.S. Dep. Agr. Res. Serv. Mimeo circ.

Chapter 17

ESTIMATING HERBAGE YIELD FROM ENERGY INTAKE OF GRAZING RUMINANTS*

VAUGHN S. LOGAN and WALLACE J. PIGDEN†
Animal Research Institute, Canada Department of Agriculture
Ottawa, Ontario

The potential yield of a pasture can be estimated from the energy used by grazing ruminants to meet their maintenance, production, and exercise requirements. The calculation gives an indirect index of herbage yield. It can measure relatively small differences in production between swards grazed by uniform animal groups. It is also valuable for comparing other estimates of productivity such as dry-matter yield and quality appraisals. In extensive grazing tests where carrying capacity of the pasture is extremely low and where it is difficult or impossible to obtain meaningful dry-matter yields, this method is a valuable tool for estimating pasture productivity. This technique is not, however, sufficiently refined to discriminate between small differences in swards grazed by different classes of livestock, for example, cattle versus sheep or beef steers versus lactating dairy cows.

In grazing trials in which forage utilization is complete, total animal productibility (maintenance plus animal product increase) is generally proportional to pasture yield. This does not mean that a grazing trial with ruminants supplies one final answer; it does mean that animal measurements under a given set of management conditions can be used as an indirect index of herbage yield. Utilization of herbage by the animals must be reasonably complete; for a complete evaluation, any excess herbage should be cut immediately and its feeding potential determined.

The energy requirements of ruminants for maintenance and production, derived chiefly from indoor feeding trials, have been used as a basis for estimating the yield and quality of grazed pastures. Several methods for estimating yield and quality from the energy requirements have been devised and used by pasture investigators (Schneider, Soni, and Harn, 1954). A popular method, which applies to several classes of animals, has been described by Sylvestre and Williams (1952). The method described below is a simplification and extension of this latter method.

---

*Contribution No. 277, Animal Research Institute.

†Now Research Coordinator (Animal Nutrition), Research Branch, Canada Department of Agriculture, Ottawa 3, Ontario.

FACTORS FOR PREDICTING ENERGY INTAKE

In evaluating forages, digestible organic matter (DOM) can be considered equivalent to digestible energy (DE) (Heaney and Pigden, 1963). Appropriate factors for estimating the energy needed for maintenance and production by different types of animals are given in Table 1 in terms of total digestible nutrients (TDN) and digestible energy (DE). Also included in the table are ratings for typical pasture conditions affecting energy evaluations of herbage production. For growing animals, these factors are used in a modification of an equation developed by Garrett, Meyer, and Lofgreen (1959), which is based on established relationships between net energy intake and body weight increase. For dairy cows, Brody and Procter (1935), using data from large numbers of lactating cows, have shown that the algebraic sum of energy for maintenance, milk production, and weight increase fit the energy in the consumed feed. Corbett (1960), Hutton (1962), and Wallace (1956, 1961) recommend this method. The equations for ewes and lambs were calculated from data of Coop and Drew (1963), and modified to measure ewe production in terms of liveweight gain of lambs; the factors for lamb liveweight increase were proportionately reduced to bring the total energy estimates in line with other reported requirements. These equations are tentative, and they should be applied only to ewes suckling lambs for 90 days or less. Energy required for wool production is included in equations in Table 1. Experimental evidence of the energy needs of nursing ewes is limited, and further data are needed to substantiate or modify this aspect of pasture evaluation. The various factors involved are discussed later in this chapter.

Examples of the calculations used to estimate TDN and DE are presented in Tables 2 and 3. These are for a lactating dairy cow, a growing steer, ewes suckling a single lamb or twins, and a weaned lamb. They take into account calculation of the exercise factor (E), and show the effects of pastures of different quality. In each equation the prediction factors from Table 1 are indicated by $\triangle$.

Maintenance energy (M) and production energy (P) should be computed separately, as the M to P ratio is a useful index of the efficiency of energy used for production. Provided that quantity of forage is not limited, this ratio is a sensitive indicator of herbage quality (Pigden and Greenshields, 1960).

The technique described here is essentially relative; treatment groups must, therefore, be well balanced. It is not sufficiently refined to compare the energy output of milking cows with that of yearling steers, or even that of sheep and cattle, except as a broad approximation.

TABLE 1. Requirements for maintenance, liveweight gain, milk production, and exercise used to predict energy intake of grazing ruminants (△ = prediction factor for each requirement)

142

	Maintenance* (M)	△ G where G = liveweight gain	△ Ge where Ge = lamb on ewe gain	△ FCM where FCM = 4% fat-corrected milk	Requirement over maintenance %	Exercise (E)† Definition
Cow					10	Forage readily available. Grazing time not over 6 hr/day. Water, salt, and milking facilities close at hand.
TDN (lb)	$0.046\ W^{0.75}$ +	$1.65G$		+ 0.32FCM		
DE (kcal)	$97\ W^{0.75}$ +	$3460G$		+ 670FCM		
Steer					25	a) Forage readily available. Distance to water or milking barn 1½ miles each way. b) Forage not readily available. Up to 8 hr/day spent in grazing. Salt, water, and milking barn close at hand.
TDN (lb)	$0.036\ W^{0.75}$ +	$M(0.57G)$				
DE (kcal)	$76\ W^{0.75}$ +	$M(0.58G)$				
Ewe and single lamb					50	Forage not readily available. Over 8 hr/day spent in grazing. Distance to water or milking barn 1½ miles each way.
TDN (lb)	$0.041\ W^{0.75}$ +	$2.3G$	+ 2.28Ge			
DE (kcal)	$86\ W^{0.75}$ +	$4830G$	+ 4780Ge			
Ewe and twin lambs					75	Forage scanty; grazing 10 to 12 hr/day; rugged terrain using vertical energy; 2 miles or more between pasture and water.
TDN (lb)	$0.041\ W^{0.75}$ +	$2.3G$	+ 3.53Ge			
DE (kcal)	$86\ W^{0.75}$ +	$4830G$	+ 7410Ge			
Sheep					100	Forage scanty; hard country; cold weather with inadequate wool or hair cover; animals losing weight.
TDN (lb)	$0.036\ W^{0.75}$ +	$M(2.3G)$				
DE (kcal)	$76\ W^{0.75}$ +	$M(2.4G)$				

*M = △ $W^{0.75}$, where △ = maintenance factor and W = liveweight in lb.
†E = % requirement over maintenance (Col. 5) × M.

TABLE 2. Calculations used to estimate TDN and DE intake of cattle on pasture from prediction factors* and animal measurements

Class of cattle	Live-weight (W)	$W^{0.75}$	Daily gain (G)	4% Fat-corrected milk (FCM)	Exercise factor % of M (E)	Calculations
	lb	lb	lb	lb	%	
Lactating dairy cow	1200	(203.8)	−0.2	30	10	Equation = M + $\triangle$G + $\triangle$FCM + E TDN = 0.046 $W^{0.75}$ + 1.65(G) + 0.32(FCM) + E = 0.046(203.8) + 1.65(−0.2) + 0.32(30) + 0.1(M) = 9.37 − 0.33 + 9.6 + 0.937 = 19.6 lb DE = 97(203.77) + 3460(−0.2) + 670(30) + 0.1(M) = 19765 − 692 + 20100 + 1976 = 41149 kcal
Growing beef steer or heifer	550	(113.6)	1.5		25	Equation = M + M $\triangle$G + E TDN = 0.036 $W^{0.75}$ + M(0.57G) + E = 0.036(113.57) + M(0.855) + 0.25(M) = 4.09 + (4.09 × 0.855) + 1.02 = 4.09 + 3.50 + 1.02 = 8.61 lb DE = 76(113.57) + M(0.87) + E = 8631 + 7509 + 2158 = 18298 kcal

*See Table 1.

143

TABLE 3. Calculations used to estimate TDN and DE intake of sheep on pasture from prediction factors* and animal measurements

Class of sheep	Live-weight (W)	$W^{0.75}$	Daily gain ewe (G)	Daily gain lamb (Ge)	Exercise factor % of M (E)	Calculations
	lb	lb	lb	lb	%	
Ewe and 1 lamb	100	(31.6)	0.3	0.4	10	Equation = M + $\triangle$ G + $\triangle$ Ge + E TDN = 0.041 $W^{0.75}$ + 2.3G + 2.28Ge + E = 0.041(31.6) + 2.3(0.3) + 2.28(0.4) + 0.1(M) = 1.30 + 0.69 + 0.91 + 0.13 = 3.03 lb DE = 86(31.6) + 4830(0.3) + 4780(0.4) + 0.1(M) = 2718 + 1449 + 1912 + 272 = 6351 kcal
Ewe with 2 lambs	150	(42.6)	−0.3	0.5	25	Equation = M + $\triangle$ G + $\triangle$ Ge + E TDN = 0.041(42.6) + 2.3 (−0.3) + 3.53(0.5) + 0.25(M) = 1.75 − 0.69 + 1.76 + 0.44 = 3.26 lb DE = 86(42.6) + 4830(−0.3) + 7410(0.5) + 0.25(M) = 3664 − 1449 + 3705 + 916 = 6836 kcal
Growing lamb	55	(20.2)	0.3		50	Equation = M + M $\triangle$ G + E TDN = 0.036(20.2) + M(0.69) + 0.5(M) = 0.73 + 0.50 + 0.37 = 1.60 lb DE = 76(20.2) + M(0.72) + 0.5(M) = 1535 + 1105 + 768 = 3408 kcal

*See Table 1.

144

SOURCE AND INTERPRETATION OF FACTORS
PRESENTED IN TABLE 1

Maintenance Requirements

Maintenance accounts for a very high proportion of the total energy needs of an animal. It has been estimated at 75 percent of energy intake for a breeding ewe (Coop, 1961), and at 49 to 62 percent for 500- to 800-pound steers on high-quality experimental pastures (Pigden and Greenshields, 1960). Proportions of energy required for maintenance vary according to level of production, ranging from approximately 100 percent for animals maintaining their weight only, to 50 percent for a 500-pound steer gaining 2 pounds per day, to 30 percent for a high-producing dairy cow. In general, maintenance energy requirements account for well over 50 percent of total energy intake.

A number of workers have assumed that maintenance requirements are directly proportional to liveweight (Gaines, 1937; Haecker, 1903). Others have recommended it be calculated as a power of live-weight: $W^{0.87}$ (Morrison, 1956), $W^{0.73}$ (Wallace, 1956), $W^{0.7}$ (Brody, 1945), and $W^{0.7}$, $W^{0.73}$, or $W^{0.75}$ (Coop, 1961). Kleiber, Regan, and Mead (1945) have recommended the equation $B = 70W^{0.75}$, where B = fasting heat production (kcal/day) and W = liveweight (lb). This point is still a matter of considerable controversy, but it is generally accepted that basal metabolism varies approximately with the $W^{0.73}$ or $W^{0.75}$ power of body weight. The index of $W^{0.75}$ has been adopted for the present discussion.

Studies using the comparative slaughter technique suggest that maintenance energy requirements of beef cattle and dry ewes or wethers are the same when animals are fed identical rations and that they can be expressed as $DE = 76W^{0.75}$ or $TDN = 0.036W^{0.75}$ (Garret and others, 1959). The same factors can be used for young growing dairy stock.

Until recently the factors used to estimate maintenance energy requirements were derived chiefly from stall-fed animals or from studies using calorimeters. Wallace (1956, 1961) conducted experiments with grazing cows on New Zealand pastures, using the Cr_2O_3 fecal-nitrogen technique, and estimated that seasonal maintenance requirements of lactating Jerseys were about 50 percent greater than those for stall-fed controls. Reid, Smith, and Anderson (1958), using the Cr_2O_3-chromogen method, have reported energy requirements of grazing cows to be about 40 percent greater than those of stall-fed cows. Conversely, Corbett (1960), Greenhalgh and Runcie (1962), and Holmes (1959) have all concluded that there is no increase in the energy requirements of strip-grazed as compared with drylot-fed cows. However, these latter workers compared systems where differences in energy expenditure would be small and could be masked by technique errors in intake measurements.

Coop (1961), Lambourne (1961), and Langlands, Corbett, and McDonald (1962) have demonstrated considerable variation, ranging

145

from 10 to 200 percent increases, in maintenance energy requirements for sheep under moderate to adverse grazing conditions. An increase of 10 to 30 percent appears to cover most conditions.

Exercise Factor

The importance of exercise as a factor in maintenance is recognized in the feeding standards for humans and draft animals; 100 to 200 percent more energy is needed for heavy work than for inactivity. This factor has not been considered previously in grazing requirements. Clapperton (1961) exercised sheep on a treadmill in a respiration chamber and reported the energy cost of horizontal work to be 0.59 cal/kg-m, which agrees well with the values of 0.54 reported for man (Smith, 1922), and 0.58 for the dog (Lusk, 1931), but it is higher than the value of 0.39 reported for the horse (Brody, 1945). The average energy expended by man in doing vertical work was 6.45 cal/kg-m; this amount decreased with speed but was not affected by steepness of gradient (Clapperton, 1961).

Information on distance walked on pasture is available. Creswell and Harris (1959) estimate that ewes travel about 1.1 to 1.3 miles daily on favorable swards. Morris (1961) and Cory (1927) estimate daily travel of range sheep at 2.9 and 3.8 miles respectively. Hancock (1953) states that cows walk 1.75 miles daily in 1-acre paddocks, and Cory (1927) reports 3.3 miles per day for cattle on range. Morris (1961) concludes that the type of vegetation and the distance between pasture and water are the main determinants of distance covered.

Lofgreen, Meyer, and Hull (1957) have found that sheep and cattle take 3.2 and 1.8 hours more time, respectively, to harvest forage on the fifth than on the second day on irrigated swards; this demonstrates the marked effect of herbage availability on the time spent grazing each day.

Pullar (1962) has shown that heat production of a fully fleeced sheep in a calorimeter is 67 percent higher when the animal is standing than when it is lying down. This confirms the work of Armsby and Fries (1916), who report a 20 to 60 percent increase for steers. Graham (1962), also using a calorimeter, found that where forage was readily available (sods transported indoors and grazed by sheep for only 4 hours per day) the grazing energy requirement was 6.9 percent above the energy needed for maintenance. Graham (1964) estimates that grazing sheep would use at least 40 percent more energy than caged sheep, and that the amount of energy expended in walking on a hilly pasture or to go a long way to water could become a major item.

There is, therefore, no doubt that a grazing energy requirement must be considered. The available evidence suggests that it is chiefly related to time spent standing, walking, grazing, and ruminating (Graham, 1964) and is also related to body weight. If herbage availability is low, expenditure of grazing energy can be high even in small

146

paddocks. Inclement weather or inadequate insulation by hair or wool increases grazing energy requirements (Blaxter, Graham, and Wainman, 1959).

The values given in Table 1 for the grazing energy factor (E) are approximate only and are expressed as percentages of maintenance requirements. The factor allows for the effect of body weight, as heavier animals have greater energy demands.

Estimates of maintenance energy requirements of Jersey crossbred cows in New Zealand (Hutton, 1962) show the requirements of dry cows fed at maintenance level, dry cows full-fed, and lactating cows full-fed, as estimated in terms of DOM, are $0.048W^{0.73}$, $0.070W^{0.73}$, and $0.095W^{0.73}$ pounds respectively. A previous estimate for lactating New Zealand Jerseys in terms of DOM is $0.053W^{0.73}$ pounds (Wallace, 1961). Other estimates for lactating cows are $0.046W^{0.73}$ pounds (Corbett, 1960), and $0.048W^{0.73}$ pounds (Langlands, 1962). Obviously, further research is required to establish maintenance energy factors for dairy cows. Meanwhile, the data suggests that the dairy cow factor should be substantially higher than the factors for beef, sheep, and growing dairy heifers (Table 1). A good intermediate value, which is comparable with that obtained by Brody and Procter (1935), is $0.046W^{0.75}$ TDN. It is conceivable that different forages may have different energy values, depending on metabolic heat losses; hence, maintenance energy values may fluctuate through a fairly wide range.

Production Energy Requirements

Determinations of the TDN required for cows of moderate production potential to produce 1 pound of fat-corrected milk (FCM) have ranged from 0.30 pound (Brody, 1945; Gaines, 1937) to 0.34 pound (Haecker, 1903). Values of 0.4 pound or more of TDN per pound FCM have been proposed as requirements for high-producing cows. The intermediate figure of 0.32 (Jensen and others, 1942; Reid, 1961) used in Table 1 conforms to average production energy requirements of cows used for grazing experiments.

Energy requirements for meat production are subject to much larger errors because changes in rumen fill affect weight measurements. The best available values are those obtained from comparative slaughter trials (Garrett and others, 1959), and they are used here for sheep and growing cattle (Table 1). Although the relationship between energy intake and energy retention is generally considered to be curvilinear, the linear equations of Garrett and others (1959) fit satisfactorily.

LIMITATIONS OF THE TECHNIQUE

Maintenance

The chief limitations in estimating maintenance energy are associated with (a) the magnitude of the exercise factor, (b) the effect of extremely adverse weather on animals inadequately protected by hair or wool, (c) the accuracy of maintenance energy factors, and (d) errors associated with gut fill. The last factor is not nearly as important as it is in estimates of weight increase. For example, the daily maintenance energy requirement of a 1000-pound steer is 6.62 pounds of TDN. Assuming this animal gains or loses 50 pounds of gut fill and the formula $TDN = 0.036W^{0.75}$ is applied, the estimate becomes 6.62 ± 0.24 pounds of TDN. This is an insignificant error, and it will be a constant percentage value, irrespective of frequency of weighings. Unless very extreme conditions are established within an experiment, (a), (b), and (c) are likely to be relative. Thus (d) is the most important source of variation, but it is still much smaller than the error associated with estimating energy intake from weight changes.

Production

Growth. There are two main problems associated with estimating energy intake from weight gain: gut fill and composition of gain. The former is by far the more important.

The daily energy requirement of a 1000-pound cow or steer for maintenance plus 2 pounds of liveweight gain is 13.9 pounds of TDN. If the gain factor of $M(0.57G)$ is applied to a 50-pound gain or loss of gut fill by this animal, the estimate for daily needs becomes 13.91 ± 195 pounds of TDN. This seems to be a fantastically large error, but it is quite possible because if allowed free access to feed and water ruminants can gain or lose 5 to 10 percent of body weight within 24 hours, depending on gut fill. For cattle gaining 1.8 pounds per day, the error of 50 pounds of gut fill is equal to the TDN required for gain during a 28-day period. Control of gut fill is therefore critical in estimates of energy required for growth.

Thus, even with strict control over gut fill changes, liveweight gains or losses by ruminants over short periods of time can be quite meaningless and estimates of energy storage should not be attempted for periods of 28 days or less (Chapter 14). If more extended periods are involved, energy expended for body weight change should be estimated. In the case of young, rapidly growing ruminants, because their gains will account for a much higher proportion of their energy intake—often more than 50 percent—errors will be lower than for animals gaining very slowly. It is extremely important that conditions of weighing be carefully standardized. Investigators should be particularly wary of situations, such as rotational grazing, where quality and availability of herbage can have marked effects on gut fill over short grazing periods. The practice of feeding a standard ration at maintenance level for several days before starting growing animals on a grazing experiment and feeding it again at the end of the experiment before final weights are taken has much to recommend it, though the procedure is not practical for lactating cows or ewes. *Water must be withheld at least 12 hours before weighing* because it has the most important effect on fill.

A further limitation of the method is that although the equations account for increasing energy requirements with increasing weight, they do not differentiate between energy required per unit gain by late- versus early-maturing animals. The former tend to have a lower energy requirement per unit weight gain than the latter at equivalent ages during the period of rapid growth.

Where critical comparisons of energy intake from pastures are required in terms of growth, an investigator should consider slaughtering the animals and using specific gravity or carcass analysis methods for estimating carcass composition. To do this it is necessary to slaughter a representative control group when an experiment starts and slaughter treatment groups at its end. Differences in energy storage between the control and treatment groups give the indices of energy intake, so that the two major problems of gut fill and carcass composition are circumvented. Appropriate equations for transforming specific gravity values to carcass energy content are now available (Garrett and others, 1959).

Milk production. Determination of energy output in milk is the most direct and accurate procedure available for estimating animal production on pasture. Pounds of milk and percent fat content are the only measurements required. For this reason, moderately high producing dairy cows that are neither gaining nor losing appreciable amounts of weight are likely to provide the most accurate index of pasture energy output. However, care must be exercised when choosing experimental animals; for example, cows whose yield has reached peak lactation must be chosen and their conception must be timed to avoid pregnancy effects on lactation during experimental grazing.

References

Armsby, H. P., and J. A. Fries. 1916. Net energy values of ruminants. Penn. Agr. Exp. Sta. Bull. 142.

Blaxter, K. L., N. McC. Graham, and F. W. Wainman. 1959. Environmental temperature, energy metabolism and heat regulation in sheep. III. The metabolism and thermal exchanges of sheep with fleeces. J. Agr. Sci. 52:41–49.

Brody, S. 1945. Bio-energetics and growth. Reinhold Publishing Corp., New York. 683 p.

Brody, S., and R. C. Procter. 1935. Growth and development with special reference to domestic animals. XXXV. Energetic efficiency of milk production and the influence of body weight thereon. Mo. Agr. Exp. Sta. Res. Bull. 222.

Clapperton, J. L. 1961. The energy expenditure of sheep in walking on the level and on gradients. Proc. Nutr. Soc. 20, 2: XXXI.

Coop, I. E. 1961. The energy requirements of sheep. Proc. New Zeal. Soc. Anim. Prod. 21:78–91.

Coop, I. E., and K. R. Drew. 1963. Maintenance and lactating requirements of grazing sheep. Proc. New Zeal. Soc. Anim. Prod. 23:53–62.

Corbett, J. L. 1960. Faecal-index for estimating herbage consumption by grazing animals. Proc. 8th Int. Grassl. Congr., p. 438–442.

Cory, V. L. 1927. Activities of livestock on the range. Texas Agr. Exp. Sta. Bull. 367.

Cresswell, E., and L. E. Harris. 1959. An improved range meter for sheep. J. Anim. Sci. 18:1447–1451.

Gaines, W. L. 1937. Working maintenance as a function of liveweight in dairy cows and its bearing on an energy-size index of lactation. J. Dairy Sci. 20:583–598.

Garrett, W. N., J. H. Meyer, and G. P. Lofgreen. 1959. The comparative energy requirements of sheep and cattle for maintenance and gain. J. Anim. Sci. 18:528–547.

Graham, N. McC. 1962. Energy expenditure of grazing sheep. Nature 196:289.

Graham, N. McC. 1964. Energy cost of feeding activities and energy expenditure of grazing sheep. Austral. J. Agr. Res. 15:969–973.

Greenhalgh, J. F. D., and K. V. Runcie. 1962. Nutritional aspects of zero grazing. Proc. Brit. Soc. Anim. Prod., 292 p.

Haecker, T. L. 1903. Investigations in milk production. Minn. Agr. Exp. Sta. Bull. 79.

Hancock, J. 1953. Grazing behaviour of cattle. Anim. Breed. Abstr. 21:1–13.

Heaney, D. P., and W. J. Pigden. 1963. Interrelationships and conversion factors between expressions of the digestible energy value of forages. J. Anim. Sci. 22:956–960.

Holmes, W. 1959. The relationship between grazing intake and animal production, p. 119–128. In J. D. Ivins (ed.) The measurement of grassland productivity. Butterworths Sci. Publications, London.

Hutton, J. B. 1962. The maintenance requirements of New Zealand dairy cattle. Proc. New Zeal. Soc. Anim. Prod. 22:12–34.

Jensen, E., J. W. Klein, E. Rauschenstein, T. E. Woodward, and R. N. Smith. 1942. Input-output relationships in milk production. U.S. Dep. Agr. Tech. Bull. 815. 88 p.

Klieber, Max, W. M. Regan, and S. E. Mead. 1945. Measuring food values for dairy cows. Hilgardia 16:511–571.

Lambourne, J. L. 1961. Relative effects of environment and liveweight on the feed requirements of sheep. Proc. New Zeal. Soc. Anim. Prod. 21:92–108.

Langlands, J. P. 1962. Energy intake and its utilization for maintenance by the intensively grazed ruminant. Ph.D. Thesis, Univ. Aberdeen, Scotland.

Langlands, J. P., J. L. Corbett, and I. McDonald. 1962. Some studies of the energy requirements of adult sheep for maintenance. Proc. 36th Meet. Brit. Soc. Anim. Prod. 4:298 p.

Lofgreen, G. P., J. H. Meyer, and J. L. Hull. 1957. Behaviour patterns of sheep and cattle being fed pasture or soilage. J. Anim. Sci. 16:773–780.

Lusk, A. 1931. The elements of the science of nutrition. Saunders Co., London. 306 p.

Morris, J. G. 1961. The influence of nitrogen and phosphorus supplements on the composition of the ruminal ingesta of sheep grazing. Ph.D. Thesis, Utah State Univ., Logan, Utah.

Morrison, F. B. 1956. Feeds and feeding. 22nd ed. Morrison Publishing Co., Ithaca, N.Y. 1165 p.

Pigden, W. J., and J. E. R. Greenshields. 1960. Interaction of design, sward and management of yield and utilization of herbage in Canadian grazing trials. Proc. 8th Int. Grassl. Congr. 8:594–597.

Pullar, J. D. 1962. Calorimetry—The heat loss in adult sheep. Annu. Rep., Rowett Res. Inst. 18:46–51.

Reid, J. T. 1961. Energy requirements for lactation by the dairy cows. Proc. Cornell Nutr. Conf. for Feed Manufacturers.

Reid, J. T., A. M. Smith, and M. J. Anderson. 1958. Difference in requirement of dairy cattle between pastured and barn feeding conditions. Proc. Cornell Nutr. Conf. for Feed Manufacturers.

Schneider, B. H., B. K. Soni, and W. E. Harn. 1954. Methods of determining consumption and digestibility of pasture forages by sheep. Wash. Agr. Exp. Sta. Tech. Bull. 16.

Smith, H. M. 1922. Pub. 309. Carnegie Inst., Washington, D.C.

Sylvestre, P. E., and S. B. Williams. 1952. Methods of measuring the relative productivity of pasture experiments with livestock. Mimeo. Rep., Can. Dep. Agr., Ottawa. 16 p.

Wallace, L. R. 1956. The intake and utilization of pasture by grazing dairy cattle. Proc. 7th Int. Grassl. Congr. 7:134–144.

Wallace, L. R. 1961. Nutrition requirements of dairy cattle. Proc. New Zeal. Soc. Anim. Prod. 21:64–88.

Chapter 18

MEASURING THE HERBAGE CONSUMPTION
OF GRAZING ANIMALS*

WALLACE J. PIGDEN†
Animal Research Institute, Canada Department of Agriculture
Ottawa, Ontario

DENNIS J. MINSON‡
National Research Council Postdoctorate Fellow
Animal Research Institute, Canada Department of Agriculture
Ottawa, Ontario

Estimates of nutrient intake by grazing animals provide indices of pasture productivity and the efficiency with which nutrients are utilized by different classes of ruminants under different management systems. Intake measurements are also used to study the effect of specific treatments, such as prepasture planes of nutrition, supplementation, or on occasion, stimulation with hormones.

Accurate intake estimates are difficult to achieve, and many different procedures have been developed. This chapter describes the techniques available and summarizes some of the most useful facts from the mass of information available.

Herbage intake can be estimated in two ways: by measuring the digestibility of the herbage that is grazed and combining this with fecal output estimates; or by taking herbage samples before and after grazing, the difference representing intake. It is important to realize that these techniques may be used individually or combined in various ways to provide nutrient intake data.

METHODS TO DETERMINE THE DIGESTIBILITY
OF GRAZED SWARDS

Representative samples of a sward can be obtained by several procedures—by mowing, clipping, or hand plucking the herbage, or by removing boluses through esophageal or rumen fistulas. In turn, there are four techniques for estimating the digestibility of herbage:

- Feeding of large samples of herbage to ruminants in digestion stalls. This may require the harvesting of one or more tons of herbage

---

*Contribution No. 251 from the Animal Research Institute.

†Now Research Coordinator (Animal Nutrition), Research Branch, Canada Department of Agriculture, Ottawa 3, Ontario.

‡Present address: Cooper Laboratory, Division of Tropical Pastures, C.S.I.R.O., Lawes, Queensland, Australia.

- Obtaining small samples by clipping or plucking herbage or by obtaining boluses through an esophageal fistula (EF) or a rumen fistula (RF), and then digesting these samples in an in vitro rumen or analyzing them for chemical constituents
- Fecal index methods, in which feces samples are analyzed for a chemical constituent, the level of which has been shown by feeding trials to be highly correlated with digestibility
- Ratio techniques, by which the level of a presumably indigestible indicator in a small sample of herbage, obtained by a recognized sampling procedure, is compared with the level of the same indicator in the resultant feces samples. The increased fecal concentration of the indicator shows the level of digestibility.

Digestibility Trials with Large Samples

Garrigus and Rusk (1935) measured the digestibility of herbage by mowing areas adjacent to those being grazed, and feeding the cut forage to steers in digestibility stalls. This method has three disadvantages: a large amount of forage is required for a standard digestibility trial; the material fed to the animals is not always representative of what is selectively grazed; the level of intake of animals fed indoors is often lower than intake on pasture, so that digestion coefficients will be higher even if selection does not have any effect (Raymond, Minson, and Harris, 1956).

Two situations exist where this technique may be used advantageously, and where the associated error will probably be small. The first is where forage is subjected to a high grazing pressure so that utilization is completed within a short period. The second situation is where the digestibility of the plant is constant in a vertical plane, and animals grazing these pastures select material of the same digestibility as that of the whole plant. Grass swards before ear emergence may fall into this second category (Minson, Raymond, and Harris, 1960; Pritchard, Folkins, and Pigden, 1963), but alfalfa swards do not (Terry and Tilley, 1964). Details of the procedure are discussed in Chapter 21.

Estimating Digestibility with Small Herbage Samples

This procedure is based on two separate techniques, one to obtain representative samples of what the animals are grazing, and the other to estimate the digestibility of these samples.

Sampling. Clipping herbage is a relatively accurate method of sampling uniform and immature swards; a rather small sample suffices for digestibility assays. But samples from mature swards are seldom representative of the herbage an animal selects. Not only will there be a selection between plant species but, because leaf:stem ratios change considerably as maturity advances, there will be a selection within plants. Under defined conditions, clipped samples can provide useful informa-

153

tion, but misleading results may be obtained when they are used carelessly. It is recommended that small clipped samples be used to estimate digestibility of the herbage only when:

- Swards are relatively uniform and immature
- There is no dead growth, nor any effect of dung patches and urine rings
- The digestibility of the herbage is similar in a vertical plane. This can be measured by estimating the digestibility of the top and bottom growth in an in vitro assay. An analysis for a chemical constituent is not a reliable indicator of sward digestibility
- Grazing defoliates a sward within 1 week, as in a rotation.

Hand plucking involves careful observation of grazing animals, and sampling of sward components to the same degree as if they were grazed by animals. The investigator must be observant and skillful. Unless the results are checked by another method, such as a reliable esophageal fistula (EF), he cannot be certain his sample is representative of that being grazed. Like the clipping technique, this method is more useful on swards with minimum variation between and within species. With the development of the EF, there seems little reason for training individuals in plucking techniques.

An esophageal fistula is an opening in the neck of an animal through which forage falls into an attached bag. An EF for sheep has been described by Torell (1954). An EF has been devised for cattle also (Van Dyne and Torell, 1964). The method represents a notable advance in sampling technique, and is one of the most promising methods for obtaining representative samples of herbage selected by grazing animals. It is also possible in this way to obtain data on species selection and chemical composition (Heady and Torell, 1959; Lesperance and others, 1960a). The digestibility of selectively grazed forage can be estimated by one of the methods described in Chapter 6.

EF animals are fasted before grazing. Sampling must be for short periods, otherwise the animals will ruminate into the collection bag. Drinking water must be withheld to prevent moisture contamination (Torell, 1954). All animals must have grazed the sward being studied for at least 3 weeks before sampling if biased results are to be avoided (Heady and Torell, 1959; Willoughby, personal communication; Hardison and others, 1954).

There are some disadvantages associated with this method. Individual cattle or sheep may show preferences for a certain species of herbage. Samples obtained by EF are contaminated with ash and water from the saliva, as about 8 pounds of saliva are secreted per pound of feed consumed (Lesperance, Bohman, and Marble, 1960b), so mineral and dry-matter analyses are meaningless. Nitrogen contamination from saliva also occurs, and this will affect the nitrogen content of samples to a variable extent.

Probably the most serious drawback of the technique is the possibility of selective sorting at the EF. Torell (1954) notes that the percentage of grazed herbage that dropped through a fistula depended on the size of the opening. Lesperance and others (1960*b*) report that an EF cannula of 1.5 inches interior diameter for cattle was too small to allow boluses to fall through, and showed some evidence of selective sorting of soluble and fibrous feed particles when boluses dropped through an EF. They suggest that decreases in crude fiber might be caused by coarser particles slipping by the EF. It is evident that each investigator must pretest the EF he intends to use by feeding materials very similar to those to be grazed, and determining if EF samples are representative of the rations fed. If this cannot be demonstrated under controlled conditions, it is unlikely that representative sampling can be obtained in the field.

When animals with both esophageal and rumen fistulas are available, a comparison of EF and RF samples indicates if selection has occurred at the EF. Where several plant species are available for selection, animals not only show individual preferences but changes in preference as a season progresses (Heady and Torell, 1959); thus, a great deal of testing is necessary. More information is needed on this important aspect of the use of fistulas. McManus (1962) notes that losses in sheep saliva have a marked effect on appetite. This has a direct bearing on the length of time sampling can be conducted. A mineral mixture containing salt must be available for EF animals.

Rumen fistulas are useful research tools. Saltonstall (1948) has demonstrated that samples selected by a grazing steer can be collected by reaching through the RF and catching the boluses at the cardia. The rumen is emptied and the animals are permitted to graze for a short time before samples are removed through the RF. There seems to be no possibility of the selective sorting that sometimes occurs with the EF. But emptying the rumen and replacing the contents after the sampling period is tedious. Also, the many pockets and creases in the rumen make it difficult to empty the rumen completely, and some contamination usually occurs (Lesperance and others, 1960*b*). It is not known whether or not an animal with a completely empty rumen will graze normally.

A second approach is to empty the rumen sufficiently to expose the cardia (Taylor and Deriaz, 1963). This procedure requires removing about two-thirds of the contents of a full rumen, or about one-third to one-half if the animal is fasted overnight. The rumen should be emptied until the cardia is above the level of the rumen contents. The investigator walks beside the grazing animal with his arm through the fistula and catches the boluses as they are discharged from the cardia. The boluses are contaminated with saliva in the same manner as EF samples. This method has been used with cattle only, but there seems to be no reason why it could not be applied to sheep with 3-inch rumen fistulas.

Digestibility estimation. The digestibility of EF, RF, and clipped or plucked samples can be estimated by in vitro rumen assays, by analysis for chemical composition of plants, or by ratio techique where both feces and plant samples are analyzed.

The nylon bag technique uses a permeable but indigestible sac as a container for the sample of forage to be tested. The dacron, nylon, or silk sac is suspended in the rumen for a period of time, then withdrawn and the loss of dry matter or cellulose determined. The method has never been well standardized and a large number of variables affect the result. It is not recommended as a procedure for estimating digestibility, though it has some applications as outlined in Chapter 6.

The in vitro rumen procedure can be used to estimate the digestibility of small samples. However, coefficients of digestibility are relative rather than absolute; therefore, feed intakes estimated are also relative. With EF or RF samples an additional complication is introduced by contamination with saliva; this is likely to cause an increase in the DM digestibility coefficients. The amount of such contaminaton is not constant with all types of forage, because it may vary with species and degree of succulence (Lesperance and others, 1960b). Salivary ash contamination increases in vitro DM digestibility values, hence a technique should be used that estimates digestible organic matter (DOM), such as the one described by Alexander and McGowan (1966).

A second approach is to use in vitro cellulose digestibility to predict DOM, digestible energy (DE), or digestible dry matter (DDM). This method circumvents the problem introduced by ash in the saliva but is subject to the limitations of the technique, as outlined in Chapter 6. The investigator is further cautioned that the changes in diets selected by an animal, both in species and in relation to leaf:stem ratios, are likely to modify the slope of the cellulose-digestibility prediction curve and lead to large prediction errors.

Chemical constituents: The same problems and errors apply here as were discussed in Chapter 6.

Ratio technique: If a plant contains a chemical component that is indigestible and completely recovered in the feces, then the digestibility of the forage can be determined accurately by analysis of representative samples of the feed eaten and feces produced. The following formula is useful:

$$D = 100 \frac{(a-b)}{a}$$

where D = dry-matter digestibility (DMD)
$\quad a$ = concentration of indigestible material in feces dry matter
$\quad b$ = concentration of indigestible material in feed dry matter.

Three plant components have been suggested as suitable indigestible indicators: silica, lignin, and chromogens. Silica has proved unsatisfactory when applied to cut samples (Raymond, 1954); but for EF and RF samples and with the better chemical methods of estimation now available, silica appears worthy of further investigation (Jones and

156

Handreck, 1965). Lignin has been widely studied but has been found to be digested in varying degrees. Plant pigments (chromogens) appear to be indigestible when measured at a particular wavelength (Reid and others, 1950), but they have the disadvantage of being light labile (Lancaster and Bartrum, 1954). The wavelength at which complete recovery of plant pigments in feces is achieved varies between plant species and with stage of growth.

Fecal Index Techniques

In order to eliminate the necessity of obtaining herbage samples that are representative of the feed eaten, methods have been developed to estimate herbage digestibility or the feed:feces ratio (R) from the chemical composition of the feces from grazing animals. The regression equations relating digestibility to feces composition are determined with animals fed the same herbage in digestibility stalls. Several chemical fractions of the feces have been proposed as suitable for this method (nitrogen—Lancaster, 1949a; chromogen—Reid and others, 1952; fiber—Raymond and others, 1954; lignin—Forbes and Garrigus, 1950; methoxyl—Richards and Reid, 1952). Fecal fiber, lignin, and methoxyl show little promise (Raymond and others, 1956).

Fecal nitrogen. Lancaster (1947, 1949a) reports a relationship between forage digestibility and percentage nitrogen in the feces of pen-fed sheep. His observation has been confirmed by others, but the regression equations are usually different (Raymond and others, 1954). Factors such as age, level of parasitism, and species of animal will alter the digestibility:fecal nitrogen (FN) ratio (Raymond, Harris, and Kemp, 1954; Minson, 1958).

Early studies showed that one simple generalized equation could not represent the relationship between FN and digestibility (Lancaster, 1949b; Homb and Brierem, 1952), so correction factors or limited regressions based on the level of nitrogen in a forage were proposed (Forbes, 1950). These corrections reduced the standard error of estimate for the herbages studied, but were seldom applicable to swards studied elsewhere (Raymond, Harris, and Kemp, 1954; Milford, 1957; Pigden and Brisson, 1955–59). This is in part due to marked "seasonal" biases (Homb and Brierem, 1952; Minson and Kemp, 1961), and is associated with the higher nitrogen content of aftermath cuts. In experiments at Ottawa (unpublished data, 1963), some species of plants have shown little relation between FN and digestibility. Milford (1957) showed a negative relationship between FN and digestibility for some tropical species. Thus, not all plant materials show a useful correlation between FN and digestibility, and there is no generalized equation suitable for application to a wide variety of plant species.

Fecal pigments. The relationship between digestibility and the concentration of a fecal pigment (FP) in an 85 percent acetone extract was first proposed by Reid and others (1952) as an indirect method for

157

estimating digestibility. The FP are mainly of plant origin—chlorophylls, zanthophylls, and carotinoids, or their degradation products (Irwin and others, 1953). After extraction, their concentration is determined by spectrophotometric analysis at some point between 390 and 425 mμ, the exact setting depending on the species and the age of the herbage (Smart and others, 1953). The measurement of light absorption on the slope of an absorption curve is likely to be less precise than at an absorption peak, and it is recommended that all values for FP be determined at a wavelength where maximum absorption occurs (Raymond and others, 1954).

Reid and others (1952) have noted that the FP formula developed at Cornell would not necessarily apply under all conditions. This limitation has been confirmed by Kennedy and Lancaster (1957) and by Kennedy, Carter, and Lancaster (1959) for New Zealand forages; by Raymond and others (1954) for British swards; by Cook and Harris (1951) for certain range forages; by Squibb, Rivera, and Jarquin (1958) for ramie; and by Troelsen (1961) for herbages grown in Western Canada. Thus, there is no general equation which has a broad application. Moreover, the relationship between FP and digestibility can change markedly within swards during the same season (Kennedy and others, 1959). Thus, if FP are used to estimate digestibility, it is unwise to use one of the published equations without checking its validity for the sward being studied. FP techniques should not be used where the pigment recoveries are low (Irwin and others, 1953), nor where there is a considerable amount of dead or dying plant material present, nor where the sward has a naturally low pigment concentration.

Use of FN and FP with Grazing Animals

Feces samples. Samples are taken from collection bags after thorough mixing, from freshly voided feces pats on a sward, or from a limited number of rectal grab samples. With sward sampling, either all dung pats should be sampled or else a system used which selects a partial number *at random* (Raymond and Minson, 1955). Increases in accuracy fall off very rapidly after 15 to 20 sward or rectal samples are taken. Thus, whatever the length of the experimental period, whether 3, 7, 21, or more days, this basic number should be taken for each digestibility estimate. It can be obtained by intensively sampling a few animals or by taking a few samples from many animals; this depends on the objective. The random variability in FP concentration is greater than in FN, hence more samples should be taken for the former (Kennedy and others, 1959; Brisson, 1960). Variation between animals is relatively low (Kennedy and others, 1959).

There is little evidence of diurnal variations in FP concentration and, though not common for FN, they have been reported (Pigden and Brisson, 1955–59); diurnal variations are more common when low-quality forages are fed.

158

Storage and analysis of feces. Fecal samples for FP analyses may be held at ordinary refrigerator temperatures for approximately 1 week. For longer periods of storage, they can be frozen and held safely for several months. Extraction procedures have never been standardized, but the procedure of Brisson and Hatina (1957) appears ideal for routine use. It is better to work with fresh feces because drying may destroy some FP.

For FN analysis, samples may be refrigerated, as for FP, or stored under acid. Oven drying results in a loss of FN, and may cause a bias unless nitrogen values for both the regression equation and the field samples are obtained from heat-dried material.

Feces samples are usually ashed, and FN and FP concentrations expressed on an OM basis to reduce the effect of variable ash intake. A convenient reference value for FP is the optical density of 100 ml of 85 percent acetone when used to extract 1 g feces OM.

Establishing regression equations. A series of conventional digestibility trials should be carried out on fresh or frozen forages obtained from areas that are adjacent to those being grazed. A full range of digestibility trials, corresponding to various swards at different stages of maturity, should be undertaken and estimates made at about 7-day intervals. Periods shorter than 7 days are not recommended because they increase end-point digestibility errors, and longer periods are relatively insensitive to changes in sward digestibility. If refrigeration facilities are available, their use will eliminate daily cutting, as well as variations in daily DM intake which can cause errors when estimating digestibility. Heat drying should not be used because it depresses the digestibility of herbage nitrogen.

An equation based on the regression of OMD, or R on FP or FN (OM basis), is calculated. Where the plant material is extremely variable, it may be necessary to calculate several regressions limited to particular swards and times of year if a low SE of estimate is to be obtained. The SE must be calculated and *applied* when using the equation to estimate feed intake. The SE of estimates of R can be applied directly to estimate the feed intake error; the computation of those from digestibility coefficients is a more complicated procedure.

Information from sheep-feeding studies suggests that these data cannot be used to construct regressions for cattle with assurance. Sheep are generally more efficient than cattle at digesting herbages of high digestibility; the reverse is true when feeds of low digestibility are fed (Blaxter, Wainman, and Davidson, 1966).

Source and magnitude of error. Provided that adequate numbers of fecal samples have been taken, and if no biases such as diurnal cycles have been introduced, the SE of prediction is determined mainly by inherent differences in the plant material between and within swards. *Increasing the number of animals or fecal samples will not reduce this error.* The SE of OM digestibility estimates from FN for a large number of British swards has been quoted as ± 3.00 percent (Minson and

Kemp, 1961). The studies of Kennedy and others (1959) have provided a CV of 7.8 and 10.6 percent for FN and FP respectively for prediction of R. Errors for more limited equations (SE of ± 2.04 to 3.24 percent— Minson and Kemp, 1961) show how errors can be reduced by employing limited regressions. By using a single sward which was cut daily while it matured, Greenhalgh, Corbett, and McDonald (1960) found a SE for FN of only ± 1.00. However, regressions limited to a particular sward or time of year are unlikely to have a consistent SE of less than ± 2 units. Translated into terms of estimating feed intake, this will result in an error of approximately ± 8 percent when the digestibility of the feed is 75 percent.

An additional hazard when using this technique is the selection error. In theory, the fecal-index technique measures the digestibility of the selected forage. Though this is true for lucerne, Lambourne and Reardon (1962) have shown different regressions for leaves and stems of grasses, indicating that the leaf:stem ratio selected by an animal will influence the slope of the fecal-index:digestibility regression.

The SE of prediction is usually quoted in one of two ways—in terms of R or as percentage digestibility units from coefficients of digestibility. The R values equivalent to a given series of digestibility coefficients are:

% Digestibility	50	60	70	80
R (feed:feces ratio)	2.00	2.50	3.33	5.00

The SE of prediction of R is directly applicable to feed intake errors, but that from digestibility coefficients is not. For example, an error of ± 3 percent digestibility units will produce an error of about ± 12 percent in feed intake when the herbage digestibility is 75 percent. This is equal to a coefficient of variability of 12 percent for R. Thus, the variability in estimates of R between swards of different species and between successive cuts or grazings on the same sward is likely to be large. It would appear that errors of acceptable size are likely only where comparisons are made between different groups of animals on the same sward, or where utilization is so complete that selection seldom occurs; then the between-sward error would not exist. Moreover, in addition to the errors in determining R values, the errors involved in feces output estimates must be considered. Together they form the total error associated with estimates of feed intake.

Estimation of Fecal Excretion

Total collection method (Direct Method). In this technique the total feces dry matter excreted is collected in bags attached to the animal by means of a harness. After being mixed, preferably with a power mixer, the feces are sampled for DM determinations. Harness and collection bags suitable for beef and dairy cattle have been developed by Garrigus and Rusk (1935), and Balch, Bartlett and Johnson (1951) respectively.

For sheep, the leather harness described by the Commonwealth Agricultural Bureaux (C.A.B., 1961) represents a very satisfactory design, which can be lightened by substituting nylon for leather. Canvas webbing rots quickly. The rubber collection bags (C.A.B., 1961) keep their shape when the animal lies down, and very low losses occur— usually less than 1 percent. However, they are much more expensive than the locally made canvas bags used at the Animal Research Institute, Ottawa. For simplicity and minimum cost, the reader is advised to consult the design of Weston (1959). With canvas bags, waterproof polyethylene bag liners (4 ml) which eliminate washing can be used, and can serve as temporary containers for transport and storage of feces. A simple apparatus to deflect urine and collect feces from grazing ewes has been described (Owen and Ingleton, 1961). Bags are usually emptied twice daily for sheep and three to four times for cattle, otherwise the weight of the feces may pull the bags out of position and losses will occur.

The method is limited largely to intensive-type experiments where animals are readily accessible. Its main advantage over the indicator method is that all feces are collected (barring accidental losses), and no errors or assumptions about sampling techniques are involved.

Before any experiment, the animals must be trained to wear the harness and bags. This requires 1 to 3 weeks for inexperienced animals. If sheep are well trained, there is little reason to think harnesses and bags affect performance in small paddocks where ample herbage is available. Cattle may be affected (Meyer, Lofgreen, and Ittner, 1956) but, in trials at Ottawa, milk production of cows on pasture was not affected by bagging during short periods of about 1 week. Keeping harnesses and bags properly adjusted to prevent loss of feces is very important. Labor requirements may be quite high, but it is doubtful if the procedure is more laborious than that involving dosing with Cr_2O_3 and the subsequent sampling and analysis, as described below.

External indicators (Indirect Method). This is a ratio technique, based on the use of an indigestible inert chemical which is quantitatively administered to an animal at regular intervals and its fecal concentration measured. DM or OM excreted in feces is calculated as follows:

$$\text{Feces DM or OM} = \frac{\text{Quantity of indicator administered}}{\text{Concentration of indicator in feces DM or OM}}$$

The chromium sesquioxide (Cr_2O_3) technique depends on three factors: accurate measurement of the amount administered and of fecal concentrations; accurate sampling methods so that the samples represent the average Cr_2O_3 fecal concentration; quantitative recovery of Cr_2O_3.

Administration of Cr_2O_3. The industrial grade of Cr_2O_3 used for paints is a satisfactory indigestible tracer, if it is low in soluble material. The most convenient and reliable method of administering the oxide is in readily filled Scherer gelatin capsules* containing chromic oxide sus-

---

*Available from R. P. Scherer Ltd., 1370 Argyle St., Windsor, Ontario.

pended in soya bean oil (Raymond and Minson, 1955). These are available in 1 and 10 g sizes for sheep and cattle respectively.

Cr_2O_3-impregnated Kraft paper* is also available and should be administered in shredded form. It is less convenient than the Scherer capsules as each pellet does require preparation by the operator. It can be compressed into pellets (Troelsen, 1963), which can then be given by balling gun. It can also be rolled or inserted in gelatin capsules. The paper currently in use contains approximately 30 to 32 percent Cr_2O_3.

The number of times Cr_2O_3 is administered daily depends on several factors. In general, the more frequent the administration, the lower the variability in fecal Cr_2O_3 concentration and the fewer the feces samples that need to be taken. But twice daily dosing is regarded as the upper practical limit. When Cr_2O_3 is given in Scherer capsules and if time sampling is employed, it is highly desirable to dose twice daily. If sward sampling is employed, fewer dung pats need to be sampled when the oxide is given twice instead of once daily. Administration of the oxide in the shredded paper form instead of as Scherer capsules reduces variability of Cr_2O_3 in feces; hence, fewer samples need to be taken. Diurnal cycles are reduced but not eliminated.

Scherer capsules and shredded Cr_2O_3 paper, provided that the latter is compactly pelleted, can be readily administered with a balling gun to cattle in stanchions or in a squeeze; sheep are easily held by hand. The operator should hold one hand against the animal's throat so that the capsule can be felt going down the esophagus. Otherwise an animal may hold the pellet in its throat for a few moments, then regurgitate and discard it. Animals should be kept under close observation for about 15 minutes after dosing, as capsules or pellets are sometimes regurgitated and discarded before they disperse in the rumen.

The length of preliminary feeding period needed to allow Cr_2O_3 intake to equilibrate with output should be at least 7 days prior to fecal sampling. When using Scherer capsules with high-quality feeds, this may be reduced to 5 days, but for poor-quality forages it should be extended to 10 or more days. When Cr_2O_3-impregnated paper is used, these times should be extended by 1 to 2 days because of the slower initial rate of passage.

Analysis for Cr_2O_3. Two analytical methods that have been well tested are those of Christian and Coup (1954), and Brisson and Hatina (1956). Although Cr_2O_3 is generally considered very insoluble, a number of investigators have noted samples in which substantial amounts were soluble and digestible. Hence, each new lot of Cr_2O_3 should be tested before use.

Recovery of Cr_2O_3. If Cr_2O_3 has been fed for a sufficiently long preliminary period, the quantity excreted each day should be equal to the quantity fed. But there are day-to-day variations (coefficient of vari-

---

*Available from J. F. D. Greenhalgh, Rowett Research Institute, Bucksburn, Aberdeen, Scotland.

ability about 10%) in excretion rates, and for short collection periods of 10 or even more days, complete recovery of the tracer is uncommon.

The day-to-day variation is caused by both dietary and random factors. When animals graze a new sward the level of intake is high, the forage selected is low in fiber, and the rate of passage through the digestive tract increases. Hence fecal excretion of Cr_2O_3 in 24 hours will be equal to the residues of a hypothetical 24-hour period plus the additional residues flushed through because of the increased rate of passage. Intake declines as a sward is grazed down; the rate of passage of digesta decreases; and fecal production per 24-hour period is less than expected. Since the Cr_2O_3 fecal concentration is not directly affected by these changes in rate of passage, fecal excretion of Cr_2O_3 each 24 hours may be more than is fed for the first few days followed by an apparent under-recovery. It has been suggested that for short-term work, the Cr_2O_3 concentration provides a more realistic measure of the feces residues produced from a hypothetical 24-hour period of intake than can be achieved by total collection (Raymond and Minson, 1955). But in most experiments the intake would be estimated for a complete grazing cycle and not on a day-to-day basis.

If an investigator is careful and the analytical techniques are satisfactory, 95 to 100 percent of the Cr_2O_3 fed will be recovered in the feces, though some may be lost during grinding (Stevenson, 1962), or by absorption and excretion in the urine (Deinum, Immink, and Deijs, 1962); in a few experiments, and for unknown reasons, its recovery has been less than 90 percent. Because low recoveries occur on occasion, care must always be taken when interpreting data obtained by this technique.

Fecal sampling. Cr_2O_3 concentration in feces fluctuates markedly over a 24-hour period. The magnitude of the diurnal cycles depends on the level and frequency of feeding and the frequency of dosing with Cr_2O_3. Techniques for releasing Cr_2O_3 at a uniform rate in the reticulorumen reduce but do not eliminate the cyclic variations (Pigden and others, 1964). Thus, an investigator must always allow for these fluctuations and use a sampling technique that reduces bias. Two methods are available: sward sampling where most if not all of the feces pads are sampled (Raymond and Minson, 1955), and time sampling where the investigator strives to sample at an hour (or combination of hours) when feces contain the average 24-hour concentration of Cr_2O_3 (Hardison and Reid, 1953).

Sward sampling is less prone to bias than time sampling and is quite satisfactory where animal group estimates of fecal excretions are required. It makes no assumptions about the diurnal excretion pattern of Cr_2O_3 or its magnitude. Either Scherer capsules or Cr_2O_3 paper can be used. According to Cowlishaw and Alder (1963), measurement of a 10 percent difference between means ($P = 0.05$) for fecal output by cattle, each with a SE ± 0.2, would require 25 to 45 samples from dung pats using Cr_2O_3 paper but 60 to 100 samples for Scherer capsules.

163

Time sampling has the advantage of a much lower labor requirement where animals are handled twice daily for other reasons; for example, lactating cows. Samples can be taken rectally prior to or after milking, and the identification of feces from individual cows requires no special technique. However, there is a much greater opportunity for bias than with sward sampling because Cr_2O_3 diurnal excretion patterns are not constant, but shift on their axis with level of feed intake, timing of feed intake, and other factors. It is essential to sample twice daily, once when the fecal Cr_2O_3 concentration is above the average and again when it is below. This introduces a compensating effect and minimizes the serious errors caused by these shifts. The investigator using time sampling, therefore, needs to know the general shape and amplitude of the diurnal cycle he is dealing with and should use harnessed and bagged animals at intervals to check on his sampling pattern and to obtain data that can be used to correct any bias that may occur. Time sampling for grazing steers can be done when animals are corralled for twice-daily Cr_2O_3 administration, but labor requirements are high.

When fecal output estimates from individual animals are required, colored polystyrene particles* can be placed in gelatin capsules and administered when dosing with Cr_2O_3 (Minson and others, 1960). One 18-g dose per day has been satisfactory for cattle. Fecal dung pats are identified with the appropriate animal by smearing a sample of each defecation to expose the color of the polystyrene particles. If ten colors are employed and two colors used per animal, the feces from 45 individual animals can be identified. The same technique can be applied to sheep if the particles are ground finely prior to administration, but color identification for sheep in the field is more difficult than for cattle.

Compositing or bulking errors present certain hazards in time sampling. Animals with high feed intakes tend to excrete feces low in dry matter whereas the reverse is true for animals with low intakes. Compositing feces of several animals on an equal wet basis can cause a between-animal bias since more Cr_2O_3 is contributed by the low-intake animals. Such biases have been estimated to reach 10 to 18 percent (Lambourne, 1957). They can be reduced by compositing on a DM basis. However, when time sampling, within-animal bias can occur because of different DM content of forenoon and afternoon samples.

A correction can be applied if data from harnessed and bagged animals are available, as was noted under diurnal cycles. The most satisfactory method to avoid the introduction of any bias is sampling all the feces excreted on the sward.

CLIPPING TECHNIQUES TO MEASURE INTAKE

Early investigations of animal intake on pasture employed a number of clipping techniques. Where relatively long-term estimates of intake are

---

*Available from the General Chemical and Pharmaceutical Co. Ltd., Judex Works, Sudbury, Wembley, Middlesex, England.

required, it is necessary to protect specific areas from grazing to estimate plant growth effects. Numerous variations of this method have been developed and excellent discussions are available (Carter, 1962; Brown, 1954; C.A.B., 1961). This section will not deal with this aspect of clipping techniques, but only where intake estimates are required for very short-term periods (less than 72 hours), and where fecal index and bagged animal methods are unsuitable because of the lag between intake and mean excretion of indigestible residues, which may vary from about 24 hours on high-quality diets to several days for relatively indigestible herbages. Moreover, digestibility of grazed forage changes rapidly and daily feed intakes are variable.

Clipping can provide quantitative estimates of intake over short periods if certain conditions are met. The magnitude of the intake error is a combination of the plant growth factor and the accuracy of sampling. Intensity of utilization determines the plant growth error. Van der Kley (1956) has shown that this will be proportional to intensity of utilization on different grazing systems, as follows:

Grazing system	Cows/hectare	Plant growth error* kg DM/cow-day
Extensive	5	8–16
Rotational	20	2–4
Strip	80–120	0.3–1

The sampling error is determined by variability in growth of the sward and losses not recovered by clipping. Sward variability can be compensated for by increasing sample numbers. The clipping technique must allow cutting *below* grazing height and pick up most trampled material. Van der Kley (1956) recommends cutting a large number of areas of limited size with hand clippers, and increasing sample numbers as a sward is grazed down.

This technique fits well into a strip-grazing routine with the back fence moved daily or every second day to minimize growth errors on grazed areas. Plant growth errors will be higher on rotational systems, and more than a 3-day grazing period per paddock is not recommended. The method is best suited to intensive grazing systems on small areas.

This technique provides useful intake estimates over short periods with simple equipment. Disadvantages include the limited scope of the method and the fact that individual animal intakes cannot be obtained unless each animal is placed on a separate plot. Errors will vary with conditions, but careful investigators should be able to estimate intake within ±10 percent.

References

Alexander, R. H., and Mary McGowan. 1966. The routine determination of in vitro digestibility of organic matter in forages—An investigation of the problems associated with continuous large-scale operations. J. Brit. Grassl. Soc. 21:140–147.

*Based on an assumed growth rate of 40 to 80 kg DM/hectare per day.

Balch, C. C., S. Bartlett, and V. W. Johnson. 1951. Apparatus for the separate collection of faeces and urine from cows. J. Agr. Sci. 41:98–101.

Blaxter, K. L., F. W. Wainman, and J. L. Davidson. 1966. The voluntary intake of food by sheep and cattle in relation to their energy requirements for maintenance. Anim. Prod. 8:75–83.

Brisson, G. J. 1960. Indicator methods for estimating amount of forage consumed by grazing animals. Proc. 8th Int. Grassl. Congr. 8:435–438.

Brisson, G. J., and G. Hatina. 1956. On the routine determination of chromic oxide in feces. Can. J. Agr. Sci. 36:210–212.

Brisson, G. J., and G. Hatina. 1957. A method for the extraction of pigments (chromogens) from the feces of cattle and sheep. Can. J. Anim. Sci. 37: 136–142.

Brown, D. 1954. Methods of surveying and measuring vegetation. Commonw. Bur. of Pastures and Field Crops, Bull. 42, Farnham Royal, Bucks., England. 223 p.

C.A.B. (Commonwealth Agr. Bur.). 1961. Research techniques in use at the Grassl. Res. Inst., Hurley, Berks. Bull. 45.

Carter, J. F. 1962. Herbage sampling for yield: Tame pastures, p. 90–101. In Pasture and range research techniques. Comstock Publishing Associates, Ithaca, N.Y.

Christian, K. R., and M. R. Coup. 1954. Measurement of feed intake by grazing cattle and sheep. 6. The determination of chromic oxide in feces. New Zeal. J. Sci. Technol. 36:328–330.

Cook, C. W., and L. E. Harris. 1951. A comparison of the lignin ratio method and the chromogen method of determining digestibility and forage consumption of desert range plants by sheep. J. Anim. Sci. 10:565–573.

Corbett, J. L. 1960. Fecal-index techniques for estimating herbage consumption by grazing animals. Proc. 8th Int. Grassl. Congr. 8:438–442.

Cowlishaw, S. J., and F. E. Alder. 1963. A comparative study of paper and oil as carriers of chromium sesquioxide administered to grazing steers to determine their fecal output. J. Brit. Grassl. Soc. 18:328–333.

Deinum, B., H. J. Immink, and W. B. Deijs. 1962. The excretion of chromium sesquioxide by cows after administration of Cr_2O_3-containing paper, p. 123–129. Jaarb. Inst. Biol. Schleik. Onderz. Land., Wageningen.

Forbes, R. M. 1950. Protein as an indicator of pasture forage digestibility. J. Anim. Sci. 9:231–237.

Forbes, R. M., and W. P. Garrigus. 1950. Some effects of forage composition on its nutritive value when cut and fed green to steers and wethers, as determined conventionally and by lignin ratio. J. Anim. Sci. 9:531–539.

Garrigus, W. P., and H. P. Rusk. 1935. The consumption of reed canary and brome grasses by grazing steers. Proc. Amer. Soc. Anim. Prod. 75–82.

Greenhalgh, J. F. D., J. L. Corbett, and I. McDonald. 1960. The indirect estimation of digestibility of pasture herbage II. Regressions of digestibility on faecal nitrogen concentration; their determination in continuous digestibility trials and the effect of various factors on their accuracy. J. Agr. Sci. 55: 377–386.

Hardison, W. A., and J. T. Reid. 1953. Use of indicators in the measurement of the dry matter intake of grazing animals. J. Nutr. 51:35–52.

Hardison, W. A., J. T. Reid, C. M. Martin, and P. C. Woolfolk. 1954. Degree of herbage selection by grazing cattle. J. Dairy Sci. 37:89–102.

Heady, H. F., and D. T. Torell. 1959. Forage preference exhibited by sheep with esophageal fistulas. J. Range Manage. 12:28–34.

Homb, T., and K. Breirem. 1952. The use of fecal nitrogen as a measure of dry matter intake and digestibility of organic matter in forage. J. Anim. Sci. 11:496–500.

Irwin, H. M., H. G. Wiseman, J. C. Shaw, and L. A. Moore. 1953. The role of plant pigments in digestion trial studies. J. Anim. Sci. 12:541–551.

Jones, L. H. P., and K. A. Handreck. 1965. The relation between the silica content of the diet and the excretion of silica by sheep. J. Agr. Sci. 65:129–134.

Kennedy, W. K., and R. J. Lancaster. 1957. Comparison of fecal pigments and fecal nitrogen for the estimation of feed-to-feces ratio of pasture-fed cattle. Proc. New Zeal. Soc. Anim. Prod. 17:56–62.

Kennedy, W. K., A. H. Carter, and R. J. Lancaster. 1959. Comparison of fecal pigments and fecal nitrogen as digestibility indicators in grazing cattle studies. New Zeal. J. Agr. Res. 2:627.

Lambourne, L. J. 1957. Measurement of feed intake of grazing sheep. II. The estimation of feces output using markers. J. Agr. Sci. 48:415–425.

Lambourne, L. J., and T. F. Reardon. 1962. Use of 'seasonal' regressions in measuring feed intake of grazing animals. Nature (London) 196:961–962.

Lancaster, R. J. 1947. The nutritional status of some N.Z. pastures. Proc. 7th Ann. Conf. New Zeal. Soc. Anim. Prod. p. 125–126.

Lancaster, R. J. 1949a. Estimation of digestibility of grazed pasture from faeces nitrogen. Nature (London) 163:330–331.

Lancaster, R. J. 1949b. The measurement of feed intake by grazing cattle and sheep. I. A method of calculating the digestibility of pasture based on the nitrogen content of faeces derived from pasture. New Zeal. J. Sci. Technol. 25A:31–38.

Lancaster, R. J., and M. P. Bartrum. 1954. Measurement of feed intake by grazing cattle and sheep. IV. A source of error in the chromogen technique for estimating the digestibility of fodders. New Zeal. J. Sci. Technol. 35A:489–496.

Lesperance, A. L., E. H. Jensen, V. R. Bohman, and R. A. Madsen. 1960a. Measuring selective grazing with fistulated steers. J. Dairy. Sci. 43:1615–1622.

Lesperance, A. L., V. R. Bohman, and D. W. Marble. 1960b. Development of techniques for evaluating grazing forage. J. Dairy. Sci. 43:682–689.

McManus, W. R. 1962. Studies on the relationship of saliva to rumen function of sheep on low feed intakes. Austral. J. Agr. Res. 13:907–923.

Meyer, J. H., G. F. Lofgreen, and N. R. Ittner. 1956. Further studies on the utilization of alfalfa by beef steers. J. Anim. Sci. 15:64–75.

Milford, R. 1957. The value of fecal nitrogen and feed crude fibre in estimating intake of four sub-tropical plant species. Austral. J. Agr. Res. 8:359–370.

Minson, D. J. 1958. The errors involved in the measurement of herbage consumption using indicator techniques. Ph.D. Thesis, Univ. Reading, England.

Minson, D. J., W. F. Raymond, and C. E. Harris. 1960. Studies in the digestibility of herbage. VIII. The digestibility of S37 cocksfoot, S23 ryegrass and S24 ryegrass. J. Brit. Grassl. Soc. 15:174–180.

Minson, D. J., and C. D. Kemp. 1961. Studies in the digestibility of herbage. IX. Herbage and fecal nitrogen as indicators of herbage organic matter digestibility. J. Brit. Grassl. Soc. 16:76–79.

Minson, D. J., J. C. Taylor, F. E. Alder, J. F. Raymond, W. E. Rudman, C. Line, and M. J. Head. 1960. A method for identifying the feces produced by individual cattle or groups of cattle grazing together. J. Brit. Grassl. Soc. 15:86–88.

Owen, J. B., and Jean W. Ingleton. 1961. A method of collecting feces from ewes. Anim. Prod. 3:63–64.

Pigden, W. J., and G. J. Brisson. 1955–59. Relationships between organic matter digestibility coefficients derived conventionally and from feces nitrogen for forages fed to sheep. Anim. Poult. Sci. Div., Exp. Farms Service, Can. Dep. Agr.

Pigden, W. J., K. A. Winter, G. J. Brisson, and G. I. Pritchard. 1964. Diurnal excretion of Cr_2O_3 by ruminants when administered in sustained-release pellets. Can. J. Anim. Sci. 44:207–214.

Pritchard, G. I., L. P. Folkins, and W. J. Pigden. 1963. The in vitro digestibility of whole grasses and their parts at progressive stages of maturity. Can. J. Plant Sci. 43:79–87.

Raymond, W. F. 1954. Studies in the digestibility of herbage. III. The use of faecal collection and chemical analysis in pasture studies: (a) Ratio and tracer methods. J. Brit. Grassl. Soc. 9:61–67.

Raymond, W. F., C. E. Harris, and C. D. Kemp. 1954. Studies in the digestibility of herbage. V. The variation, with age, of the ability of sheep to digest herbage, with observations on the effect of season on digestive ability. J. Brit. Grassl. Soc. 9:209–220.

Raymond, W. F., C. D. Kemp, A. W. Kemp, and C. E. Harris. 1954. Studies in the digestibility of herbage. IV. The use of faecal collection and chemical analysis in pasture studies: (b) Faecal index methods. J. Brit. Grassl. Soc. 9:69–82.

Raymond, W. F., and D. J. Minson. 1955. The use of chromic oxide for estimating the faecal production of grazing animals. J. Brit. Grassl. Soc. 10:282–296.

Raymond, W. F., D. J. Minson, and C. E. Harris. 1956. The effect of management on herbage consumption and selective grazing. Proc. 7th Int. Grassl. Congr. 123–133.

Reid, J. T., P. G. Woolfolk, C. R. Richards, R. W. Kaufmann, J. K. Loosli, K. L. Turk, J. I. Miller, and R. E. Blaser. 1950. A new indicator method for the determination of digestibility and consumption of forages by ruminants. J. Dairy Sci. 33:60–71.

Reid, J. T., P. G. Woolfolk, W. A. Hardison, C. M. Martin, A. L. Brundlage, and R. W. Kaufman. 1952. A procedure for measuring the digestibility of pasture forage under grazing conditions. J. Nutr. 46:255–269.

Richards, C. R., and J. T. Reid. 1952. The use of methoxyl groups in forage and fecal materials as an index of the feeding value of forages. J. Dairy Sci. 35: 595–602.

Saltonstall, L. 1948. The measurement of the quantity and quality of the herbage consumed by sheep. M.Sc. Thesis, Cornell Univ., Ithaca, N.Y.

Smart, W. G. Jr., F. W. Sherwood, G. Matrone, and G. H. Wise. 1953. Digestibility of forages: Pigments involved in the chromogen(s) ratio method. J. Agr. Food Chem. 1:318–321.

Squibb, R. L., C. Rivera, and Roberto Jarquin. 1958. Comparison of chromogen method with standard digestion trial for determination of the digestible nutrient content of kikuyu grass and ramie forages for sheep. J. Anim. Sci. 17: 318–321.

Stevenson, Audrey E. 1962. Measurement of feed intake by grazing cattle and sheep. 8. Some observations on the accuracy of the chromic oxide technique for the estimation of faeces output of dairy cattle. New Zeal. J. Agr. Res. 5:339–345.

Taylor, J. C., and R. E. Deriaz. 1963. The use of rumen-fistulated steers in the direct determination of nutritive value of ingested herbage in grazing experiments. J. Brit. Grassl. Soc. 18:29–38.

Terry, R. A., and J. M. A. Tilley. 1964. The digestibility of the leaves and stems of perennial ryegrass, cocksfoot, timothy, tall fescue, lucerne and sanfoin, as measured by an in vitro procedure. J. Brit. Grassl. Soc. 19:363–372.

Torell, D. T. 1954. An esophageal fistula for animal nutrition studies. J. Anim. Sci. 13:878–884.

Troelsen, J. E. 1961. Plant chromogens as an indicator in estimating the digestibility of forage crops by sheep. Can. J. Plant Sci. 41:732–739.

Troelsen, J. E. 1963. Note on chromic oxide paper pellets for administration to ruminants. Can. J. Anim. Sci. 43:389–390.

Van der Kley, F. K. 1956. A simple method for the accurate estimation of daily variation in the quality and quantity of herbage consumed by rotationally grazed cattle and sheep. Netherlands J. Agr. Sci. 4:197–204.

Van Dyne, G. M., and D. T. Torell. 1964. Development and use of the esophageal fistula: A review. J. Range Manage. 17:7–19.

Weston, R. H. 1959. The efficiency of wool production of grazing Merino sheep. Austral. J. Agr. Res. 10:865–885.

168

Chapter 19

HOW TO INSERT STOMACH TUBES AND FISTULAS*

G. IAN PRITCHARD†

Animal Research Institute, Canada Department of Agriculture
Ottawa, Ontario

A fistula provides a method for sampling ingesta at specific points in the alimentary tract of an animal. Its insertion is a simple operation, though great care is needed to prevent leakage and ulceration, which may result from poorly fitted cannulas. To calculate digestion rates and production of intermediate compounds, or to remove inoculum for in vitro fermentations, samples are taken by one of two methods: by inserting a tube through the esophagus or by installing a fistula at a selected site. These methods vary widely; examples of only the more useful are given here.

STOMACH TUBE

Fluid ingesta can be aspirated from the rumen through a rubber tube inserted through the mouth and esophagus. Smooth, thick-walled tubing, of less than ⅝ inch outside diameter is used for sheep; and of 1¼ inches outside diameter for cattle.‡ This method is usually preferred when growth and carcass data are required simultaneously, but it takes longer than collecting samples through fistulas. Caution must be exercised to prevent an animal from biting the tube, and to avoid its entry into the trachea. Listen at the open end of the tube to make sure it is not in the trachea. Blockage of the tube with solid materials can be avoided by perforating the sides of the tube near the distal end, or by using a suction strainer (Raun and Burroughs, 1962). There are disadvantages to inserting a tube in this way: the operator does not know from which part of the rumen a sample is collected, nor whether the end of the tube will be at the same location in successive collections.

For cattle, a more convenient procedure that avoids these difficulties is to insert a special metal probang, ⅞ inch in outside diameter and 6 feet long,§ through the esophageal route. The small end is wrapped with latex rubber. It is this small end that is inserted, rather than the cup end, which is normally used for repelling foreign bodies. Once the probang is in place, a rubber or plastic tube is inserted through the

---
*Contribution No. 278, Animal Research Institute.
†Present address: Fisheries Research Board, Ottawa, Ontario.
‡Laboratory tubing is adequate, though tubes prepared specially for this purpose and aspirator pumps are available from most veterinary supply houses.
§Available from veterinary supply houses.

probang and samples of rumen ingesta are aspirated. This system has several advantages over conventional stomach tubes: the operation is faster, the tubes are not damaged by an animal's teeth, and the probang penetrates the feed mass midway in the dorsal sac to collect samples from a uniform position.

ESOPHAGEAL FISTULAS

Esophageal fistulas provide a means of distinguishing between the quality of herbage when it is growing in a pasture and herbage actually consumed by animals (Edlefsen, Cook, and Blake, 1960; Weir, Meyer, and Lofgreen, 1959; Weir and Torell, 1959; Van Dyne and Torell, 1964). Esophageal fistulas are not easy to install, proper healing and leakage being the chief problems. Nevertheless, they have been installed successfully in calves (Chapman and Hamilton, 1962), dairy cows (Rusoff and Foote, 1961), yearling steers (Lesperance, Bohman, and Marble, 1960; Lesperance and others, 1960), and sheep (Torell, 1954; Cook and others, 1958; Cook, Mattox, and Harris, 1961; McManus, Arnold, and Hamilton, 1962; Bath, Weir, and Torell, 1956). The method described here is patterned after that of Chapman (personal communication, 1963).

To prevent regurgitation, animals should be starved for 36 hours before the operation, and then placed under deep anesthesia (intravenous sodium pentobarbitol or equivalent). Nasotracheal intubation will ensure unobstructed breathing. A needle is inserted through the abdominal wall into the rumen to release gas, and a plastic tube with the end cut at 45 degrees is passed into the esophagus to serve as a location aid.

The initial incision is made on the top of the convexity formed by the trachea when the animal is lying on its side. The anterior end of the incision should be at least 5 cm from the larynx in sheep or 10 cm in cattle. This location is preferable to the jugular groove because it avoids incision of muscle lateral to the jugular vein and makes collection more convenient. If the incision is made at the midline, pressure from the trachea will impede extrusion from the fistula. Access to the esophagus is gained by blunt dissection between the trachea and thyroid on one side and the brachio-cephalic muscle on the other. The esophagus is easily located and extruded with the sloped end of the stomach tube until the surface is parallel to the skin. A clean stab incision is made into the lumen of the esophagus, and the mucosa and tunica are grasped with Allis clamps. Only large spurting blood vessels need be ligated. The stomach tube can then be drawn back, the incision enlarged to fit the size of fistula to be used, and the esophageal wall attached to the skin with interrupted sutures. The ends of the esophageal incision can be sutured if the orifice is too large. Antibiotic treatment should be applied locally at the time of the operation and systemically thereafter.

The fistula can be closed with a suitable stoppering device. Split-plug stoppers, as described by Hamilton, McManus, and Larsen (1960), McManus and others (1962), and Chapman and Hamilton (1962), are satisfactory. They can be bought,* or they can be cut in different sizes with a small emery wheel from blocks of surgical rubber. Once inserted, they are held in place with a flat ring about 3 inches in diameter *followed* by an elastic band. The split-plug stopper, by itself and installed in a calf, is shown below. These plugs are better than the permanent cannulas of Rusoff and Foote (1961), and of Cook and others (1958), as they can be installed at any time and are less liable to break. Leakage is less with this method than with the rigid-wire method of Torell (1954) or the molded latex plug of McManus (1962).

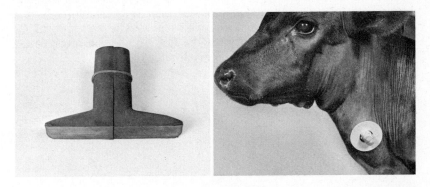

Left: Split-plug stopper for esophageal fistulas. *Right:* Esophageal fistula with split-plug stopper installed in a calf.

Any sign of ulceration around the fistula requires prompt attention. If excess infection occurs, it is usually desirable to sacrifice the animal and fistulate another. Sufficient time must be allowed for healing (often 2 to 3 months) before pasture sampling is attempted.

Herbage is collected by suspending a canvas or plastic bag tied around the neck and to a girth cord. Samples, adequate in size for most analyses, can usually be obtained from grazing animals within 30 minutes. Saliva contamination increases the ash content of these samples (Bath and others, 1956; McManus, 1961) but other constituents collected in this manner represent those eaten. Lesperance and others (1960) warn that with very fibrous hay, it is possible for the more fibrous part of the bolus to continue down the esophagus while the less fibrous parts are collected.

*Available from McAliece Industrial Rubber Co. Ltd., 49 St. Francis St., Melbourne C1, Australia.

RUMEN FISTULAS

Rumen fistulas are used extensively in pasture research. They are fairly easy to install and can be kept in place for months or years without causing discomfort.

The surgical process outlined here is based on the procedure of Schalk and Amadon (1928), as modified by Jarrett (1948) and Dougherty (1955). It is suitable for all types of ruminants and, once the fistula is established, it allows for cannulas to be removed or replaced at any time. It is better than single-stage techniques (Dougherty, 1955; Michael and McKinley, 1954; Ash, 1957; Schnautz, 1957) because the ingesta are contaminated less during the operation and peritonitis is less likely to occur.

The operation is done in two stages: the first produces an adhesion between the rumen and abdominal wall, and the second removes a section of rumen tissue for inserting the cannula. The conventional site is on the left side, midway between the last rib and the tuber coxae, where the rumen is close to the abdominal wall.

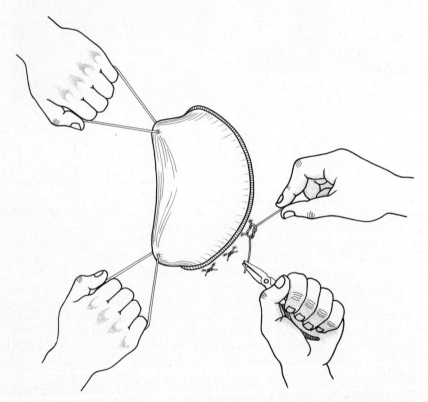

Rumen pouch being held out through incision, and sutures being placed through skin and rumen wall.

An animal need not be starved before the operation. Enough tranquilizer (acepromazine malate or equivalent) is injected intravenously to restrain the animal but to leave it standing. The operation site is clipped and shaved, then washed with a low-toxicity germicide before being anesthetized with procaine. The site needs to be high enough to prevent large losses of fluid ingesta. A vertical incision is made through the skin, the length of the incision determining the size of the fistula. Abdominal muscles are then separated with minimal surgery, the peritoneum incised, and the rumen exposed. A pouch of the rumen is pulled through the incision, two pieces of umbilical tape having been attached for handholds. The skin is then sutured to the rumen wall with interrupted sutures (No. 2 plasticized nylon), starting at the ventral end of the incision. Muscles of the abdominal wall are not included in the sutures. Care should be taken to keep the needle from puncturing the rumen wall and to prevent folds between sutures. The sutures are removed after 6 to 8 days.

Some variation in the procedure is possible at this stage. Balch and Cowie (1962), and Schalk and Amadon (1928) suggest leaving a wide clamp attached to the rumen wall; when sloughed off this leaves a direct opening into the rumen. Jarrett (1948) describes how to invert the rumen fold and suture the skin along the line of incision, so that the next stage of the operation may be performed at any time between 15 days and several months later. The third procedure, which is usually preferred, is to cover the operation area with a sterile bandage for 6 to 8 days, and then remove a plug of rumen tissue by cutting about ⅛ inch from the skin. When the fistula is finished, the cannula may be installed immediately or a temporary plug used until healing is complete (Balch and Cowie, 1962).

The advantages and disadvantages of various cannulus, stoppers, and pneumatic plugs have been discussed by Mendel (1961). The two-piece pneumatic plug,* described by Balch and Johnson (1948), and Balch and Cowie (1962), and shown below, has proved very satisfactory under most conditions. Small, molded rubber cannulus, also shown below, patterned after the design by Jarrett (1948), are suitable for sheep, goats, or calves.† A wide variety of cannula designs and their manufacturing details are available (Mendel, 1961; Watts, 1948; Hentschl, Berry, and Huffman, 1954; Johnson and Prescott, 1959; Yarns and Putman, 1962; Stoddard and others, 1951; Komarek and Leffel, 1961; Harrison, 1961; Dougherty, 1955; Nichols, 1954).

Cannulas need to be kept clean and in good repair. If the area around a cannula shows any sign of irritation, the spot should be washed with sterile saline solution and dusted with antibiotic powder.

Ingesta are sampled readily through a cannula with cap or bung removed. If the fistula is large, a hand may be placed directly into the

---

*Available from the Avon India Rubber Co., Melksham, Wilts.
†Available from the S.A. Rubber Mills Ltd., 672 South Road, Edwardston, South Australia.

Left: A two-piece pneumatic plug (Balch and Cowie, 1961) that has been in use for about one year. *Right:* Molded rubber cannula and bung of the Jarrett (1948) type.

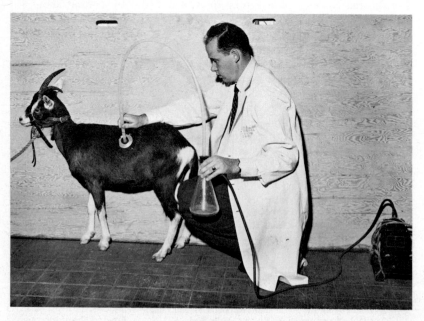

Aspirating ingesta from a goat fitted with a rumen fistula.

rumen and the ingesta removed, but when smaller fistulas are used contents must be aspirated through a tube (*see* page 174). Thus, large fistulas are necessary when large particles of ingesta are required or when samples must be collected from specific locations within the rumen. Taylor and Deriaz (1963) have expanded these procedures by describing the collection of boluses as they reach the cardia.

ABOMASAL AND INTESTINAL FISTULAS

To obtain samples of ingesta in different parts of the tract posterior to the rumen, transintestinal intubation similar to that described by Blankenhorn, Hirsh, and Ahrens (1955) for humans (except that the tube must be inserted through a rumen fistula) is not satisfactory because tubes get tangled, and the back flow of ingesta through the abomasum and omasum makes insertion difficult. It is preferable to install fistulas in the abomasum (Jarrett, 1948), or intestine (Doughtery, 1955). Surgical techniques for installing a variety of these fistulas in ruminants are detailed by Markowitz and others (1954).

References

Ash, R. W. 1957. A large-diameter rumen cannula for sheep. J. Physiol. 139: 6 p.
Balch, C. C., and V. W. Johnson. 1948. A pneumatic cannula and bung for rumen fistulas in cattle. Vet. Rec. 60:446.
Balch, C. C., and A. T. Cowie. 1962. Permanent rumen fistulae in cattle. Cornell Vet. 52:206–214.
Bath, D. L., W. C. Weir, and D. T. Torell. 1956. The use of the esophageal fistula for the determination of consumption and digestibility of pasture forage by sheep. J. Anim. Sci. 15:1166–1171.
Blankenhorn, David H., Jules Hirsch, and Edward H. Ahrens, Jr. 1955. Transintestinal intubation: Technic for measurement of gut length and physiologic sampling of known loci. Proc. Soc. Exp. Biol. Med. 88:356–362.
Chapman, H. W., and F. J. Hamilton. 1962. Oesophageal fistulation of calves. Austral. Vet. J. 38:400.
Cook, C. W., J. L. Thorne, J. T. Blake, and J. Edlefsen. 1958. Use of an esophageal-fistula cannula for collecting forage samples by grazing sheep. J. Anim. Sci. 17:189–193.
Cook, C. W., J. E. Mattox, and L. E. Harris. 1961. Comparative daily consumption and digestibility of summer range forage by wet and dry ewes. J. Anim. Sci. 20:866–870.
Dougherty, R. W. 1955. Permanent stomach and intestinal fistulas in ruminants; some modifications and simplifications. Cornell Vet. 45:331–357.
Edlefsen, J. L., C. W. Cook, and J. T. Blake. 1960. Nutrient content of the diet as determined by hand-plucked and esophageal fistula samples. J. Anim. Sci. 19:560–567.
Hamilton, F. J., W. R. McManus, and L. H. Larsen. 1960. An improved method of oesophageal fistulation for food intake studies in the sheep. Austral. Vet. J. 36:111–112.
Harrison, F. A. 1961. A modified rumen cannula for cattle. Vet. Rec. 73:942.
Hentschl, A. F., R. N. Berry, and C. F. Huffman. A plastic plug for use in the bovine rumen fistula. Mich. State Coll. Vet. 14:77.

Jarrett, I. G. 1948. The production of rumen and abomasal fistulae in sheep. J. Council Sci. Ind. Res. 21:311–317.

Johnson, C. E., and J. M. Prescott. 1959. A pneumatic plug for rumen fistulas. J. Anim. Sci. 18:830–835.

Komarek, R. J., and E. C. Leffel. 1961. Gas-tight cannula for rumen fistula. J. Anim. Sci. 20:782–784.

Lesperance, A. L., V. R. Bohman, and D. W. Marble. 1960. The development of techniques for evaluating grazed forage. J. Dairy Sci. 43:682–689.

Lesperance, A. L., E. H. Jensen, V. R. Bohman, and R. A. Madsen. 1960. Measuring selective grazing with fistulated steers. J. Dairy Sci. 43:1615–1622.

Markowitz, J. 1954. In collaboration with J. Archibald and H. G. Downie. Experimental surgery, including surgical physiology. 3rd ed. Williams and Wilkins, Baltimore, Md.

McManus, W. R. 1961. Properties of roughage feedstuffs collected from oesophageal fistulas. Austral. J. Exp. Agr. 1:159–163.

McManus, W. R. 1962. Oesophageal fistulation studies in the sheep. Austral. Vet. J. 38:85–91.

McManus, W. R., G. W. Arnold, and F. J. Hamilton. 1962. Improved techniques in oesophageal fistulation of sheep. Austral. Vet. J. 38:275–281.

Mendel, V. E. 1961. Pneumatic and semipneumatic plugs for large-diameter rumen fistulas in cattle. J. Dairy Sci. 44:679–686.

Michael, S. J., and R. E. McKinley. 1954. Rumenatomy simplified. J. Amer. Vet. Med. Ass. 124:26–27.

Nichols, R. E. 1954. An inflatable plug for small rumen fistulas. Amer. J. Vet. Res. 15:246.

Raun, N. S., and W. Burroughs. 1962. Suction strainer technique in obtaining rumen fluid samples from intact lambs. J. Anim. Sci. 21:454–457.

Rusoff, L. L., and L. E. Foote. 1961. A stainless steel esophageal-fistula cannula for dairy cattle nutrition studies. J. Dairy. Sci. 44:1549–1550.

Schalk, A. F., and R. S. Amadon. 1928. Physiology of the ruminant stomach (bovine). N. Dak. Agr. Exp. Sta. Bull. 216.

Schnautz, J. C. 1957. A rumen fistula modification. Amer. J. Vet. Res. 66:73–75.

Stoddard, G. E., N. N. Allen, W. H. Hale, A. L. Pope, D. K. Sorensen, and W. R. Winchester. 1951. A permanent rumen fistula cannula for cows and sheep. J. Anim. Sci. 10:417–423.

Taylor, J. C., and R. E. Deriaz. 1963. The use of rumen-fistulated steers in the direct determination of nutritive value of ingested herbage in grazing experiments. J. Brit. Grassl. Soc. 18:29–38.

Torell, D. T. 1954. An esophageal fistula for animal nutrition studies. J. Anim. Sci. 13:878–884.

Van Dyne, George M., and D. T. Torell. 1964. Development and use of the esophageal fistula: A review. J. Range Manage. 17:7–19.

Watts, P. S. 1948. Metal plug for permanent rumen fistula in bovines. Vet. Rec. 60:4.

Weir, W. C., and D. T. Torell. 1959. Selective grazing by sheep as shown by a comparison of the chemical composition of range and pasture forage obtained by hand clipping and that collected by esophageal-fistulated sheep. J. Anim. Sci. 18:641–649.

Weir, W. C., J. H. Meyer, and G. P. Lofgreen. 1959. Symposium on forage evaluation: The use of esophageal fistula, lignin, and chromogen techniques for studying selective grazing and digestibility of range and pasture by sheep and cattle. Agron. J. 51:235–237.

Yarns, D. A., and P. A. Putnam. 1962. An economical rumen cannula. J. Anim. Sci. 21:744–745.

Chapter 20

MICROBIOLOGICAL TECHNIQUES OF IN VITRO AND IN VIVO FERMENTATION*

G. IAN PRITCHARD†
Animal Research Institute, Canada Department of Agriculture
Ottawa, Ontario

J. EBBE TROELSEN
Research Station, Canada Department of Agriculture
Swift Current, Saskatchewan

Two microbiological techniques are being used to evaluate herbage quality. They give estimates of the rate of digestion and the total digestibility of a herbage. The first is an in vitro fermentation in which herbage is digested by microorganisms removed from a rumen (Pigden and Bell, 1955; Hershberger and others, 1959; Quicke and others, 1959; Donefer, Crampton, and Lloyd, 1960; Sheldon and Reid, 1960; Baumgardt, Cason, and Taylor, 1962; Tilley and Terry, 1963; Pritchard, Folkins, and Pigden, 1963). In the second, an in vivo fermentation, permeable sacs containing herbage are suspended in the rumens of fistulated animals (McAnnally, 1942; Pigden and others, 1961; Van Dyne, 1962; Hopson, Johnson, and Dehority, 1963). Both techniques have been used successfully under quite different conditions. Their value has been shown by their accuracy in estimating the nutritional value of herbages and in predicting the response of livestock to a herbage. Because several herbage samples can be tested at one time and because only very small samples are required, these techniques are less time-consuming and expensive than conventional digestibility trials.

IN VITRO FERMENTATIONS

The essential components of an in vitro fermentation are the medium, the substrate, and the inoculum. Temperature, pH, and atmospheric conditions must be controlled. A batch system is commonly used when herbages are being fermented, though continuous fermentation systems have been described (Stewart and Warner, 1959). The system chosen determines the type of fermentation vessel, the fermentation time, and the component of the herbage to be measured. Centrifuge tubes, equipped with stoppers that permit the release of gas, are satisfactory incubation vessels (Quicke and others, 1959; Tilley and Terry, 1963).

---

*Contribution No. 279, Animal Research Institute.
†Present address: Fisheries Research Board, Ottawa, Ontario.

It is not necessary to remove the end products of fermentation, as their cumulative levels do not deter microbial activity (Johnson, Dehority, and Bentley, 1958).

Substrate

The substrate accounts for 1 to 3 percent of the fermentation mix. Most herbages are satisfactory substrates when they are prepared properly. Dried, medium-ground (20-mesh) material permits ease of sampling, and exposes a large surface of tissue for microorganisms to attack. Extra-fine grinding should be avoided as it influences rate of digestion (Dehority and Johnson, 1961).

Buffers

Buffers are based on the composition of saliva (McDougall, 1948). When a crude or strained inoculum is used, no additive is necessary. However, if nutritional factors that occur naturally in rumen fluid are removed during purification of the inoculum, they must be added to the buffer. Common additives are glucose, biotin, valeric acid, para-amino-benzoic acid, urea, casein, iron, and calcium (Quicke and others, 1959; Donefer and others, 1960). A buffer is set at a pH of 6.9 or 7 after saturation with carbon dioxide.

Inoculum

The inoculum is the most critical component of the fermentation mix, and care must be taken to prevent chilling, aeration, and contamination after the ingesta is taken from the rumen. The ingesta collected should contain a considerable amount of fibrous material because the microorganisms are concentrated on it.

Donor animals are usually fistulated, though ingesta can be obtained through a stomach tube. Cattle are the most useful donors, because the larger the fistula the easier it is to aspirate the ingesta from the rumen. The ingesta of sheep and goats are equally useful, but often more difficult to obtain. If an aspirator is not available, sheep and goats can be placed on their backs, the fistula plugs removed, and the ingesta caught in a thermos as it flows from the rumen, as illustrated.

Crude inoculum can be prepared by straining ingesta through six to eight layers of cheesecloth. This procedure removes the coarser material in the ingesta, but provides a strong inoculum that ensures active fermentation. Johnson and others (1958), and Donefer and others (1960) have described techniques to purify crude inoculum, but these are time-consuming processes. For most analyses, crude inoculum suffices.

178

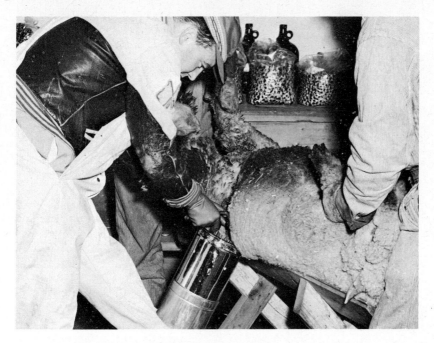
Removing fluid from the rumen of a wether.

There are a few precautions that minimize variations in the inoculum from one collection to the next. These include:

- Compositing the ingesta from two or more donors
- Collecting the ingesta at a set time each day, and at least 12 hours after the last feeding and watering
- Feeding a uniform ration of medium-quality grass or grass–legume hay as a basic diet (Barnett and Reid, 1961; Quicke and others, 1959)
- Using a preheated thermos to collect the ingesta. A gallon of ingesta will produce enough crude inoculum to inoculate 100 or more 50-ml or cc tubes
- Minimizing the time between collection and inoculation to reduce aeration and chilling.

Incubation

Fermentation mixes are kept under temperature and atmospheric conditions comparable to those in a rumen. Temperature is maintained at 39 to 40 C by placing the vessels in a water bath or an incubator. Anaerobic conditions are maintained by the use of CO_2 in either continuous- or self-gassing systems. Continuous-gassing systems require a manifold with enough valves to regulate the flow of CO_2 through each tube. When self-gassing systems are used, the tubes are flushed with

179

A continuous-gassing in vitro system, showing manifold (upper right) and water bath

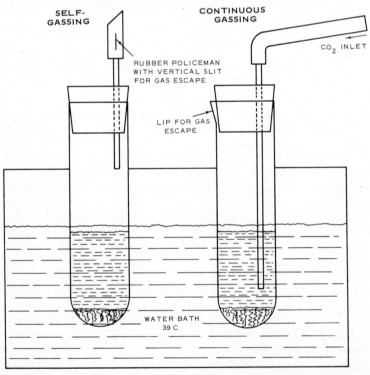

SELF-GASSING

CONTINUOUS GASSING

CO_2 INLET

RUBBER POLICEMAN WITH VERTICAL SLIT FOR GAS ESCAPE

LIP FOR GAS ESCAPE

WATER BATH 39 C

Self-gassing and continuous-gassing rumens for in vitro fermentation.

CO₂ before capping; they depend on the subsequent fermentation to exclude oxygen. A gas release device is required.

Incubation may continue for 3 to 96 hours. The length of time depends on the system employed, and what component of the herbage is being used as an index of the extent of digestion. The shorter incubation periods are used mainly to estimate fermentation rates; the longer periods to estimate total digestion. Fermentation is stopped by deproteinization or by bacterial inhibitors.

Different components of herbages have been used to estimate both the rate and the extent of digestion. These include cellulose, other carbohydrates, dry matter, organic matter, and energy. The end products of fermentation have also been measured to estimate the amount of herbage digested, including the release of CO_2 or total gases and the accumulation of short-chain fatty acids. Reid (1962), and Reid, Jung, and Murray (1964) report no difference in using disappearance of cellulose instead of dry matter to estimate total digestion. Hargus (1963) has suggested that the digestion of organic or dry matter might give better estimates of herbage digestibility than would the digestion of cellulose only.

Standard errors should be kept below 3 percent (Barnes, 1964; Tilley and Terry, 1963). In vitro values may be used to estimate in vivo criteria such as digestible energy, digestible dry matter, or total digestible nutrients (Baumgardt, Taylor, and Cason, 1962; Bowden and Church, 1962), or nutritive value indices (Donefer and others, 1960). Correlations of in vitro and in vivo estimates may vary with the system used and with the laboratory. Check herbages of known nutritive value should, therefore, be included frequently in the fermentation.

Sometimes a comparison of the potential quality of several herbages is all that is required. It is generally agreed that presently employed

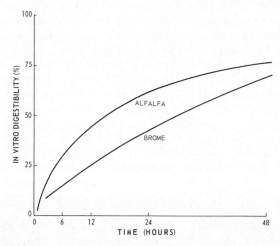

The influence of time on the in vitro digestibility of alfalfa and brome grass.

181

techniques give relative rather than absolute nutritive values, so that in vitro estimates should always be reported as such and not be considered absolute values of animal digestion (Balch, 1960; Pritchard and others, 1963). Also, it is important to watch for atypical herbages that do not follow the same pattern in vitro as they do in vivo (Reid, 1962).

Examples of Incubation

A self-gassing batch system, as used at the Animal Research Institute, Ottawa, is a modification of methods described by Alexander and McGowan (1961), Pritchard and others (1963), and Tilley and Terry (1963). Incubations are carried out in tared 50-ml centrifuge tubes containing 250 mg of substrate, 25 ml of buffer at pH 6.9, and 5 ml of crude inoculum (*see* illustration on page 180). Following an initial gassing with CO_2, the tubes are incubated at 39 C for up to 48 hours. The tubes are shaken occasionally. After 48 hours, the assay may be stopped; the tubes and their contents placed in a vacuum oven and dried at 70 C; the loss of dry matter or a specific component computed; and the results compared with known time–weight data (*see* graph on page 181). However, a more complete assay includes the digestion of crude protein. If this is planned, the procedure continues as follows. Five ml of freshly prepared pepsin solution (14 g pepsin in 500 ml of 1.5 N HCl), together with an antifoaming agent, are added to each mix. Incubation is continued for 48 hours. The tubes are then centrifuged and decanted. The residue is washed once with distilled water, and dried for 16 hours at 70 C in a vacuum oven. Each tube is then weighed and its dry-matter loss is computed.

At the Research Station, Swift Current, Saskatchewan, a continuous-gassing batch system has been used (Troelsen and Hanel, 1966). The fermentation mix comprises 30 ml of buffer, 25 ml of inoculum, and 1 g of substrate. Incubation is carried out in 90-ml centrifuge tubes that have a lip for gas escape. Carbon dioxide is supplied from a tank through a manifold at the rate of 40 bubbles per minute (*see* photograph on page 180). At regular intervals the pH is adjusted to 6.9 by adding a $NaCO_3$ solution. At termination of digestion the content of each tube is transferred to a 300-ml beaker, made to volume (140 ml) with dilute HCl, and adjusted to pH 1.2. Pepsin is added (0.2 g per beaker), and the mix incubated at 39 C for 24 hours. Residues are recovered by filtration through a glass-fiber pad in a tared porcelain filtration crucible in the presence of 1 g of preignited Hyflo supercel (Alexander and McGowan, 1961). Measurements are made of the dry and organic matter to estimate in vitro digestibility.

IN VIVO FERMENTATION

In vivo assays require a fistulated animal and sacs made from silk, nylon, or dacron (McAnnally, 1942; Pigden and others, 1961; Lusk,

182

Browning, and Miles, 1962; Van Dyne, 1962; Van Keuren and Heinemann, 1962; Hopson and others, 1963). Sacs measuring about 2 by 4 inches will hold up to 3 g of substrate. The substrate should not be ground too fine, as small particles will pass through the pores of the sacs; a grind that will pass through a 20- to 40-mesh screen is adequate. Ten to twenty sacs, each identified by a plastic or a metal tag, may be placed in the rumen through the fistula at one time. Rates of digestion can be measured by removing one or more sacs at regular intervals; the digestibility of any component can be estimated after a predetermined period of incubation. Bacterial action should be stopped immediately after the sacs are removed from the rumen. Residues can be dried in the sacs and the dry-matter loss determined from initial and final weights. Alternatively, the sacs may be emptied, and the residue analyzed to estimate the disappearance of one or more components.

Hopson and others (1963) warn that the ration fed to a fistulated animal may influence results. Their work indicates that the ration fed should be the same as the substrate.

References

Alexander, R. H., and Mary McGowan. 1961. A filtration procedure for the *in vitro* determination of digestibility of herbage. J. Brit. Grassl. Soc. 16:275–276.

Balch, C. C. 1960. Review of some papers read at the 9th International Grassland Congress at Reading, July 1960. II. Grass and animal nutrition. J. Brit. Grassl. Soc. 16:164–168.

Barnes, R. F. 1964. Collaborative *in vitro* studies on standard forages. Proc. Amer. Soc. Anim. Sci., 56th Annu. Meet., Knoxville, Tenn.

Barnett, A. J. G., and R. L. Reid. 1961. Reactions in the rumen. Edward Arnold Ltd., London. 252 p.

Baumgardt, B. R., J. L. Cason, and M. W. Taylor. 1962. Evaluation of forages in the laboratory. I. Comparative accuracy of several methods. J. Dairy Sci. 45:59–61.

Baumgardt, B. R., M. W. Taylor, and J. L. Cason. 1962. Evaluation of forages in the laboratory. II. Simplified artificial rumen procedure for obtaining repeatable estimates of forage nutritive value. J. Dairy Sci. 45:62–68.

Bowden, D. M., and D. C. Church. 1962. Artificial rumen investigations. II. Correlations between *in vitro* and *in vivo* measures of digestibility and chemical components of forages. J. Dairy Sci. 45:980–985.

Dehority, B. A., and R. R. Johnson. 1961. Effect of particle size upon the *in vitro* cellulose digestibility of forages by rumen bacteria. J. Dairy Sci. 44:2242.

Donefer, E., E. W. Crampton, and L. E. Lloyd. 1960. Prediction of the nutritive value index of a forage from *in vitro* rumen fermentation data. J. Anim. Sci. 19:545–552.

Hargus, W. A. 1963. Ovine bioenergetics and nutritional efficiency, with special reference to forage utilization. Diss. Abstr. 23:2272.

Hershberger, T. V., T. A. Long, E. W. Hartrook, and R. W. Swift. 1959. Use of the artificial rumen technique to estimate the nutritive value of forages. J. Anim. Sci. 18:770–779.

Hopson, J. D., R. R. Johnson, and B. A. Dehority. 1963. Evaluation of the dacron bag technique as a method for measuring cellulose digestibility and rate of forage digestion. J. Anim. Sci. 22:448–453.

Johnson, R. R., B. A. Dehority, and O. G. Bentley. 1958. Studies on the *in vitro* rumen procedure: Improved inoculum preparation and the effects of volatile fatty acids on cellulose digestion. J. Anim. Sci. 17:841–850.

Lusk, J. W., C. B. Browning, and J. T. Miles. 1962. Small-sample *in vivo* cellulose digestion procedure for forage evaluation. J. Dairy Sci. 45:69–73.

McAnnally, R. A. 1942. Digestion of straw by the ruminant. Biochem. J. 36:392–399.

McDougall, E. I. 1948. Studies on ruminant saliva. I. The composition and output of sheep saliva. Biochem. J. 43:99–109.

Pigden, W. J., and J. M. Bell. 1955. The artificial rumen as a procedure for evaluating forage quality. J. Anim. Sci. 14:1239.

Pigden, W. J., G. I. Pritchard, K. A. Winter, and V. S. Logan. 1961. Freezing— A technique for forage investigation. J. Anim. Sci. 20:796–801.

Pritchard, G. I., L. P. Folkins, and W. J. Pigden. 1963. The *in vitro* digestibility of whole grasses and their parts at successive stages of maturity. Can. J. Plant Sci. 43:79–87.

Quicke, G. V., O. G. Bentley, H. W. Scott, and A. L. Moxon. 1959. Cellulose digestibility *in vitro* as a measure of the digestibility of forage cellulose in ruminants. J. Anim. Sci. 18:275.

Reid, R. L. 1962. Investigations of plant species and maturity stage on forage nutritive value as determined by *in vitro* digestion techniques. Final Rep. U.S.D.A. Contract No. 12-14-100-4524 (24), Univ. West Virginia, Morgantown.

Reid, R. L., G. A. Jung, and S. Murray. 1964. The measurement of nutritive quality in a bluegrass pasture using *in vivo* and *in vitro* techniques. J. Anim. Sci. 23:700–710.

Shelton, D. C., and R. L. Reid. 1960. Measuring the nutritive value of forages using the *in vitro* rumen technique. Proc. 8th Int. Grassl. Congr. 8:524–528.

Stewart, D. G., and R. G. Warner. 1959. Continuous culture for studying mixed rumen microorganisms. J. Dairy Sci. 42:913–914. (Abstr.)

Tilley, J. M. A., and R. A. Terry. 1963. A two-stage technique for the *in vitro* digestion of forage crops. J. Brit. Grassl. Soc. 18:104–111.

Troelsen, J. E., and Donna Hanel. 1966. Ruminant digestion in vitro as affected by inoculum donor, collection day, and fermentation time. Can. J. Anim. Sci. 46:149–156.

Van Dyne, G.M. 1962. Micro-methods for nutritive evaluation of range forages. J. Range Manage. 15:303–314.

Van Keuren, R. W., and W. W. Heinemann. 1962. Study of a nylon bag technique for *in vivo* estimation of forage digestibility. J. Anim. Sci. 21:340–345.

Chapter 21

INDOOR FEEDING TRIALS FOR ESTIMATING DIGESTIBILITY AND INTAKE*

DAVID P. HEANEY and WALLACE J. PIGDEN†
Animal Research Institute, Canada Department of Agriculture
Ottawa, Ontario

DENNIS J. MINSON‡
National Research Council Postdoctorate Fellow
Animal Research Institute, Canada Department of Agriculture
Ottawa, Ontario

The efficiency with which ruminants process herbages into animal products depends largely on the feeding value or quality of those herbages. Feeding value may be measured by indoor feeding trials that estimate apparent digestibility and ad libitum intake—two parameters that are recognized as basic measurements of quality. Certain procedures must be complied with to ensure accurate estimates of these important parameters.

The digestibility and daily dry-matter herbage intake of animals can be estimated by allowing them to graze a sward under controlled conditions. But because this method is slow, expensive, and subject to many errors and uncontrollable variables, most investigators resort to cutting herbage and feeding it indoors as fresh or conserved fodder. This method gives a satisfactory control over many important variables, though it has limitations that must be accepted. For example:

- The chemical composition and the nutrient availability of herbage may change during conservation or storage
- Indoor feeding trials will not duplicate herbage selection of grazing animals
- Herbage must be cut at least once a day, or preserved for a period of time.

The following are among the advantages of indoor feeding trials:

- Accurate direct measurements of individual animal feed consumption and digestibility are obtained
- The characteristics of herbage or forage, as consumed, can be defined
- The environment of experimental animals can be controlled
- Use of animals and facilities is not restricted to the pasture season.

---

*Contribution No. 280, Animal Research Institute.
†Now Research Coordinator (Animal Nutrition), Research Branch, Canada Department of Agriculture, Ottawa 3, Ontario.
‡Present address: Cooper Laboratory, Division of Tropical Pastures, C.S.I.R.O., Lawes, Queensland, Australia.

Thus, indoor feeding trials provide a valuable measure of herbage quality, when the feed is prepared properly and the trial is conducted according to standardized experimental procedures.

FEED PREPARATION AND CONSERVATION

Conservation is required to provide sufficient herbage of near-constant quality for a feeding period of 1 day to 4 or more weeks. The conservation method employed depends on the facilities available, the length of the storage period, and the objectives of a study.

Fodder is prepared for feeding by cutting it into 1- to 3-inch lengths. This may be done with either a forage harvester in the field prior to conservation, or a cutting box in the laboratory. There are three reasons for cutting: to minimize wastage during feeding and reduce rejection of the less acceptable portions of a ration; to facilitate storage; and to obtain a constant feed length for tall- and short-growing crops.

Preparation of Fresh Herbage

Herbage may be cut daily and fed fresh to avoid conserving it. It is advisable to cut enough feed for two feedings each afternoon, thereby avoiding the morning dew. The portion to be kept overnight should be placed in a polyethylene bag with ½ to 1 kg of dry ice and closed fairly tightly but not sealed. The bags should be stored in a cool place, preferably in a refrigerator at 0 to 5 C. The gas released from the dry ice decreases the rate of tissue metabolism and prevents heating. Animals eat this feed as readily as freshly harvested forage (Pigden and others, 1961). Refrigeration without dry ice at 0 to 5 C is less satisfactory. Where neither dry ice nor refrigeration can be provided, it is usually necessary to cut herbage twice a day for the morning and afternoon feedings.

Feeding freshly cut herbage is satisfactory when the objective of a feeding trial is to determine digestibility and intake patterns as a crop matures. But other methods of harvesting or conservation are necessary if the objective is to estimate the digestibility and intake of herbages at defined stages of crop growth.

Two practical problems associated with harvesting once or twice daily are the extra weekend labor required and the difficulty of harvesting during a rainy period.

Preservation by Freezing and Storing

Quick freezing and storing at low temperatures is probably the conservation method that results in the least change in plant nutrient composition, but it is relatively expensive per unit of forage. Approximately 2.5 to 3 m³ of freezer storage space is required to store 550 to

186

650 kg of freshly chopped forage—enough for three sheep for 3 to 5 weeks. This is an average figure, and it varies considerably with type of forage. Because of volumes involved, it is impractical to freeze and store forage for cattle-feeding trials (calves possibly excepted) except for very special purposes or for very short-term studies.

At the Animal Research Institute, Ottawa, a moderate-sized facility with sufficient capacity to carry on an effective program of intake and digestibility studies with sheep has been built up gradually by purchasing portable units over a period of several years. These basic units consist of an insulated plywood box built in panels or sections and bolted together. A unit can be moved from one location to another, enlarged by adding extra panels, and located wherever electricity is available. When outdoors it has to be roofed over to keep off the rain. The compressor is an air-cooled unit that will not freeze in cold weather. It may be located beside the box or at a considerable distance, but needs a solid concrete base. If covered, the cover must not interfere with free air flow over the cooling coil. Electrical defrost systems operate better than hot gas defrosters in cold weather, and they are recommended if a unit is outdoors or in an unheated building.

The units in use at Ottawa are approximately 4 by 3.4 by 2.6 m (outside measurements), giving about 27 m³ of interior space. Shelves or bins are constructed lengthwise along the sides. Plywood

Storing bagged forage for freezing.

Bagging chopped forage and adding dry ice prior to freezer storage.

and dexion angle metal provide a variety of shelf and bin designs at minimum cost. The freezing coil is normally placed high and at the rear, and incorporates the automatic defrost system. Three freezers of this type are currently in operation at the Institute. The total cost for materials and installation is about $4500 per unit. Further details of freezers for experimental purposes are available (Pigden and others, 1961; and C.A.B., 1961).

Fresh herbages are stored in 8-ml polyethylene bags approximately 66 by 40 cm in size. These are filled with chopped grass and closed with wire ties. Unless a forage harvester is used, the herbage is chopped by a hay cutter prior to packaging unless the material is very short and immature. Each bag holds about 5.5 kg of fresh herbage.

Up to 700 kg of fresh herbage has been frozen at one time in each of the units, though 275 to 400 kg is normally introduced at one time. Freezing capacity is boosted by packing dry ice (10 to 20 percent by weight) with the fresh herbage. This chills the material and also tends to inhibit enzymatic action during the freezing process.

Use of dry ice has permitted fairly large-scale operations without an expensive sharp freezer unit. However, the quantities of carbon dioxide can be dangerous if personnel are unaware of its presence or ignorant of its lethal properties. Thus, when dry ice is used, special precautions must be taken. Freezers are kept locked, and are opened only by authorized personnel to clear out most of the gas before normal routine is resumed. Freezers are clearly labeled as dangerous during this period.

Preservation by Ensiling

Ensiled herbage often gives much lower animal intake estimates than corresponding fresh or dried material, although digestibility estimates are likely to be very similar (Harris and Raymond, 1963). Consequently, ensiling is not recommended where intake of preserved material is to be employed as an estimate of herbage intake in the field.

Sampling of Succulent Roughages

Fresh, frozen, or ensiled herbages are difficult to sample adequately for dry-matter and chemical analysis. The chopper illustrated is a com-

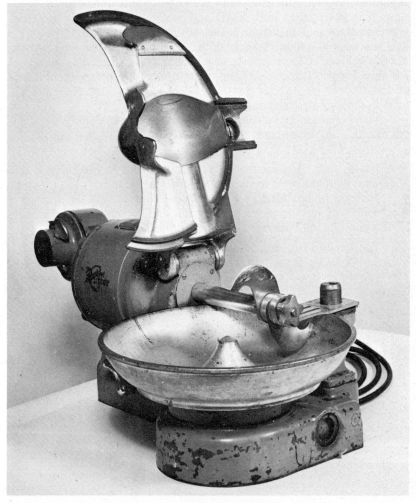

Salad chopper used to chop and mix fresh herbage or silage. More accurate sampling is possible following this technique of preparation.

189

mercial machine used by restaurants to chop raw vegetables for salads. The herbage is placed in the bowl, the top is lowered, and the bowl and material rotate below the spinning blades. Several pounds of fresh herbage or silage can be finely chopped and mixed in a few minutes with this machine. The machine can also chop the hard pellets often found in sheep and rabbit feces. Duplicate samples of 200 g can be removed for dry-matter and laboratory determinations.

Preservation by Drying

The purpose of drying is to preserve fodder in a form that can be compared readily with fresh herbage. Drying with unheated air is too slow. It is slower than heat drying and prolongs the period when enzymatic changes and metabolic losses occur. It is essential to introduce into the drying system clean heat that can be produced directly from electric heating coils or from a heat-exchanger connected to an oil- or gas-fired burner. Direct heat from a gun-type oil burner, without a heat exchanger, carries an oily soot that contaminates feed and makes it unacceptable to experimental animals.

Many efficient drying systems can be constructed readily. A simple but effective unit consists of:

- A heat source with a heat exchanger
- A fan to pass air over the heat exchanger and to discharge it into an air duct that carries the heated air to the herbage
- A platform or box with a mesh or slatted floor to hold the herbage
- A source of electric power for the fan and for either the electrodes of a gun-type oil burner or for electrical heating coils.

The weight of fresh herbage that can be dried at one time is determined by the size of the heating unit and the box or platform. The drying system illustrated is a commercial heating unit that uses 2¼ to 8

Oil-fired gun-type heating unit with heat exchanger attached to duct and tarpaulin-covered drying box.

gallons of oil per hour, and produces 250,000 to 890,000 Btu per hour, with an air duct and box that were constructed at the Research Institute, Ottawa.

The floor of the box measures approximately 5.5 by 8.5 m and is divided into four compartments, each with a floor area of about 2.75 by 4.25 m. Air ducts are constructed so that the air flow can be directed to either or both of the front compartments, either of the side pairs, one side pair and the front compartment of the other pair, or all four compartments. The herbage is distributed over the floor to a depth of up to ¾ m. Uniformity of distribution is very important because the heated air penetrates thinly spread herbage most readily. This herbage dries and, when dry, allows a high proportion of the heated air to funnel through and be wasted. With material of low initial dry-matter content it is often necessary to redistribute the material after 3 to 6 hours to ensure even drying. The unit will put out 225 to 275 kg of dried forage per compartment, or up to 1100 kg of dried forage every 24 hours.

RATION CONTROL

When either digestibility or intake is being measured, the quantity of dry matter consumed must be accurately determined. Several alternative procedures to achieve this objective can be used; a few of the more useful ones are outlined below. Regardless of which procedure is used, the validity of the entire experiment depends on obtaining truly representative samples for dry-matter determinations. Therefore, care should be exercised when samples are taken, and only the best sampling techniques should be used.

Daily weighing and dry-matter determinations of each animal's feed, with daily calculation of dry matter offered, is unnecessarily laborious and time-consuming. This procedure also allows the accumulation of daily errors.

For digestion trials, in which the same amount of feed is offered each day, the simplest procedure is to weigh out in one operation, before the trial begins, all the feedings required to carry each animal through the collection period. With this procedure, only one dry-matter determination per feeding is required, and only one dry-matter value needs to be used to calculate the dry-matter consumption of a given animal.

For intake trials, in which the daily feed allotment must fluctuate to maintain control of the amount of weighback, further modification is required. A method that is particularly well adapted to the use of freezing as a method of conservation is to mix thoroughly all the fresh, chopped herbage required for a trial and then to weigh it into sacks so that each sack contains exactly the same amount of material. As the sacks are filled, representative samples are taken for dry-matter determination and subsequent chemical analysis. Each sack, therefore, contains the same known amount of dry matter. During a feeding trial, the

191

only record required is the total number of sacks fed to each animal. Daily weighings of animal feed are made only to maintain control of the daily amount offered. Any spilled or uneaten feed is collected and dried, and the weight is subtracted from the total dry matter offered. Further details of this method of feed handling have been published (C.A.B., 1961).

Although the above procedure could be adapted for use when drying forages, experience at Ottawa indicates that the following procedure is better when dried forages are fed. A container of feed, sufficient to last the duration of the measurement period, is weighed and assigned to each animal. When the feed allotments are prepared and weighed, representative samples of each feed are taken for dry-matter determinations. At the end of the feeding period, the feed remaining in each container is weighed and resampled for dry-matter determinations. Dry matter consumed by each animal is calculated by subtracting from the quantity of dry matter in its container at the beginning of the trial the dry matter remaining unfed at the end, and also subtracting, of course, the dry weight of any spilled or uneaten feed. As with frozen feeds, daily weighings of the feed placed in the feed box are made only to maintain the approximate desired daily feed offering.

CONDUCT OF DIGESTION TRIALS

When measuring digestibility coefficients with ruminants, the method employed is "to give the experimental ration in exact quantities for long periods, in order to ensure that a 'steady state' of fecal excretion is reached, and then to collect the feces excreted during a measured interval of time" (Blaxter, Graham, and Wainman, 1956). Though this ideal is attained readily with conserved rations fed below appetite, fresh herbages present many unique problems because of their continually changing composition. Many pasture studies have been made with herbage cut daily and, despite difficulties in interpreting the results, this technique is still used widely—probably more from necessity than choice.

Number of Animals

The number of animals needed to measure the digestibility of each feed depends on the expected size of the differences in digestibility between the feeds being compared. The standard error of an individual dry-matter digestibility coefficient is usually between 1.0 and 1.3 digestibility units percent (Raymond, Harris, and Harker, 1953; Forbes and others, 1946). Raymond and others (1953) have reported the number of sheep needed for each feed to obtain an 80 percent chance that the digestibility difference will be significant at the 5 percent level of significance (graph, page 193). In most digestibility trials the herbage is fed to three, four, or five sheep.

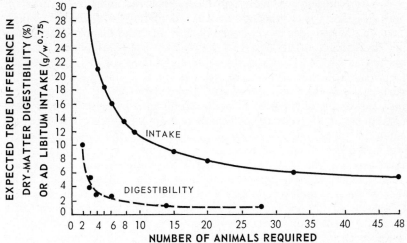

The number of animals needed to obtain an 80 percent chance that the digestibility or intake difference will be significant at the 5 percent level.

Length of Trial

A digestibility trial is divided into preliminary and measurement periods. During the preliminary period, the animals become accustomed to a given feed and begin to eat the same quantity each day at the same time residues of previous feeds are expelled from the digestive tract. Most studies have shown that 6 to 8 days are sufficient for preliminary periods when ordinary forages are fed, but with problem feeds such as silages, straws, and ground or pelleted hays, longer preliminary periods are desirable.

Measurement periods of 4 to 12 days are usually used, but it is advisable to avoid periods of less than 7 days because endpoint errors in fecal measurement decrease in direct proportion to the length of the collection periods (Blaxter and others, 1956).

Level of Feeding

To obtain accurate digestibility estimates, an even intake must be maintained and this necessitates feeding below appetite. When fed below appetite, an animal will consume all the less palatable and less digestible parts of a ration.

When comparing the digestibility of two feeds, there is always the question of whether they should be fed at the same level or as close to appetite as possible. Because digestibility may be depressed slightly by increased intake, there is a logical reason to feed at the same level. However, the results of indoor trials are usually applied to field conditions where feeding is ad libitum. If one feed is more palatable than another, allowances should be made in the indoor trials by feeding as close to appetite as possible without selection occurring.

193

With the current interest in the appetite of animals for different herbages, there is a tendency to feed ad libitum in digestibility trials. Though this provides useful intake data, it increases the error in estimating digestibility in at least two ways. The day-to-day fluctuations in normal ad libitum intake increase the endpoint error in fecal measurement, and selection of the more digestible parts of the ration may occur, particularly of poor-quality rations. The degree of selection by an animal increases as the quantity of excess feed offered is increased. Under these conditions the digestibility coefficients that are measured are for the feed eaten and not for that offered. With high-quality, immature grasses, in which the digestibility of the various parts and segments is relatively homogeneous, the errors are minimal. With mature alfalfa, on the other hand, the digestibility error caused by selection can be serious, as indicated in the graph below. One way to overcome this serious objection is to feed ad libitum but to remove uneaten feed only at the end of a trial, the quantity of residues being kept to a minimum at all times. This method cannot be used with fresh or frozen grass that decomposes if left in feed boxes for more than a day. *The safest method is to measure digestibility and appetite in separate periods.* A satisfactory procedure is to measure ad libitum intake during the week immediately after a suitable preliminary period, then measure digestibility at 90 percent of the ad libitum consumption after a 2-day period.

Collection of Feces

Feces can be weighed each day and samples taken for dry-matter and chemical analysis. However, when cold storage is available, a less laborious method is to store in a freezer all the feces produced by each

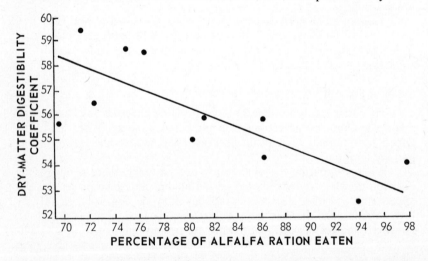

The decrease in measured digestibility of mature alfalfa as the proportion of feed consumed varies from 70 to 98 percent of the amount offered.

sheep, in 5-gallon cans fitted with lids. At the end of a trial, the feces are thawed, weighed, mixed thoroughly, and sampled for dry-matter and chemical analysis. Feces that fail to be retained in the collection bag should be gathered and dried, and their weight added to the dry weight of the bulk collection.

Calculation of results. The digestibility coefficient (*D*) of dry matter (DM) is:

$$D = \frac{(\text{Wt of DM in herbage eaten}) - (\text{Wt of DM in feces produced})}{(\text{Wt of DM in herbage eaten})} \times 100 \quad (1)$$

The digestibility of other plant components can be calculated from Equation 1 by substituting for weight of dry matter the weights of the other components eaten and excreted. For routine work, it is often simpler to use Equation 2 to calculate the digestibility coefficients of other herbage components from the dry-matter digestibility (*D*), the percentage of the component (*C*) in the dry matter (*Y*), and feces dry matter (*X*):

$$\text{Digestibility coefficient of } C = \frac{100\,(Y-X) + XD}{Y} \quad (2)$$

Metabolism stalls. Descriptions of many types of metabolism stalls are available in the literature. Where intake and digestibility of forages are the only considerations, simple, wooden, inexpensive stalls of a type used at Ottawa are suitable. They are constructed in multiples of four and can be taken apart for moving or storage (plans are available on request). Each animal is tied loosely and is fitted with a simple harness that supports a canvas collection bag with a polyethylene liner. This arrangement allows the animal more freedom than apron-type collection apparatus. Urine passes through a mesh floor to a collecting tray that directs it through a funnel into a bottle.

Feces Mixing

Thorough mixing of feces prior to sampling for analysis is essential. The mixer that has proved most useful at Ottawa is one used by bakeries. It has sufficient capacity to handle all the feces produced by one sheep during an 8-day collection, or all the feces produced by one cow in 24 hours.

With sheep, the daily feces outputs of each animal are accumulated in a single container in a deepfreeze until the end of the collection period; they are then thawed and mixed. Cattle feces are mixed daily and a sample taken for freezing; the daily samples are thawed and mixed for each collection period. Sheep and cattle feces are mixed for 15 and 10 minutes respectively.

Inexpensive reconditioned machines of the type used at Ottawa are available commercially and are generally satisfactory. Meat-grinding attachments are also available, making the machine useful for a variety of tasks.

A commercial "dough" mixer employed for large-scale mixing of feces from digestion studies.

CONDUCT OF INTAKE TRIALS

The use of the measured voluntary, or ad libitum, intake of forage as one of the parameters characterizing its feeding value is a comparatively recent innovation. The assay procedures currently used at the Animal Research Institute, Ottawa, to determine intake are in general agreement with those of most other institutions active in this field, and are adequate to give satisfactory measurements. However, they are subject to further change as more complete information becomes available.

Number of Animals

The inherent animal-to-animal variability associated with the measurement of intake is usually very high compared with that of other biological assay procedures. In an analysis of 441 determinations of ad libitum intake involving 2427 individual animal-period measurements, standard errors of the 441 determinations averaged 9.7, but ranged from 0.9 to 40.6 intake units. The average coefficient of variability was 16.4 (Heaney, Pritchard, and Pigden, 1965). The number of sheep needed per determination to obtain an 80 percent chance that the true intake difference is significant at the 5 percent level of significance is shown in the graph on page 193.

Length of Trial

A preliminary feeding period is required for animals to become accustomed to a feed and to reduce daily fluctuations in feed consumption to a minimum, though some fluctuation will continue indefinitely. For ordinary forages, a preliminary period of 9 to 12 days is adequate (Blaxter, Wainman, and Wilson, 1961). For problem forages like silages and straws, longer preliminary periods are required. Experience at Ottawa indicates that a measurement period of 7 days is usually sufficient to minimize errors due to daily fluctuations in consumption.

Level of Feeding

If the objective is to measure true ad libitum intake, each animal must have access to feed at all times, and the feeding level must be sufficient to provide some feed weighback each day. The actual amount of weighback should be kept small because it is logical to assume that selection influences intake: an animal should consume more of the desirable portions of the forage if it is allowed to reject that which is undesirable. Results of experiments at Ottawa, when intake was measured against levels of rejection (daily weighback) ranging to 40 percent of the daily consumption, have shown that:

- Although the general assumption stated above is true, ad libitum intake is affected much less by level of selection allowed than is digestibility

- Levels of rejection up to 10 percent of daily consumption cause negligible errors in measured intake
- Fluctuations in normal day-to-day consumption make it difficult to maintain a precise level of rejection.

The above considerations show that intake should be measured with animals receiving sufficient feed to provide 2 to 10 percent daily weighback. Uneaten feed should be removed from feed boxes daily. Experienced livestock feeders will have little difficulty in maintaining daily weighbacks within the recommended range.

Calculation of Results

If intake measurements are to have any general comparative value, they must be recorded in a manner that makes them independent of body weight. Relating intake to absolute units of body weight (lb or kg) only partially achieves this objective. The best correction is to record intake per unit of metabolic size (Crampton, Donefer, and Lloyd, 1960; Blaxter and others, 1961). Although there have been inconsistencies in choice of exponent, most North American animal research workers, as well as the European Association for Animal Production (Kleiber, 1965), are now using the three-fourths power of body weight to represent metabolic size.

Accurate records of total dry matter offered and total dry-matter weighback must be kept for each animal during the measurement period. From these data, it is easy to calculate the average daily consumption per animal. Each animal is weighed at the beginning and at the end of the measurement period, and the average to the two weights is converted to units of metabolic size (Heaney and Love, 1964). The average daily consumption divided by the metabolic size produces the index of ad libitum intake—g consumed daily/$W^{0.75}$ kg.

References

Blaxter, K. L., N. McC. Graham, and F. W. Wainman. 1956. Some observations on the digestibility of food by sheep, and on related problems. Brit. J. Nutr. 10:69–91.

Blaxter, K. L., F. W. Wainman, and R. S. Wilson. 1961. The regulation of food intake by sheep. Anim. Prod. 3:51–61.

C.A.B. 1961. Research techniques in use at The Grassland Research Institute, Farnham Royal, Bucks. Bull. 45.

Crampton, E. W., E. Donefer, and L. E. Lloyd. 1960. A nutritive value index for forages. J. Anim. Sci. 19:538–544.

Forbes, E. B., R. F. Elliott, R. W. Swift, W. H. James, and V. F. Smith. 1946. Variation in determinations of digestive capacity of sheep. J. Anim. Sci. 5:298–305.

Harris, C. E., and W. F. Raymond. 1963. The effect of ensiling on crop digestibility. J. Brit. Grassl. Soc. 18: 204–212.

Heaney, D. P., and J. C. Love. 1964. Tables of conversion of body weight to metabolic size. Anim. Res. Inst., Can. Dep. Agr.

Heaney, D. P., G. I. Pritchard, and W. J. Pigden. 1965. Between-animal variability in ad libitum forage intakes by sheep. J. Anim. Sci. 24:909. (Abstr.)

Kleiber, M. 1965. Metabolic body size. Proc. 3rd energy symposium European Ass., Anim. Prod. 11:427–435.

Pigden, W. J., G. I. Pritchard, K. A. Winter, and V. S. Logan. 1961. Freezing—a technique for forage investigations. J. Anim. Sci. 20:796–801.

Raymond, W. F., C. E. Harris, and V. G. Harker. 1953. Studies on the digestibility of herbage. I. Technique of measurement of digestibility and some observations on factors affecting the accuracy of digestibility data. J. Brit. Grassl. Soc. 8:301–314.

Chapter 22

DESIGN OF EXPERIMENTS

PETER ROBINSON
Statistical Research Service, Canada Department of Agriculture
Ottawa, Ontario

Design is often taken to mean only the physical layout of an experiment, but design is far more. Design is involved at all stages of a research program—in the preliminary thinking at the formative stage, in the discussion at the planning stage, in the layout of experimental units, in the collection of data at the execution stage, in the tests of significance at the analysis stage, and in the conclusions at the decision-making stage. In the earlier stages, the type of design appropriate to a particular investigation must be considered in relation to the practical limitations of the facilities available. In the later stages, choice of tests of significance and permissible conclusions are dependent upon the design used.

In general, use of a design built to the specifications of a particular investigation, and the use of appropriate tests of significance will:

- Reduce the time required for completion of a study
- Ensure use of available resources to the best advantage
- Avoid wasting effort in obtaining data that contain no information pertinent to the problem being studied
- Clarify aims and objectives and rule out unproductive lines of investigation quickly
- Give a measure of the reliance that may be placed on conclusions reached.

It should be stated most emphatically that a statistical design is not, of itself, complex and unwieldy. On the contrary, a statistician will very often simplify a design suggested by a research worker in the field.

BASIC IDEAS OF DESIGN

Two fundamental principles are involved in design: replication and randomization.

Replication is necessary to obtain a measure of the variability in experimental material. This measure then serves as a yardstick to judge whether an observed difference between means is of an order that can be expected on the basis of this measure, or whether it is substantially larger.

Randomization is necessary for the laws of chance to operate. Statistical theory is built upon these laws; if they do not hold, tests of significance are invalid and the conclusions drawn may be erroneous. It is usually impossible to ensure that all experimental units are exactly alike. Even if randomization increases the practical difficulties of conducting an experiment, it is still necessary.

Certain restrictions may be placed on the randomization procedure to surmount practical difficulties. But these restrictions must be taken into account when analyzing data and drawing conclusions.

SELECTION OF AN APPROPRIATE DESIGN

To select a design that is suited to a given investigation, it is essential to specify as exactly as possible the question to be answered. For example, in the question, "Is there a response to fertilizer?", presence and absence is all that is involved. However, "What is the optimum level of application of fertilizer?" requires the calculation of several rates to estimate the response curve.

Only when a problem has been clearly specified should the type and number of treatments or the sampling procedure be determined. The first step is to decide whether the investigation concerns a single factor, such as a variety trial or sampling to estimate different stand densities, or whether it is factorial, involving combinations of different levels of two or more factors. Other points that may be considered are the inclusion of "unrealistic" or "impractical" treatments to obtain a better understanding of the observed results, or the inclusion of extra checks or standards.

It is also necessary to decide how to group observations to eliminate extraneous sources of variation. The type of grouping to use depends on a number of considerations. It may be possible by good grouping to eliminate two or more sources of variation, such as fertility in two directions, or day of sampling and time within day of sampling. If the number of treatments to be tested is very large, grouping in incomplete blocks is desirable. Grouping may be influenced appreciably by the facilities available or practical limitations in applying treatments or taking samples. In many sampling problems the only feasible design is one leading to nested classifications, a method that has a parallel in the split-plot design in field experimentation.

Further Reading

Cochran, W. G., and G. M. Cox. 1957. Experimental designs. 2nd ed. J. Wiley and Sons, New York. xiv and 611 p.

Cox, D. R. 1958. Planning of experiments. J. Wiley and Sons, New York. vii and 306 p.

Davies, O. L. (ed.) 1956. Design and analysis of industrial experiments. Hafner Co., New York.

Finney, D. J. 1960. An introduction to the theory of experimental design. Univ. of Chicago Press, Chicago.

Kempthorne, O. 1952. Design and analysis of experiments. J. Wiley and Sons, New York.

Quenouille, M. H. 1953. The design and analysis of experiments. Hafner Co., New York.

Yates, F. 1937. The design and analysis of factorial experiments. Tech. Commun. 35, Imperial Bureau Soil Science.

Some experimental designs, their advantages and limitations

Design	When to use	Advantages	Limitations
Completely randomized	When grouping will not increase precision, i.e., when experimental units are relatively uniform. With few treatments and few degrees of freedom where error can occur.	Simple calculations. Missing data do not complicate calculations.	Usually inefficient because of lack of uniformity of experimental units.
Randomized complete block	When grouping will increase precision, and when number of treatments is not large enough to necessitate grouping within a complete replication.	Removes variation in one direction. Simple calculations. Missing data easy to deal with.	Usually inefficient with a large number of treatments.*
Latin square	When grouping in two crossed classifications will increase precision. In investigations carried out over a period of time to remove effect of variations with time.	Removes variation in two directions. Simple calculations. Missing data easy to deal with.	Few degrees of freedom are available for error with less than 4 treatments. Becomes unwieldy with more than 7 treatments. Requires assumption that 1st order interactions between rows, columns, and treatments are all negligible.
Graeco-Latin and higher order squares	Under same conditions as for Latin square.	As for Latin square design. Removes extraneous variation from 3 or more sources.	As for Latin square design.
Youden square (incomplete Latin square)	When a Latin square is desirable, but number of treatments would make the design unwieldy. In greenhouse experiments.	Removes variation in two directions.	Analysis complex. Number of treatments that can be accommodated is limited.
Confounded designs for	When number of treatment combinations in a full replication of a factorial	Increases efficiency of large factorial experiments.*	Information lost on the interactions that are confounded.

Design	When to use	Advantages	Limitations
Split-plots (main effects confounded) for factorial experiments	When full information on the main effects of one (or more) factors not required. When physical limitations necessitate large plots for some treatments.	Only advantageous when conditions in previous column hold.	Information lost on the main effects that are confounded. Interpretation can be difficult if splitting extended to a number of levels.
Composite and rotatable designs for factorial experiments	When sequential experimentation is possible, i.e., when conditions and material remain relatively uniform from one test to the next. This is more likely to hold in chemical and physical than in biological experiments. When a full factorial experiment involves a large number of treatment combinations.	Allows speedier progress to the treatment combinations of major interest in sequential experimentation.	Computations more tedious than in some other designs for factorial experiments. Mathematical model rather restrictive.
Lattices (for single factor experiments)	When number of treatments is large, and other types of grouping are impracticable.	Advantageous when conditions in "When to use" column hold.	Calculations tedious. Different precisions for different comparisons.
Fractionally replicated designs for factorial experiments	When number of treatment combinations is so large that it is impracticable to include them all. When further treatments are to be superimposed on an existing experiment.	Reduces number of experimental units required. Work can be continued on an existing experiment instead of starting afresh.	Main effects are confounded with some of the higher order interactions.
Other incomplete block designs for single factor experiments	When grouping is desirable or essential because of practical limitations, i.e., in paired comparisons.	Increases efficiency of experiment.*	Calculations can be tedious. Number of blocks required for balanced design may be high.

*The efficiency of one design relative to another is defined as the ratio of their error variances.

Chapter 23

RECORDING HERBAGE YIELD DATA

THOMAS H. ANSTEY*
Research Station, Canada Department of Agriculture
Lethbridge, Alberta

DOUGLAS A. COOKE
Research Station, Canada Department of Agriculture
Melfort, Saskatchewan

To facilitate the orderly tabulation of herbage yield data, appropriate record forms should be designed for each experiment. Form design is an integral part of good research planning. Not only are the items of data collected in an experiment important, but also the order in which they are recorded. This is particularly true when data are to be analyzed by computer.

Well-planned forms simplify an experiment, provide continuity, facilitate interpretation of results, and save time. They are especially valuable for long-term experiments where the importance of a statistic may not be realized until data have been recorded for a year or more.

Illustration of record forms are rarely found in the literature. This is understandable since even similar experiments seldom have identical requirements. However, a number of basic forms have been illustrated by Brown (1954), and by Sylvestre and Williams (1952). These are useful to anyone designing forms for recording pasture data. The form designed by Sylvestre and Williams, on page 205, is particularly useful when herbage production and consumption are calculated by the Difference Method. In this form, consumption is estimated by subtracting the weight of ungrazed herbage (Column 2) from that of the caged yield (Column 1). Production is estimated by subtracting the weight of uncaged herbage from the previous harvest (Column 3) from that of the current caged yield (Column 1).

DATA COLLECTION FOR COMPUTER ANALYSIS

Ideally, all data, as they are collected, should be transposed directly from a measuring device to punch cards, paper tape, or magnetic tape. This saves time and minimizes error. Many research projects are not sufficiently long-term to warrant a fully automated recording system, but every research worker should come as close to this objective as possible.

---

*Now Assistant Director General (Western), Research Branch, Canada Department of Agriculture, Ottawa 3, Ontario.

Form for recording production and consumption of dry matter estimated by the Difference Method

Melfort—1961 Project No. and Title—*Ag.5.24.01 The carrying capacity and productivity of pastures.*
Treatment—*Inter. Wht. & Alf (check)*

Cutting	Dry weight of herbage harvested from cages lb/ac				Dry weight of ungrazed herbage on field at time cages harvested lb/ac				Dry matter of ungrazed herbage covered by cages when moved to new location lb/ac				Dry-matter amount of herbage consumed by livestock (total consumption) lb/ac				Dry-matter yield of herbage (total production) lb/ac			
	Replicate				Replicate				Replicate				Replicate				Replicate			
	1	2	3	Total	1	2	3	Total	1	2	3	Total	1	2	3	Total	1	2	3	Total
1	1332	1004	597	2933	256	339	156	751	256	339	156	751	1076	665	441	2182	1332	1004	597	2933
2	908	1430	1335	3673	355	348	538	1241	355	348	538	1241	553	1082	797	2432	652	1091	1179	2922
3	429	524	820	1773	103	162	215	480	103	162	215	480	326	362	605	1293	74	176	282	532
4	200	251	302	753	92	65	101	258					108	186	201	495	97	89	87	273
5																				
6																				
Totals of cuttings	2869	3209	3054	9132	806	914	1010	2730	714	849	909	2472	2063	2295	2044	6402	2155	2360	2145	6660
Average pounds of dry matter per acre			3044				910				824				2134				2220	

There are several methods for recording data directly on cards. In some survey-type systems the data are recorded on the left-hand side of the card, and then are visible to the key punch operator for direct punching on the same card. More complex systems use mark sensing, which allows for automated punching. A small hand-operated card punch, which has been introduced recently, allows direct punching of up to six digits simultaneously.

There are four principles that are basic to data collection for computer use:

- Plan ahead
- Arrange for the computer to do all the sorting; this permits data collection in the same order as in the experimental design. If this is not possible without reprogramming, try to record data so that the original sheets can be used by the key punch operator
- Let the computer do the arithmetic
- Use source card punching of data whenever possible.

Before any plans for data collection and recording are made, the type of computer program should be selected. There are two types. The first are general-purpose programs available in the library of each machine. The others are specialized programs, each of which is usually suitable for only one particular experiment (Anstey and Smillie, 1963).

Let us consider a library program. In the simple matter of calculating plot dry-matter yields, the order of data recording might be: treatment number, plot fresh weight, sample fresh weight, and sample dry weight. If the drying pans are not tared, a fifth measurement (container weight) must be recorded. Then sample fresh weight and dry weight would include container weight. Where should container weight be recorded? Has the computer program been designed to make the subtraction? Because data should be recorded in a form directly suitable for computer input, it is important to scrutinize the program specifications carefully before collecting data.

The situation is somewhat different with a specialized program. This can be designed to accept data in the most convenient form. The programmer should be consulted about recording sequence early in the planning stage, not after the data have been recorded. A specialized program gives ample opportunity for imaginative thinking, because the computer may be used to:

- Test data for completeness
- Determine if data meet the requirements for statistical hypotheses
- Make all mathematical calculations
- Make decisions on methods of calculation based on intermediate results
- Present tables suitable for direct interpretation.

References

Anstey, T. H., and K. W. Smillie. 1963. Use of a remote digital computer on an open-shop basis in agricultural research. Computer J. 6:118–120.

Brown, D. 1954. Methods of surveying and measuring vegetation. Commonwealth Bureau of Pasture and Field Crops. Bull. 42. Farnham Royal, Bucks. 223 p.

Sylvestre, P. E., and S. B. Williams. 1952. Methods of measuring the relative productivity of pasture experiments with livestock. Anim. Husb. Div., Can. Dep. Agr., Ottawa. 16 p.

Chapter 24

LIVESTOCK PRODUCTION RECORDS

STANLEY E. BEACOM
Research Station, Canada Department of Agriculture
Melfort, Saskatchewan

Animal response is one of the most meaningful measures of the yield and quality of herbages and pasture treatments. But this response does not depend on pasture treatment alone. To assess the response of animals, detailed and complete records must be kept of their breed, age, sex, and condition, their performance during grazing trials, their pre-grazing performance, their environment, and the way they are managed. All these factors affect the rate and efficiency of pasture utilization and have to be taken into account in reporting experimental results. If records are kept in a systematic way, they do much to facilitate the interpretation of results.

FACTORS TO CONSIDER
WHEN RECORDING PRODUCTION DATA

Management of Animals

Records should make it possible to determine the best system of management to use in grazing trials. Mott (1960) has described a system whereby stocking rates are adjusted throughout the grazing season to equalize grazing pressure between treatments. Kennedy, Reid, and Anderson (1960) recommend that stocking rates be held constant regardless of differences in optimum grazing pressures for herbages or treatments.

Apparent discrepancies between similar treatments in different experiments have been explained by differences in animal management. If the entire forage production on a given treatment is used by grazing animals, liveweight gain is greatest when the stocking rate and the available amount of pasture are balanced. If applied to all treatments, this technique can be used to compare productivity, but it may give production figures that cannot be duplicated under actual conditions.

To assess the effect of adjusting stocking rates by the "put-and-take" method, it is best to summarize data by periods. In a test requiring optimum production or optimum maintenance, and where the only factor influencing gain is the *quantity* of forage available per head, adding extra animals to a treatment is usually justified if very little reduction in average daily gain occurs relative to the gain on comparable treatments. On an unpalatable herbage, livestock might not consume enough for a reasonable rate of gain, irrespective of stocking rate or other management practice.

Stocking Rate

Stocking rate is usually indicated by the average number of head of livestock per acre or acres per head. Since stocking rate tells nothing about rate of gain, it cannot, by itself, measure pasture productivity, unless all treatments are managed to promote a uniform level of production per animal. Stocking rate does indicate grazing load, and it can help to point up differences in total gain between treatments. The range in stocking rate over a grazing period is important; pastures or management practices that give efficient utilization with a near-constant stocking rate are preferable to those that require widely fluctuating stocking rates.

Initial and Final Weights of Animals

Initial and final weights and total gain should be presented in summarizing performance. The weights of animals of similar breeding and background indicate their physiological age. Other factors being equal, larger weight gains per acre can be expected from lighter than from heavier animals because tissues of lower energy content are being laid down. The gain per head is often an important factor to the producer, as it influences the time required to finish the animals. Thus, large gains per head may be more desirable than large gains per acre, particularly if they are obtained by using extra animals during flush growth periods. Gains obtained under these conditions are not always too meaningful, and the fact that extra animals must be available to capitalize on flush growth is a disadvantage. Production figures obtained under these experimental conditions may not be applicable under farm conditions.

Length of Grazing Season

Under farm or ranch conditions, it is almost essential that animals be placed on pasture in the early spring and left there until late fall. For example, this applies to a breeding herd that has a regular year-round "productive" cycle. It is not so essential with growing or fattening animals, where rapid gains per head are important, and where it may be more desirable to have the same gain but over a shorter period of time. Rates of gain near the end of a pasture season may not be sufficiently high to justify keeping animals on pasture; they can then be placed on supplemental annual pasture or in a feedlot.

Under range conditions, maximum gain per head is usually the principal consideration. Sarvis (1923) states that "the most efficient system of grazing is one that will insure sufficient forage during the entire season to produce the greatest total gain, with the least number of cattle on the minimum unit of land, without permanent injury to the native vegetation."

It is essential to study length of grazing period, together with the seasonal pattern of liveweight gain, in order to evaluate a variety of treatments to meet specific needs.

Average Daily Gain and Rate of Gain

Average daily gain must be assessed in the light of the method of grazing management employed. Where put-and-take stocking is practiced, average daily gain is usually a reflection of stocking rate, and may have no relation to an experimental treatment. In some situations, it is desirable to aim for a uniform average daily gain across treatments and to use liveweight gain per acre as a relative measure of treatment effects. Where stocking rates are kept constant across treatments, daily gain may reflect differences in the quantity or quality of a herbage, and it is an index of pasture differences when the stocking rate is high enough for the most productive treatments to be used efficiently.

Rate-of-gain indicates the efficiency with which consumed herbage is being used. For this reason, it is usually desirable to manage pastures to assure high gains, provided herbage is being utilized efficiently.

Where grazing pressure is high so that daily dry-matter intake per head is reduced, or where the quality of a herbage limits dry-matter intake, both the rate-of-gain and the efficiency of pasture utilization are reduced. Average daily gain may be quite misleading as a measure of treatment effect if treatments are not stocked to their production potentials. Mott (1960) discusses relationships between stocking rates and production per animal and per acre.

Gain per Acre

Total liveweight gain per acre must be assessed in relation to such factors as stocking rate, length of pasture period, gain per animal, and seasonal variation in herbage production. For comparative purposes the gross gain per acre may be quite satisfactory. However, most animals coming off pasture carry varying amounts of "fill," much of which may be lost when the animals are removed from pasture, and some allowance for this must be made. If weighing is impractical after an overnight shrink, a 3 percent reduction from off-pasture weights will largely offset the effect of "nonproductive" fill. See Chapter 14 for further information about weighing techniques.

Production of Total Digestible Nutrients

The quantity of total digestible nutrients (TDN) produced by a pasture can be estimated by a technique based on "reverse feeding standards." This technique takes into account the energy needed for maintenance, work, and production. Since liveweight gain is influenced by grazing pressure, liveweight gain alone may not be a fair criterion to use for assessing productivity under different grazing intensities. The reverse feeding standard technique, first described by Sylvestre and Williams (1952), is discussed in Chapter 17.

Efficiency of Dry-matter Utilization

Accurate determinations of dry-matter intake give a useful indication of grazing capacity. The correlation between average daily gain and efficiency of utilization is usually high. An unusually high dry-matter consumption per pound of liveweight gain might indicate a low dry-matter intake, an excess stocking rate, a low herbage palatability, adverse weather conditions, or excessive use of energy to meet high maintenance requirements (Campbell, 1963).

Seasonal Variations in Herbage Production

Seasonal variations in herbage production are rarely referred to in the literature, but they pose problems for both research workers and producers. Perhaps these variations are not usually presented in tables because no concise, easily understood method for doing this has been devised. A series of percentages, covering successive approximately equal pasture periods, could be used to give a seasonal picture of pasture productivity. Thus, periodic (32:29:33:5:1) or cumulative (32:61: 94:99:100) gains could be used to indicate the pattern of liveweight gains and dry-matter production as a season progresses. Three or four periods could be used instead of five. Stocking rate, and dry-matter and TDN production trends could be illustrated similarly but would probably reflect fluctuations in weight gains.

FORMS FOR RECORDING ANIMAL PERFORMANCE

The forms described below have been in use for 10 years at the Research Station, Melfort, Saskatchewan, and have simplified the keeping of up-to-date records for pasture experiments as well as the preparation of the tables and graphs required to interpret field data.

The recording system used at Melfort has the following advantages:

- Field data, recorded for each grazing period and cumulatively, are complete as soon as an experiment is finished
- Few additional calculations are needed to summarize field data for statistical and economic evaluation
- The records provide information that can be plotted readily to indicate trends in daily gain, total gain, TDN, or other utilization criteria
- All mathematical values required for interpretation of experimental results are readily available.

211

All forms are versatile, as they can be used to record individual animal performance on one replicate or on an entire treatment, the performance of permanent and put-and-take grazers separately, or all treatments used in an experiment for any class of livestock where gains and maintenance are the "production" criteria studied.

The weight and over-winter rate of gain, as well as any special over-winter treatments, are taken into account when allotting animals to pasture treatments and replicates. The animals that show a good average gain during the winter are used as permanent grazers.

Because it is sometimes desirable at a later date to trace the performance of certain or all animals over an entire pasture season, or to relate winter and pasture performances, it is important to record the kind of pasture from which put-and-take animals come and where they go when removed. It is also useful to record any and all previous ear-tag numbers lost by an animal, as well as the current number.

At present no provision is made to incorporate pasture consumption or digestibility data, but these could easily be recorded on an extra form.

Form 1

Form 1 is used to record sequential liveweights through a grazing season for all animals on any one treatment. It is the form on which all original field data are entered. The form can be extended to record data for as many periods as required. Note that initial and final weights are averaged over a 2-day period, with the exception of put-and-take animals.

When it is necessary to use put-and-take animals, their records are added to the form or removed, as appropriate. It is practical to record the weights of put-and-take animals as they are moved on or off a treatment. This procedure ensures that the weights of all animals are recorded immediately. If the records of put-and-take animals are always added or removed below those of permanent grazers, a glance down the left-hand side of the form will reveal the number of head pastured during any one period.

Form 2

"Grazing Period"— Enter starting and ending date for each period, from Form 1. If different fields or pasture types are included in any one treatment (for example, three fields of different pasture species grazed in rotation), a note should be made in this column to indicate the portion of the treatment involved.

Column 1— Enter the number of days in each period.

Column 2— Enter the number of animals pastured during each period, from Form 1. (At Melfort, no animals are removed or added except at the time of weighing the whole group. If it is felt that stocking rate should be adjusted more often, all animals must be weighed and the adjustments made. The Melfort method simplifies calculations and record keeping.)

Column 3— Multiply Column 1 by Column 2.

Column 4— Enter the total final weight of animals grazing during each period, from Form 1.

Column 5— Enter the total initial weight of animals grazing during each period, from Form 1.

Column 6— Subtract Column 5 from Column 4 to arrive at live-weight gains during the period.

Column 7— Divide Column 6 by Column 3 to arrive at average daily gain.

Column 8— Summate animal days to date.

Column 9— Summate liveweight gains to date.

Column 10— Divide cumulative liveweight gains by cumulative steer days to give a cumulative average daily gain.

Column 11— By adding each entry in Column 4 to the corresponding one in Column 5 and dividing by 2, the average total weight during each period is obtained.

Column 12— Divide Column 11 by Column 2. This figure may also be obtained by adding Columns 4 and 5 and dividing by twice the number in Column 2.

Form 3

Form 3 is designed to facilitate calculation of TDN production, based on energy requirements for animal maintenance and gain. The equations used to estimate these criteria are given in Chapter 17.

Column 13— Activity increment (included in factor shown in Column 14).

Column 14— Pounds of TDN required to maintain 100 pounds of liveweight per day for the weight of animal involved. Includes the activity increment shown in Column 13.

Column 15— Pounds of TDN required for maintenance.

Column 16— Summation of Column 15.

Column 17— Pounds of TDN required per pound of gain for the weight of animal involved.

Column 18— TDN required for production.

Column 19— Cumulative TDN required for production.

Column 20— Total TDN (maintenance plus production) required during each period.

Column 21— Cumulative TDN to date.

Column 22— Total TDN per acre for each period.

Column 23— Cumulative TDN production per acre to date.

Form 4

This form illustrates the factors that are used to convert the live-weight and gains recorded in Form 2 to the TDN values that are summarized in Form 3. Sample liveweights are shown in the left-hand column. The six center columns indicate the pounds of TDN required for daily maintenance per 100 pounds liveweight plus activity increments of zero, 10, 25, 50, 75, and 100 percent. The right-hand column shows the TDN required per pound of liveweight gain. For steers of weights shown in the left-hand column, the estimates for maintenance plus a designated activity increment can be entered directly in the pertinent space in Form 3. However, a more accurate estimate of TDN values is assured by calculating directly from the equations in Table 1, Chapter 17, using the exact weight of the animal.

SPECIAL CONSIDERATIONS

Our hypothetical example shows the performance of a group of steers, flexible as to number, continuously grazing the same pasture treatment. In other experiments, a herd or flock might graze a rotation of two or more paddocks in one treatment, or a nonsystematic rotation where two or more different types of pasture comprise a single experimental treatment (the repeated-seasonal method). In these cases, on the top line of Form 1 under the date, indicate the pasture into which the animals are placed on that date. Since the kind of pasture from which the animals came can be noted, it is important that the form indicate the management method used, so that no confusion will arise as to when the animals were moved from one pasture to another. Records should be transferred promptly to Form 2 and this notation made in Column 1. An experienced pasture manager can adjust grazing pressure to allow for optimum dry-matter intake across treatments. But a check on average daily gains before and after changes in stocking rate may indicate discrepancies in grazing intensity on different replicates, particularly on replicates of the same treatment.

When Form 2 is used, it can be decided whether to segregate the records and calculations according to subtreatments right away, or whether this separation can be made later. Separate sheets can be used for each subtreatment and for each treatment as a whole, or data from different subtreatments or treatments can be entered in different-colored ink on the same sheet to facilitate the interpretation of each subtreatment at a later date.

Additional columns could be added to the forms for recording milk production and converting it to TDN or digestible energy (DE) equivalent and for recording and subtracting the TDN equivalent of feed other than pasture.

It is difficult to know whether weight changes occurring when animals are moved from one paddock to the next within a treatment, or from one pasture mixture to another in the same treatment, are due to

214

changes in fill or to a true difference in pasture productivity. For this reason, the data are usually treated as being representative of a treatment as a whole. They are not broken down into subtreatments, although this could be done readily.

Brown (1951) has presented a number of forms that have been used to record and summarize pasture productivity. These appear to be more applicable to farm conditions than to grazing trials, as they provide space to record numerous factors occurring under farm practice that would not be encountered in most grazing experiments. However, anyone planning to organize a record system will find several of their features of interest.

Liveweight gains may be high when animals are weighed off wet pasture. Normally, this is compensated for by apparently lower gains during the following period. Weather records should be maintained separately, or such environmental factors as rainfall, temperature, and insect annoyance may be noted on the weigh sheet itself. If at all possible, avoid removing or adding animals under unusual or adverse environmental conditions, as relative performance between treatments may be disproportionately affected. For example, the removal of an animal when apparent weight gains are high because of the consumption of moist forage would give an excessively high estimate of true gains in that lot; conversely, adding the animal to another lot at this time would underestimate true gains for that lot during the next period. The desirability of weighing at regular intervals and of removing or adding animals on weigh days indicates the need for devising some systematic method of adjusting the performance of put-and-take grazers over short periods where "gains" appear to be unusual. This adjustment should be based on the performance of the permanent grazers before, during, and after the period in question. This would, of course, involve the assumption that put-and-take grazers were physiologically comparable to permanent grazers. The original records must be kept "as recorded," with any adjustments or corrections being carried out on a separate set of forms. The original picture must never be lost.

References

Brown, Dorothy. 1954. Methods of surveying and measuring vegetation. Bull. 42, xv and 223 p. Commonwealth Agr. Bur., Farnham Royal, Bucks.

Campbell, J. B. 1963. Grass–alfalfa versus grass-alone pastures grazed in a repeated-seasonal pattern. J. Range Manage. 16:78–81.

Kennedy, W. K., J. T. Reid, and M. J. Anderson. 1960. Evaluation of animal production under different systems of grazing. J. Dairy Sci. 42:679–685.

Mott, G. O. 1960. Grazing pressure and the measurement of pasture production. Proc. 8th Int. Grassl. Congr. 8:606–611.

Sarvis, J. T. 1923. Effects of different systems and intensities of grazing upon the native vegetation at the Northern Great Plains Field Station. U.S. Dep. Agr. Bull. 1170.

Sylvestre, P. E., and S. B. Williams. 1952. Methods of measuring the relative productivity of pasture experiments with livestock. Anim. Husb. Div., Can. Dep. Agr., Ottawa. 16 p.

Form 1. Animal liveweight in pounds

Project: Comparison of continuously grazed brome grass – alfalfa vs. a three-field system comprising crested wheat grass – alfalfa, brome grass – alfalfa, and Russian wildrye grazed in rotation.

Lot #1 *Rep.* #1 *Area:* 6 acres *Year:* 1966

Starting and Ending Dates of Grazing Periods

Animal Number	Av. May 24 & 25	May 31	June 7	June 14	June 21	June 28	July 5	July 12	July 19	July 26	August 2	August 9	August 16	August 23	Av. August 30 & 31
Permanent grazers															
1	688	726	737	750	765	780	795	808	828	843	855	870	882	889	895
2	650	685	698	710	720	740	753	768	786	802	810	828	838	848	853
3	635	672	682	696	712	722	737	749	767	774	784	800	810	815	818
4	600	630	642	654	670	683	696	710	730	740	748	765	779	785	790
Put-and-take grazers															
5		650	665	680	692	708	720	735	750	760	775	790			
6		570	590	605	617	640	655	670	690	700	708	715			
7			610	620	635	660	670	685	710	730					
8			630	650	665	675	690	708	728	746					
9					680	690	706	720							
10					765	775	790	809							
11					690	700	710	725							
Total weight	2573	3933	5254	5365	7611	7773	7922	8087	5989	6095	4680	4768	3309	3337	3356
Weight, less animals added or removed	—	2713	4014	—	5476	—	—	5833	—	4619	—	3263	—	—	—
Initial weight of animals in period	—	2573	3933	5254	5365	7611	7773	7922	5833	5989	4619	4680	3263	3309	3337
Gain for period	—	140	81	111	111	162	149	165	156	106	61	88	46	28	19
Cumulative gain	—	140	221	332	443	605	754	919	1075	1181	1242	1330	1376	1404	1423

216

Form 2. Summary of weight data from Form 1, in pounds

Project: Comparison of continuously grazed brome grass – alfalfa vs. a three-field system comprising crested wheat grass – alfalfa, brome grass – alfalfa, and Russian wildrye grazed in rotation.

Lot #1   *Rep.* #1   *Area:* 6 acres   *Year:* 1966

Grazing period	Number of days in period	Number of animals	Animal days	Total final weight	Total initial weight	Total gain	Average daily gain	Cumulative data			Average total weight	Average weight per animal over period
								Animal days	Liveweight gain	Average daily gain		
	Column 1	Column 2	Column 3	Column 4	Column 5	Column 6	Column 7	Column 8	Column 9	Column 10	Column 11	Column 12
Form 1*	Form 1*	Form 1*	$(1)\times(2)$* Form 1*	Form 1*	Form 1*	$(4)-(5)$* Form 1*	$(6)\div(3)$*	$\Sigma(3)$*	$\Sigma(6)$*	$(9)\div(8)$*	$\dfrac{(4)+(5)}{2}$*	$(11)\div(2)$*
May 24–31	7	4	28	2713	2573	140	5.00	28	140	5.00	2643	661
May 31–June 7	7	6	42	4014	3933	81	1.93	70	221	3.16	3974	662
June 7–14	7	8	56	5365	5254	111	1.98	126	332	2.63	5310	664
June 14–21	7	8	56	5476	5365	111	1.98	182	443	2.43	5421	678
June 21–28	7	11	77	7773	7611	162	2.10	259	605	2.34	7692	699
June 28–July 5	7	11	77	7922	7773	149	1.94	336	754	2.24	7848	713
July 5–12	7	11	77	8087	7922	165	2.14	413	919	2.23	8005	728
July 12–19	7	8	56	5989	5833	156	2.79	469	1075	2.29	5911	739
July 19–26	7	8	56	6095	5989	106	1.89	525	1181	2.25	6042	755
July 26–Aug. 2	7	6	42	4680	4619	61	1.45	567	1242	2.19	4650	775
Aug. 2–9	7	6	42	4768	4680	88	2.10	609	1330	2.18	4724	787
Aug. 9–16	7	4	28	3309	3263	46	1.64	637	1376	2.18	3286	822
Aug. 16–23	7	4	28	3337	3309	28	1.00	665	1404	2.11	3323	831
Aug. 23–30	7	4	28	3356	3337	19	.68	693	1423	2.05	3347	837

*Source (Form 1 or column number in Form 2).

Form 3. Calculation of TDN production from animal weight and gain data in Form 2.

Project: Continuously grazed brome grass – alfalfa vs. a three-field system comprising crested wheat grass – alfalfa, brome grass – alfalfa, and Russian wildrye grazed in rotation.

Lot #1   *Rep. #1*   *Area:* 6 acres   *Year:* 1966

Grazing period	TDN for maintenance				TDN for liveweight gain			Total TDN produced			
	Column 13 A.I.* (%)	Column 14 A.I.* Factor	Column 15 TDN (lb)	Column 16 Cumul. TDN (lb)	Column 17 Factor	Column 18 TDN	Column 19 Cumul. TDN liveweight gain	Column 20 For period	Column 21 To date	Column 22 Per acre	Column 23 Per acre to date
		From Form 4†	$\frac{(11)\times(1)\times(14)†}{100}$	$\Sigma(15)†$	From Form 4†	$(17)\times(6)†$	$\Sigma(18)†$	$(15)\times(18)†$	$\Sigma(20)†$	$(20)\div 6†$	$\Sigma(22)†$
May 24–31	10	.778	144	144	2.72	381	381	525	525	88	88
May 31–June 7	10	.778	216	360	2.72	220	601	436	961	73	161
June 7–14	10	.778	289	649	2.72	302	903	591	1552	99	260
June 14–21	10	.778	295	944	2.72	302	1205	597	2149	100	360
June 21–28	10	.778	419	1363	2.72	441	1646	860	3009	143	503
June 28–July 5	10	.763	419	1782	2.87	428	2074	847	3856	141	644
July 5–12	10	.763	428	2210	2.87	474	2548	902	4758	150	794
July 12–19	10	.763	316	2526	2.87	448	2996	764	5522	127	921
July 19–26	10	.751	318	2844	3.01	319	3315	637	6159	106	1027
July 26–Aug. 2	10	.751	244	3088	3.01	184	3499	428	6587	71	1098
Aug. 2–9	10	.751	248	3336	3.01	265	3764	513	7100	86	1184
Aug. 9–16	10	.739	170	3506	3.16	145	3909	315	7415	53	1237
Aug. 16–23	10	.739	172	3678	3.16	88	3997	260	7675	43	1280
Aug. 23–30	10	.739	173	3851	3.16	60	4057	233	7908	39	1319

*Activity increment (source—Chapter 17).
†Source or method of derivation.

Form 4. Estimated TDN requirements of grazing steers, in pounds*

Liveweight (lb)	TDN required per day to maintain 100 pounds of liveweight and to provide for an activity increment of						TDN required per pound of liveweight gain
	0%	10%	25%	50%	75%	100%	
425	0.794	0.872	0.991	1.190	1.388	1.588	1.93
475	0.771	0.849	0.965	1.158	1.351	1.542	2.09
525	0.752	0.827	0.940	1.128	1.316	1.504	2.25
575	0.736	0.810	0.920	1.104	1.288	1.472	2.41
625	0.720	0.792	0.900	1.080	1.260	1.440	2.57
675	0.706	0.778	0.884	1.061	1.237	1.412	2.72
725	0.693	0.763	0.868	1.041	1.215	1.386	2.87
775	0.682	0.751	0.854	1.025	1.195	1.364	3.01
825	0.671	0.739	0.840	1.008	1.176	1.344	3.16
875	0.662	0.728	0.828	0.993	1.159	1.324	3.30
925	0.652	0.718	0.816	0.980	1.143	1.304	3.44
975	0.644	0.708	0.805	0.966	1.127	1.288	3.58

*Calculations from Table 1, Chapter 17, and Sylvestre and Williams (1952).

INDEX